Test Bank
to accompany

D1643736

For All Practical Purposes
Eighth Edition

John Emert

W. H. Freeman and Company
New York

ISBN-10: 1-4292-2651-X
ISBN-13: 978-1-4292-2651-6

Printed in the United States of America

First printing

W. H. Freeman and Company
41 Madison Avenue
New York, NY 10010
Houndmills, Basingstoke
R621 6XS, England
www.whfreeman.com

CONTENTS

Part V: The Digital Revolution

Part VI: On Size and Growth

Part VII: Your Money and Resources

Chapter 1: Multiple-Choice

1. What is the valence of vertex A in the graph below?

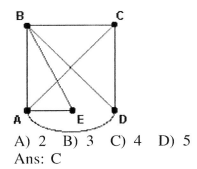

A) 2   B) 3   C) 4   D) 5
Ans: C

2. What is the valence of vertex A in the graph below?

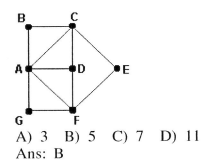

A) 3   B) 5   C) 7   D) 11
Ans: B

3. What is the valence of vertex A in the graph below?

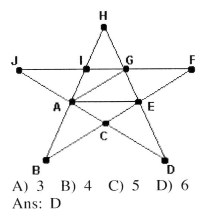

A) 3   B) 4   C) 5   D) 6
Ans: D

4. What is the valence of vertex A in the graph below?

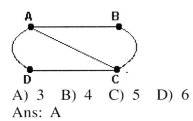

A) 3   B) 4   C) 5   D) 6
Ans: A

5. Which of the following defines the *valence of vertex A* of a graph?
   A)   The total number of vertices of the graph
   B)   The number of edges meeting at vertex A
   C)   The total number of edges of the graph
   D)   None of the above
   Ans: B

6. The valence of vertex A in the graph shown below is 1.

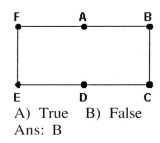

A) True   B) False
Ans: B

7. Which of the graphs below are connected?

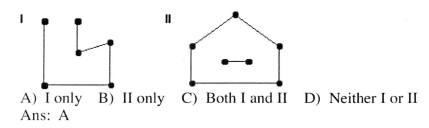

A) I only   B) II only   C) Both I and II   D) Neither I or II
Ans: A

8. Which of the graphs below are connected?

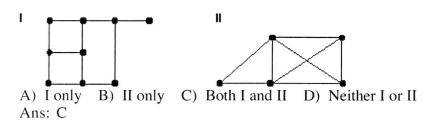

A) I only   B) II only   C) Both I and II   D) Neither I or II
Ans: C

9. Which of the graphs below are connected?

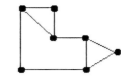

A) I only   B) II only   C) Both I and II   D) Neither I nor II
Ans: B

10. Which of the following statements about a connected graph is always true?
   A)   Every pair of vertices is joined by a single edge.
   B)   A path of edges exists between any two vertices of the graph.
   C)   There are an even number of vertices on the graph.
   D)   There are an even number of edges on the graph.
   Ans: B

11. A graph that is not connected must have at least one vertex with valence 0.
   A) True   B) False
   Ans: B

12. If a graph of four vertices has a vertex with valence 0, then the graph is not connected.
   A) True   B) False
   Ans: A

13. If a graph of six vertices has only four edges, it is not connected.
   A) True   B) False
   Ans: A

14. Which of the graphs below have Euler circuits?

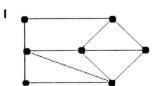 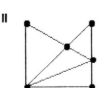

A) I only   B) II only   C) Both I and II   D) Neither I nor II
Ans: B

15. Which of the graphs below have Euler circuits?

A) I only   B) II only   C) Both I and II   D) Neither I nor II
Ans: C

16. Which of the graphs below have Euler circuits?

A) I only   B) II only   C) Both I and II   D) Neither I nor II
Ans: A

17. Which of the graphs below have Euler circuits?

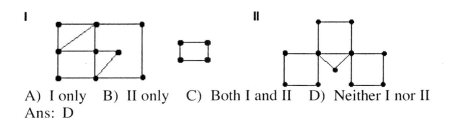

A) I only   B) II only   C) Both I and II   D) Neither I nor II
Ans: D

18. Every graph with an Euler circuit has an even number of vertices.
A) True   B) False
Ans: B

19. Every graph with an Euler circuit has an even number of edges.
A) True   B) False
Ans: B

20. Every graph that has an Euler circuit is connected.
A) True   B) False
Ans: A

21. Every connected graph has an Euler circuit.
A) True   B) False
Ans: B

22. Every graph with an Euler circuit has only vertices with even valences.
A) True   B) False
Ans: A

23. It is possible for a graph with all vertices of even valence to *not* have an Euler circuit.
A) True   B) False
Ans: A

24. Consider the paths represented by the numbered sequence of edges on the graphs below. Which path represents an Euler circuit?

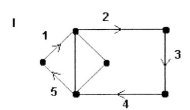   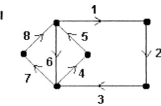

A) I only   B) II only   C) Both I and II   D) Neither I nor II
Ans: B

25. Consider the paths represented by the numbered sequence of edges on the graphs below. Which path represents an Euler circuit?

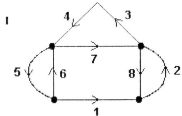   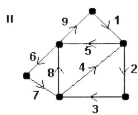

A) I only   B) II only   C) Both I and II   D) Neither I nor II
Ans: B

26. Consider the paths represented by the numbered sequence of edges on the graphs below. Which path represents an Euler circuit?

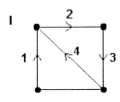   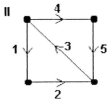

A) I only   B) II only   C) Both I and II   D) Neither I nor II
Ans: D

27. Consider the path represented by the sequence of numbered edges on the graph below. Why does the path *not* represent an Euler circuit?

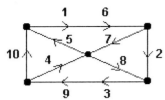

A)   The path does not start and stop at the same vertex.
B)   The path does not cover every edge of the graph.
C)   The path uses some edges more than one time.
D)   The path does not touch each vertex of the graph.
Ans: C

28. Consider the path represented by the sequence of numbered edges on the graph below. Why does the path *not* represent an Euler circuit?

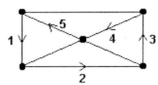

A)   The path does not start and stop at the same vertex.
B)   The path does not cover every edge of the graph.
C)   The path uses some edges more than one time.
D)   The path does not touch each vertex of the graph.
Ans: B

29. Consider the path represented by the numbered sequence of edges of the graph below. Which statement is true?

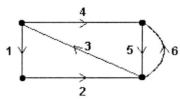

A)   The path is not a circuit.
B)   The path is an Euler circuit.
C)   The path is a circuit, but not an Euler circuit.
D)   None of the above
Ans: A

30. Consider the path represented by the numbered sequence of edges on the graph below. Which statement is true?

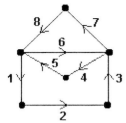

A)   The path is not a circuit.
B)   The path is an Euler circuit.
C)   The path is a circuit, but not an Euler circuit.
D)   None of the above
Ans: B

31. Consider the path represented by the numbered sequence of edges on the graph below. Which statement is true?

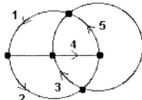

A)   The path is not a circuit.
B)   The path is an Euler circuit.
C)   The path is a circuit, but not an Euler circuit.
D)   None of the above
Ans: C

32. For which of the two situations below is it desirable to find an Euler circuit or an efficient eulerization of a graph?
I. A pizza delivery person takes pizzas to ten houses in a neighborhood and then returns to pick up the next set to be delivered.
II. A postal carrier picks up mail from six collection boxes around a city.
A) I only   B) II only   C) Both I and II   D) Neither I nor II
Ans: D

33. For which of the two situations below is it desirable to find an Euler circuit or an efficient eulerization of a graph?
    I. After a storm, a health department worker inspects all the houses of a small village to check for damage.
    II. A veteran planning a visit to all the war memorials in Washington, D.C. plots a route to follow.
    A) I only   B) II only   C) Both I and II   D) Neither I nor II
    Ans: D

34. For which of the two situations below is it desirable to find an Euler circuit or an efficient eulerization of a graph?
    I. A street department employee must check the traffic signals at each intersection in a downtown area to be certain they are working.
    II. An employee of a power company reads the electric meters outside each house along the streets in a residential area.
    A) I only   B) II only   C) Both I and II   D) Neither I nor II
    Ans: B

35. For which of the two situations below is it desirable to find an Euler circuit or an efficient eulerization of a graph?
    I. Plowing the streets of a small village after a snow.
    II. Painting the lines down the center of the roads in a town with only two-way roads.
    A) I only   B) II only   C) Both I and II   D) Neither I nor II
    Ans: C

36. After a major natural disaster, such as a flood, hurricane, or tornado, many tasks need to be completed as efficiently as possible. For which situation below would finding an Euler circuit or an efficient eulerization of a graph be the appropriate mathematical technique to apply?
    A)   Relief food supplies must be delivered to eight emergency shelters located at different sites in a large city.
    B)   The Department of Public Works must inspect traffic lights at intersections in the city to determine which are still working.
    C)   An insurance claims adjuster must visit 10 homes in various neighborhoods to write reports.
    D)   The Department of Public Works must inspect all streets in the city to remove dangerous debris.
    Ans: D

37. After a major natural disaster, such as a flood, hurricane, or tornado, many tasks need to be completed as efficiently as possible. For which situation below would finding an Euler circuit or an efficient eulerization of a graph be the appropriate mathematical technique to apply?
    A)   The electric company must check several substations for malfunctions.
    B)   The gas company must check along all gas lines for possible leaks.
    C)   The phone company must respond to customers' needs in several parts of town.
    D)   The water company must spot-check the integrity of eight water towers located throughout the city.
    Ans: B

38. In order to eulerize the graph below, give the fewest number of edges that need to be added or duplicated.

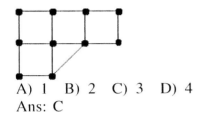

    A) 1   B) 2   C) 3   D) 4
    Ans: C

39. In order to eulerize the graph below, give the fewest number of edges that need to be added or duplicated.

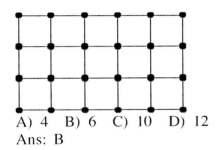

    A) 4   B) 6   C) 10   D) 12
    Ans: B

40. In order to eulerize the graph below, give the fewest number of edges that need to be added or duplicated.

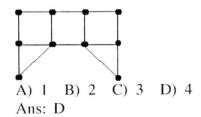

    A) 1   B) 2   C) 3   D) 4
    Ans: D

41. If a graph had eight vertices of odd valence, what is the absolute minimum number of edges that would need to be added (duplicated) to eulerize the graph?
    A) 2   B) 4   C) 6   D) 8
    Ans: B

42. If a graph had 12 vertices of odd valence, what is the absolute minimum number of edges that would need to be added (duplicated) to eulerize the graph?
    A) 2   B) 4   C) 6   D) 8
    Ans: C

43. Which of the graphs shown below gives the best eulerization of the given graph? (In the graphs below, added edges are denoted with zig-zag lines.)

a.
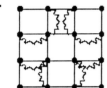

b.
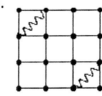

c.
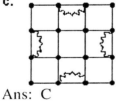

d.
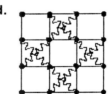

Ans: C

44. Which of the graphs shown below gives the best eulerization of the given graph? (In the graphs below, added edges are denoted with zig-zag lines.)

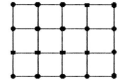

a.
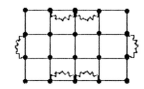

b.
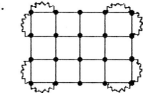

c.
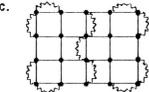

d.
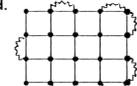

Ans: D

45. Which of the graphs shown below gives the best eulerization of the given graph? (In the graphs below, added edges are denoted with zig-zag lines.)

a.
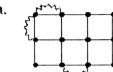

b.
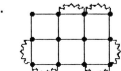

c.

d.
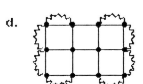

Ans: C

46. Which of the graphs shown below gives the best eulerization of the given graph? (In the graphs below, added edges are denoted with zig-zag lines.)

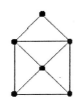

a. 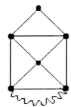   b.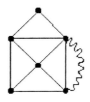

c. 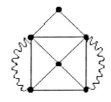   d.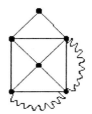

Ans: A

47. Suppose the edges of a graph represent streets that must be checked by a worker from the Department of Public Works. In order to eulerize the graph, we must add three edges. The real world interpretation of this is:
   A)   we must travel three blocks twice in our circuit.
   B)   the street department will build three new streets.
   C)   three blocks will not be checked by the Department of Public Works.
   D)   it will take three workers to check all the streets in the city.
   Ans: A

48. The map shown below illustrates part of a postal carrier's territory. The dots indicate mailboxes to which mail must be delivered. Which graph would be most useful for finding an efficient route for mail delivery?

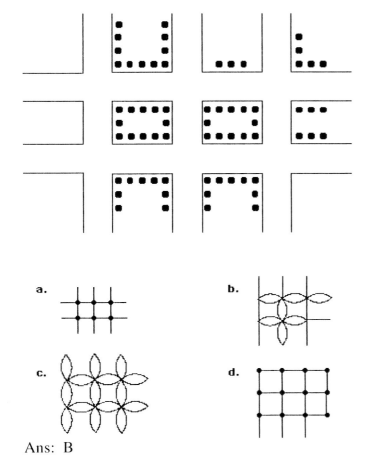

Ans: B

49. For the street network shown below, which graph would be most useful for routing a garbage truck? Assume all streets are two-way and that passing down a street once would be sufficient to collect from both sides.

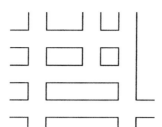

a.   b.

c.   d.

Ans: A

50. The map below shows the territory for a parking control officer. The dots represent parking meters that need to be checked. Which graph would be useful for finding an efficient route?

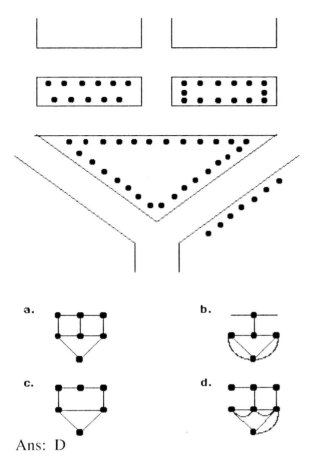

Ans: D

51. In the graph below, find the largest number of paths from A to G that do not have any edges in common.

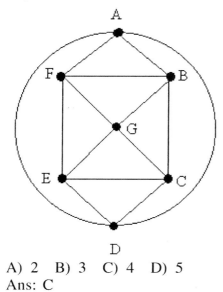

A) 2   B) 3   C) 4   D) 5
Ans: C

52. What is the valence of vertex A in the graph below?

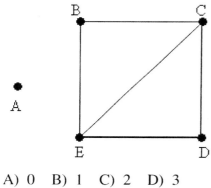

A) 0   B) 1   C) 2   D) 3
Ans: A

53. Which of the graphs below are connected?

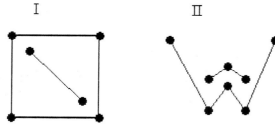

A) I only   B) II only   C) Both I and II   D) Neither I nor II
Ans: D

54. In order to eulerize the graph below, give the fewest number of edges that need to be added or duplicated.

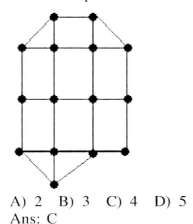

A) 2   B) 3   C) 4   D) 5
Ans: C

55. What is the smallest number of edges that would need to be removed to disconnect the graph below?

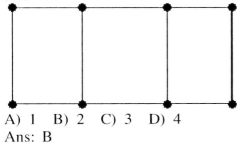

A) 1   B) 2   C) 3   D) 4
Ans: B

56. What is the smallest number of edges that would need to be removed to disconnect the graph below?

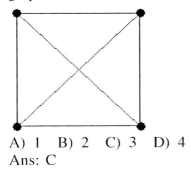

A) 1   B) 2   C) 3   D) 4
Ans: C

57. Which of the graphs below have Euler circuits?

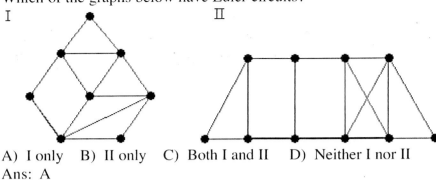

I   II

A) I only   B) II only   C) Both I and II   D) Neither I nor II
Ans: A

58. Consider the path represented by the numbered sequences of edges in the graph below. Which path represents an Euler circuit?

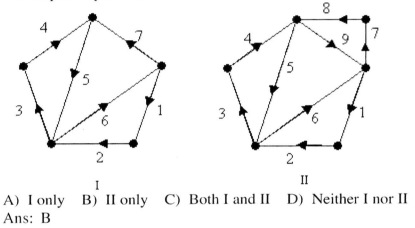

I   II

A) I only   B) II only   C) Both I and II   D) Neither I nor II
Ans: B

59. Consider the path represented by the numbered sequences of edges in the graph below. Which statement is true?

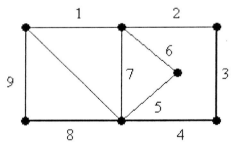

A)   The path is not a circuit.
B)   The path is an Euler circuit.
C)   The path is a circuit, but not an Euler circuit.
D)   None of the above
Ans: C

60. If a graph had 16 vertices of odd valence, what is the absolute minimum number of edges that would need to be added (duplicated) to eulerize the graph?
    A) 2 B) 4 C) 6 D) 8
    Ans: D

Chapter 1: Free-Response

1. On a graph that represents six cities and the roads between them, the valence of vertex A is 4. What does this mean in real-world terms?
   Ans: If the valence of vertex A is four, it means there are four roads which lead to town A.

2. A graph that represents six cities and the roads among them is not connected. What does this mean in real-world terms?
   Ans: If the graph that represents six cities and the roads among them is not connected, it means that it is not possible to travel among all cities. More specifically, it means at least one pair of cities has no connecting path of roads.

3. Draw a graph representing four cities, A, B, C, and D, with a road that connects each pair of cities given:
   AB, AC, BC, BD, CD
   Ans:

   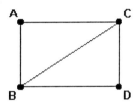

4. Draw a graph with vertices A, B, C, and D in which the valence of vertices A and D is 3 and the valence of vertices B and C is 2.
   Ans:

   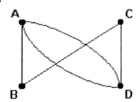

5. Draw a graph with vertices A, B, C, and D in which the valence of each vertex is 3.
   Ans:

   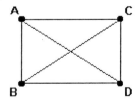

6. Consider the path represented by the sequence of numbered edges on the graph below. Explain why the path is *not* an Euler circuit.

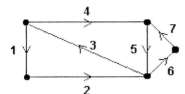

   Ans: The path is not an Euler circuit because it does not start and stop at the same vertex.

7. Consider the path represented by the sequence of numbered edges on the graph below. Explain why the path is *not* an Euler circuit.

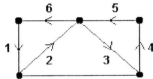

   Ans: The path is not an Euler circuit because it does not cover every edge of the graph.

8. Draw a graph with eight vertices, with the valence of each vertex even, that does *not* have an Euler circuit.
   Ans: Answers may vary. One solution is:

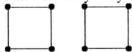

9. Explain why the graph shown below does *not* have an Euler circuit.

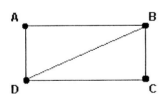

   Ans: The graph does not have an Euler circuit because the valences of vertex B and vertex D are odd.

10. Explain why the graph shown below does *not* have an Euler circuit.

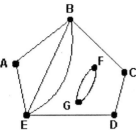

    Ans: The graph does not have an Euler circuit because it is not connected.

Use the following to answer questions 11-14:

Identify an Euler circuit on the following graphs by numbering the sequence of edges in the order traveled.

11.

    Ans: Answers may vary. One solution is:

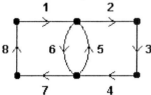

12.

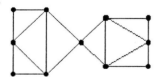

    Ans: Answers may vary. One solution is:

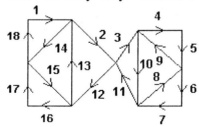

13.

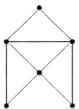

Ans: Answers may vary. One solution is:

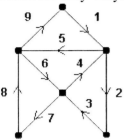

14.

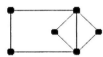

Ans: Answers may vary. One solution is:

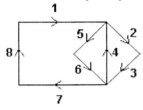

Use the following to answer questions 15-18:

Add wiggly edges to find an efficient Eulerization of the following graphs.

15.

Ans: Answers may vary. One solution is:

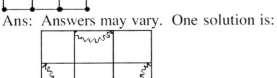

16.

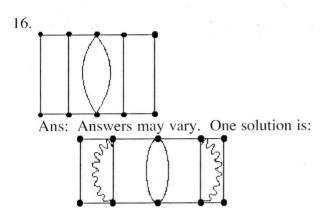

Ans: Answers may vary. One solution is:

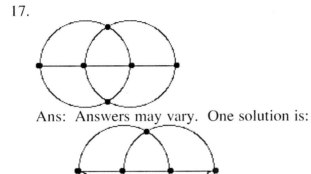

17.

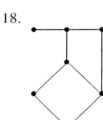

Ans: Answers may vary. One solution is:

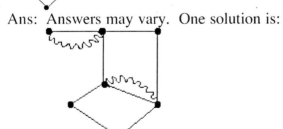

18.

Ans: Answers may vary. One solution is:

19. The map below gives the territory of a parking control officer. The dots represent meters that must be checked. Draw the graph that would be useful for finding an efficient route.

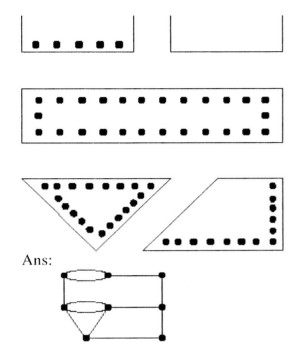

Ans:

20. For the street network shown below, draw a graph that would be useful for routing a garbage truck. Assume all streets are two-way and that passing once down the street is sufficient for collecting trash from both sides.

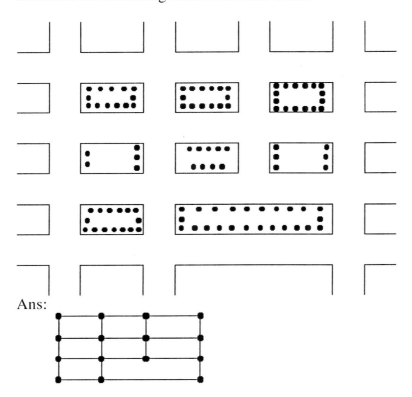

Ans:

21. Find an Euler circuit on the graph on the left and use it to find a circuit on the graph on the right that reuses one edge.

Ans: Answers may vary. One solution is:

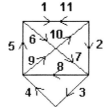

22. Find an Euler circuit on the graph on the left and use it to find a circuit on the graph on the right that reuses 4 edges.

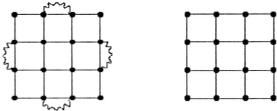

Ans: Answers may vary. One solution is:

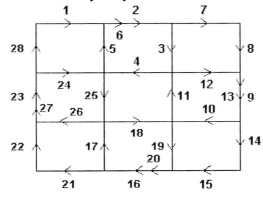

23. Find an Euler circuit on the graph on the left and use it to find a circuit on the graph on the right that reuses 3 edges.

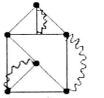

Ans: Answers may vary.

24. Why would a city street department want its snow plow operator's path to follow an Euler circuit if possible?

Ans: If the snow plow operator followed an Euler circuit, he would end his route at the city garage where he started. Also, no time or gas would be wasted traveling down streets that were already plowed.

25. Give three real-world applications in which a worker would want to find an Euler circuit on a street network.
    Ans: Answers may vary. Some situations include:
    Plowing snow
    Painting lines down the center of streets
    Trash collection
    Checking gutters on the corners of all streets
    Checking parking meters along the edge of all streets
    Delivering mail to all houses on all streets

26. Draw a connected graph with 7 vertices where each vertex has valence 4.
    Ans: Answers will vary. One solution is:

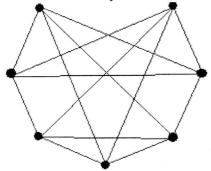

27. Draw a graph with 6 vertices where the valences are 1, 2, 2, 3, 4, and 4.
    Ans: Answers will vary. One solution is:

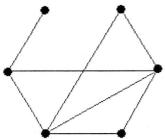

28. Find an eulerization with 9 added edges for a 3×6-block rectangular street network.
    Ans:

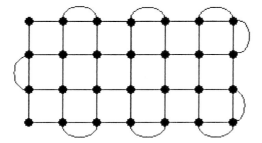

29. Draw a graph where every vertex has a valence of at least 2, but removing a single edge disconnects the graph.
Ans: Answers will vary. One solution is:

30. Draw a graph with 5 vertices where the valence of each vertex is 4.
Ans: Answers will vary. One solution is:

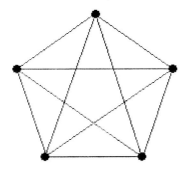

Chapter 2: Multiple-Choice

1. Which of the following describes a Hamiltonian circuit for the graph below?

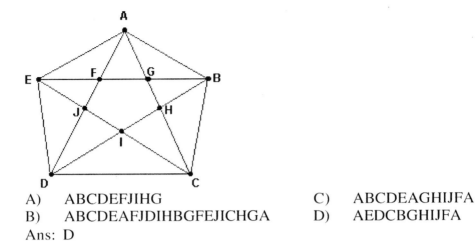

A)   ABCDEFJIHG   C)   ABCDEAGHIJFA

B)   ABCDEAFJDIHBGFEJICHGA   D)   AEDCBGHIJFA

Ans: D

2. Which of the following describes a Hamiltonian circuit for the graph below?

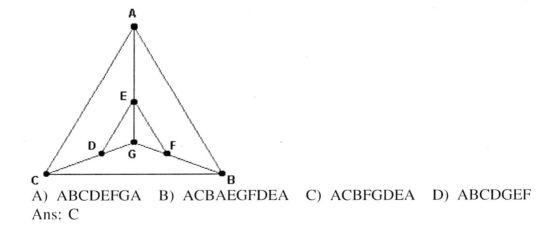

A) ABCDEFGA B) ACBAEGFDEA C) ACBFGDEA D) ABCDGEF

Ans: C

3. Which of the following describes a Hamiltonian circuit for the graph below?

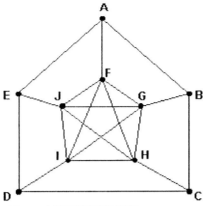

A)   ABCDEJHIGF   C)   ABCDEAFGHIJFA
B)   AEDCBGIHJFA   D)   ABCDEAFGBGIDIHCHJEJFA

Ans: B

4. On the graph below, which routing is produced by using the nearest-neighbor algorithm to solve the traveling salesman problem?

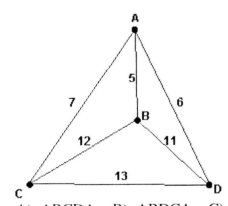

A) ABCDA   B) ABDCA   C) ACBDA   D) ABCD

Ans: B

5. For the graph below, what is the cost of the Hamiltonian circuit obtained by using the nearest-neighbor algorithm, starting at A?

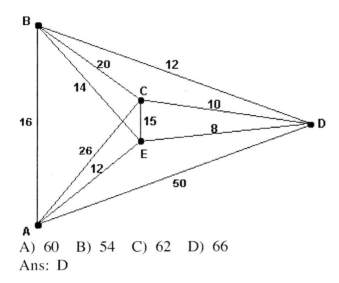

A) 60   B) 54   C) 62   D) 66
Ans: D

6. For the graph below, what is the cost of the Hamiltonian circuit obtained by using the nearest-neighbor algorithm, starting at A?

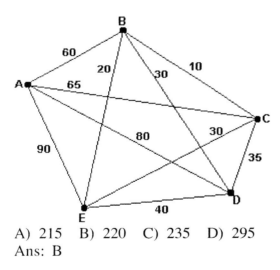

A) 215   B) 220   C) 235   D) 295
Ans: B

7. Which path listed forms a Hamiltonian circuit on the graph below?

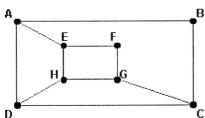

A)   ADCBFGHEA
B)   ABCDHGFE

C)   ABCDHGFEA
D)   ABCDHGFEHDA

Ans: C

8. On a map there are roads from town A of length 10, 26, 12, and 50 miles. Using the nearest-neighbor algorithm for finding a Hamiltonian circuit starting at town A, which road would be traveled first?
A)   road of length 10
B)   road of length 26

C)   road of length 12
D)   road of length 50

Ans: A

9. For the traveling salesman problem (Hamiltonian circuit) applied to six cities, how many tours are possible?
A) 60   B) 120   C) 360   D) 720
Ans: B

10. For the traveling salesman problem (Hamiltonian circuit) applied to five cities, how many distinct tours are possible?
A) 120   B) 60   C) 24   D) 12
Ans: C

11. For the traveling salesman problem (Hamiltonian circuit) applied to four cities, how many distinct tours are possible?
A) 3   B) 6   C) 12   D) 24
Ans: B

12. For the traveling salesman problem applied to seven cities, how many distinct tours are possible?
A) 360   B) 720   C) 2520   D) 5040
Ans: B

13. On the graph below, which routing is produced by using the sorted-edges algorithm to solve the traveling salesman problem?

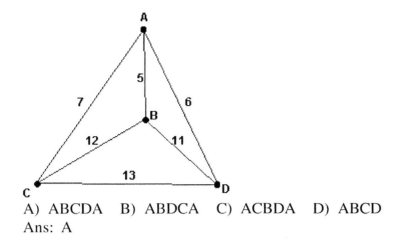

A) ABCDA B) ABDCA C) ACBDA D) ABCD
Ans: A

14. For the graph below, what is the cost of the Hamiltonian circuit obtained by using the sorted-edges algorithm?

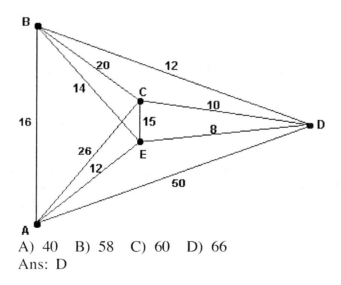

A) 40 B) 58 C) 60 D) 66
Ans: D

15. For the graph below, what is the cost of the Hamiltonian circuit obtained by using the sorted-edges algorithm?

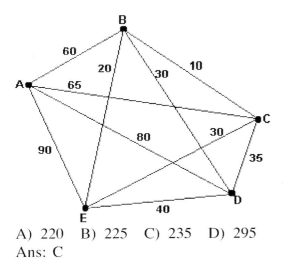

A) 220   B) 225   C) 235   D) 295
Ans: C

16. Use Kruskal's algorithm for minimum-cost spanning trees on the graph below. The cost of the tree found is:

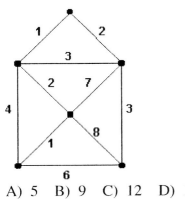

A) 5   B) 9   C) 12   D) 15
Ans: B

17. Use Kruskal's algorithm for minimum-cost spanning trees on the graph below. The cost of the tree found is:

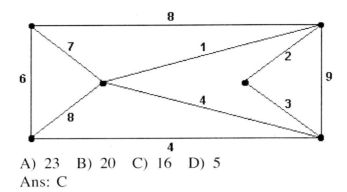

A) 23   B) 20   C) 16   D) 5
Ans: C

18. Use Kruskal's algorithm for minimum-cost spanning trees on the graph below. The cost of the tree found is:

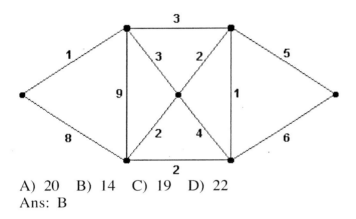

A) 20   B) 14   C) 19   D) 22
Ans: B

19. Use Kruskal's algorithm for minimum-cost spanning trees on the graph below. The cost of the tree found is:

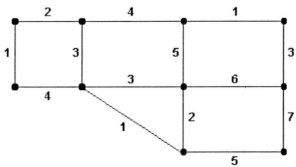

A) 47   B) 25   C) 22   D) 15
Ans: C

20. Use Kruskal's algorithm for minimum-cost spanning trees on the graph below. The cost of the tree found is:

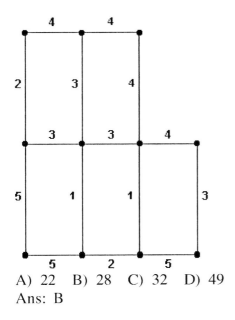

A) 22   B) 28   C) 32   D) 49

Ans: B

21. Given the order-requirement digraph for a collection of tasks shown below, the critical path would be:

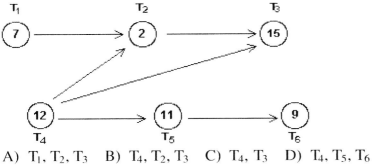

A) T_1, T_2, T_3 B) T_4, T_2, T_3 C) T_4, T_3 D) T_4, T_5, T_6

Ans: D

22. If the order-requirement digraph for a collection of tasks is shown below, then what is the minimum completion time for the collection of tasks?

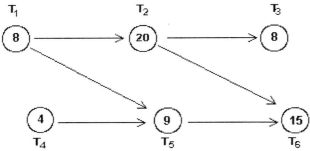

A) 64 minutes   B) 43 minutes   C) 36 minutes   D) 28 minutes
Ans: B

23. What is the earliest possible completion time for a job whose order-requirement is shown below?

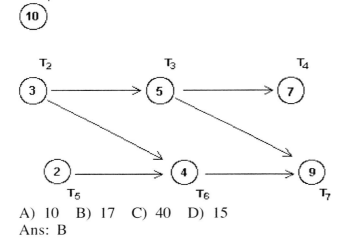

A) 10   B) 17   C) 40   D) 15
Ans: B

24. What is the earliest possible completion time for a job whose order-requirement digraph is shown below?

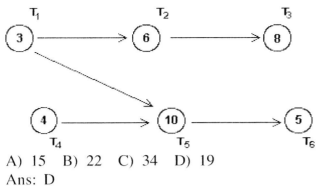

A) 15   B) 22   C) 34   D) 19
Ans: D

25. What is the earliest possible completion time for a job whose order-requirement is shown below?

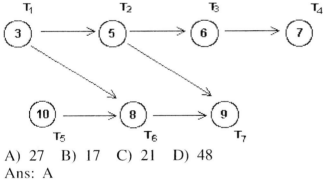

A) 27   B) 17   C) 21   D) 48
Ans: A

26. The nearest-neighbor algorithm for solving the traveling salesman problem always gives optimal results.
A) True   B) False
Ans: B

27. The sorted-edges algorithm for solving the traveling salesman problem always gives optimal results.
A) True   B) False
Ans: B

28. Kruskal's algorithm for finding minimum-cost spanning trees always gives optimal results.
A) True   B) False
Ans: A

29. The nearest-neighbor algorithm for solving the traveling salesman problem always produces the same result as the sorted-edges algorithm.
    A) True   B) False
    Ans: B

30. The path produced by the nearest-neighbor algorithm when solving the traveling salesman problem may be dependent on the starting city.
    A) True   B) False
    Ans: A

31. The path produced by the sorted-edges algorithm when solving the traveling salesman problem may be dependent on the starting city.
    A) True   B) False
    Ans: B

32. The minimum-cost spanning tree produced by applying Kruskal's algorithm will always contain the lowest cost edge of the graph.
    A) True   B) False
    Ans: A

33. The minimum-cost spanning tree produced by applying Kruskal's algorithm may contain the most expensive edge of the graph.
    A) True   B) False
    Ans: A

34. A heuristic algorithm will always produce optimal results.
    A) True   B) False
    Ans: B

35. A heuristic algorithm may produce optimal results.
    A) True   B) False
    Ans: A

36. When Kruskal's algorithm is used to find a minimum-cost spanning tree on a graph, which of the following is false?
    A)   Circuits are not permitted in the tree.
    B)   The tree contains the edge of the graph of minimum cost.
    C)   The tree is not necessarily connected.
    D)   The tree may contain the edge of the highest cost.
    Ans: C

37. A spanning tree of a graph must contain every edge of the graph.
    A) True   B) False
    Ans: B

38. A digraph is a graph with exactly two vertices.
    A) True   B) False
    Ans: B

39. Suppose an architect needs to design an intercom system for a large office building. The technique most likely to be useful in solving this problem is:
    A)   finding an Euler circuit on a graph.
    B)   applying the nearest-neighbor algorithm for the traveling salesman problem.
    C)   applying Kruskal's algorithm for finding a minimum-cost spanning tree for a graph.
    D)   None of these techniques is likely to apply.
    Ans: C

40. Suppose a veteran is planning a visit to all the war memorials in Washington, D.C. The technique most likely to be useful in solving this problem is:
    A)   finding an Euler circuit on a graph.
    B)   applying the nearest-neighbor algorithm for the traveling salesman problem.
    C)   applying Kruskal's algorithm for finding a minimum-cost spanning tree for a graph.
    D)   None of these techniques is likely to apply.
    Ans: B

41. Suppose an employee of a power company needs to read the electricity meters outside of each house along the streets in a residential area. The technique most likely to be useful in solving this problem is:
    A)   finding an Euler circuit on a graph.
    B)   applying the nearest-neighbor algorithm for the traveling salesman problem.
    C)   applying Kruskal's algorithm for finding a minimum-cost spanning tree for a graph.
    D)   None of these techniques is likely to apply.
    Ans: A

42. Suppose a pizza delivery person needs to take pizzas to 10 houses in different neighborhoods and then return to pick up the next set to be delivered. The technique most likely to be useful in solving this problem is:
    A)   finding an Euler circuit on a graph.
    B)   applying the nearest-neighbor algorithm for the traveling salesman problem.
    C)   applying Kruskal's algorithm for finding a minimum-cost spanning tree for a graph.
    D)   None of these techniques is likely to apply.
    Ans: B

43. Suppose a college campus decides to install its own phone lines connecting all of the buildings where calls may be relayed through one or more buildings before reaching their destination. The technique most likely to be useful in solving this problem is:
    A)   finding an Euler circuit on a graph.
    B)   applying the nearest-neighbor algorithm for the traveling salesman problem.
    C)   applying Kruskal's algorithm for finding a minimum-cost spanning tree for a graph.
    D)   None of these techniques is likely to apply.
    Ans: C

44. Suppose that after a storm an inspection needs to be made of the sewers along the streets in a small village to make sure local flooding is not due to clogging. The technique most likely to be useful in solving this problem is:
    A)   finding an Euler circuit on a graph.
    B)   applying the nearest-neighbor algorithm for the traveling salesman problem.
    C)   applying Kruskal's algorithm for finding a minimum-cost spanning tree for a graph.
    D)   None of these techniques is likely to apply.
    Ans: A

45. Suppose a maintenance worker needs to empty garbage dumpsters from five locations on the grounds of a park in the most efficient way possible. The technique most likely to be useful in solving this problem is:
    A)   finding an Euler circuit on a graph.
    B)   applying the nearest-neighbor algorithm for the traveling salesman problem.
    C)   applying Kruskal's algorithm for finding a minimum-cost spanning tree for a graph.
    D)   None of these techniques is likely to apply.
    Ans: B

46. Phyllis has her office in Middleton and must visit four clients, each in a different city. The graph below shows each city and the distances between each pairs of cities. How many miles would Phyllis travel if she chooses the Hamiltonian circuit for her trip by using the sorted-edges algorithm?

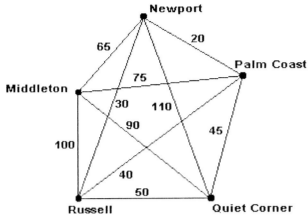

A) 265 miles   B) 300 miles   C) 285 miles   D) 345 miles
Ans: C

47. The graph below shows the cost (in hundreds of dollars) of installing telephone wires between the work spaces in an office complex. Use Kruskal's algorithm for minimum-cost spanning trees to find the cost for establishing this phone network.

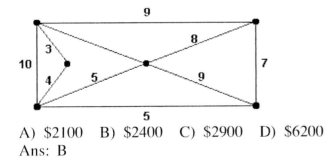

A) $2100   B) $2400   C) $2900   D) $6200
Ans: B

48. A local cafeteria offers a choice of 5 meats, 6 vegetables, and 3 salads. A complete dinner includes 1 meat, 1 vegetable, and 1 salad. How many different dinners can be created?
A) 14   B) 45   C) 90   D) 120
Ans: C

49. Kris has 3 pairs of pants of different colors, 5 shirts of different colors, and 2 pairs of shoes. How many different outfits can Kris create?
A) 2   B) 10   C) 30   D) 50
Ans: C

50. Given the two graphs shown below, which one represents a tree?

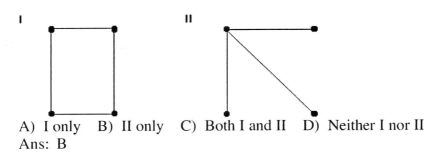

A) I only   B) II only   C) Both I and II   D) Neither I nor II
Ans: B

51. Given the two graphs shown below, which one represents a tree?

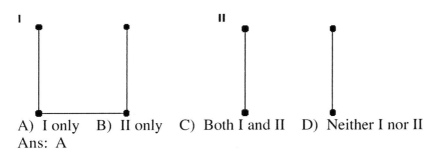

A) I only   B) II only   C) Both I and II   D) Neither I nor II
Ans: A

52. In which of the diagrams below do the wiggled edges represent spanning trees?

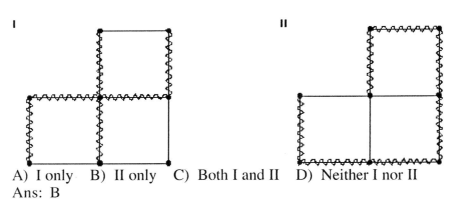

A) I only   B) II only   C) Both I and II   D) Neither I nor II
Ans: B

53. In which of the diagrams below do the wiggled edges represent spanning trees?

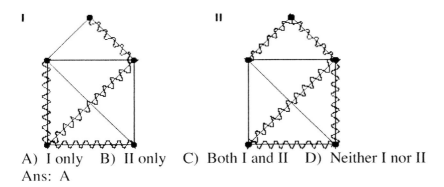

A) I only   B) II only   C) Both I and II   D) Neither I nor II
Ans: A

54. For the graph below, which routing is produced by using the nearest-neighbor algorithm to solve the traveling salesman problem?

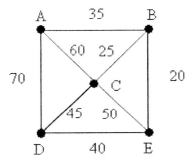

A) ABCEDA   B) ABEDCA   C) ADCEBA   D) ABCED
Ans: B

55. For the graph below, what is the cost of the Hamiltonian circuit obtained by using the nearest-neighbor algorithm, starting at A?

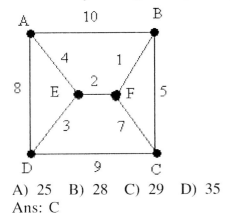

A) 25   B) 28   C) 29   D) 35
Ans: C

56. A college student has six pairs of pants, eight tee shirts, three sweatshirts, and two pairs of tennis shoes. If an outfit consists of pants, a tee shirt, a sweatshirt, and a pair of tennis shoes, how many different outfits can the student wear before repeating one?
    A) 19   B) 124   C) 288   D) 328
    Ans: C

57. An on-line banking service requires its customers to select a password that is four characters long. The password is case-sensitive, so upper-case letters are considered to be different than lower-case letters. The first character of the password must be an upper-case letter and the second character must be a digit. The remaining two characters may each be a digit, an uppercase letter, or a lowercase letter. What is the number of possible passwords?
    A) 175,760   B) 336,960   C) 999,440   D) 1,406,080
    Ans: C

58. A connected graph G has 32 vertices. How many edges does a spanning tree of G have?
    A) 30   B) 31   C) 32   D) 33
    Ans: B

59. A connected graph G has 32 vertices. How many vertices does a spanning tree of G have?
    A) 30   B) 31   C) 32   D) 33
    Ans: C

60. For the graph below, which routing is produced by using the sorted-edges algorithm to solve the traveling salesman problem?

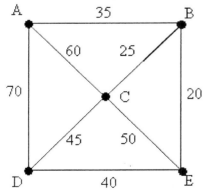

    A) ACBEDA   B) ABCEDA   C) ABEDCA   D) ADCEBA
    Ans: A

61. For the graph below, what is the cost of the Hamiltonian circuit obtained by using the sorted-edges algorithm?

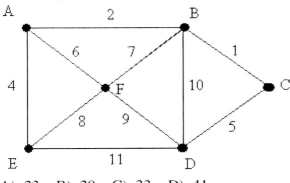

A) 23   B) 29   C) 33   D) 41
Ans: B

62. Which of the following describes a Hamiltonian circuit for the graph below?

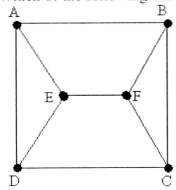

A) ABFEDCBA   B) ABCFEA   C) ABCFBAEDA   D) ABCFEDA
Ans: D

63. Use Kruskal's algorithm for minimum-cost spanning trees on the graph below. What is the cost of the tree found?

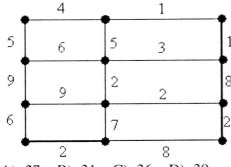

A) 27   B) 31   C) 36   D) 39
Ans: C

Chapter 2: Free-Response

1. Construct a complete graph on 4 vertices.
   Ans:

   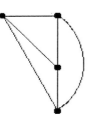

2. Construct a complete graph whose vertices represent the six largest islands of Hawaii: Kauai, Oahu, Molokai, Lanai, Maui, and Hawaii.
   Ans:

   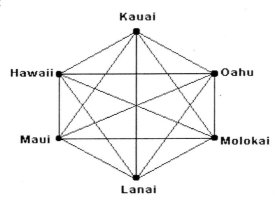

3. Construct an example of a spanning tree on the graph given below.

   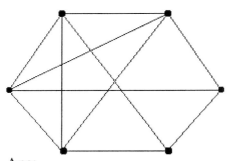

   Ans:

   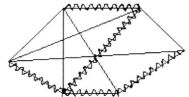

4. Construct an example of a graph with no Hamiltonian circuit.
   Ans:

5. Construct a digraph for the following tasks necessary when building a house: get a building permit, install wiring, pour foundation, build walls, build doghouse, pass final inspection.
   Ans:

   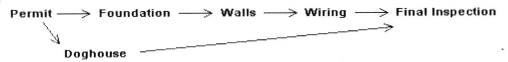

6. Identify six tasks necessary when building a sandwich, and construct a digraph for these tasks.
   Ans:

   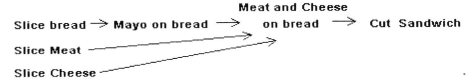

7. Identify six tasks necessary when preparing for a picnic, and construct a digraph for these tasks.
   Ans:

8. Use the brute force algorithm to solve the traveling salesman problem for the graph of the four cities shown below.

   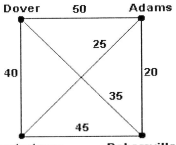

   Ans: Route ABCDA and ACBDA have cost 155. Route ABDCA has (minimum) cost 120.

9. Use the brute force algorithm to solve the traveling salesman problem for the graph of the four cities shown below.

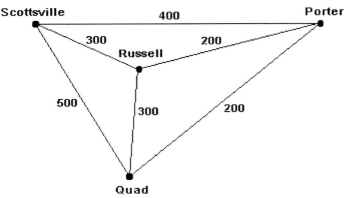

Ans: Route PQRSP and PQSRP have (minimum) cost 1200. Route PRQSP has cost 1400.

10. Use the brute force algorithm to solve the traveling salesman problem for the graph of the four cities shown below.

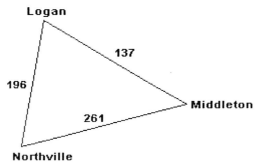

Ans: Only one route, with cost 594.

11. You own a chain of 12 apartment complexes (including your residence) and you want to plan a trip to visit each of your properties. If it takes 1/2 minute to compute the total length of a tour, how long will it take to apply the brute force algorithm to find the optimal tour?
Ans: $(11!/2)(1/2) = 9979200$ minutes, approximately 19 years.

12. You own a chain of 10 one-day photo development kiosks and a lab where the photos are developed. Each morning and evening a delivery truck leaves the lab, visits each kiosk, and returns to the lab. If it takes 1/3 minute to compute the total length of a tour, how long will it take to apply the brute force algorithm to find the optimal tour for the delivery truck?
Ans: $(9!/2)(1/3) = 60480$ minutes, or 42 days.

13. You want to create a mileage grid showing the distance between every pair of the 50 U.S. state capitals. How many numbers will you have to compute?
    Ans: $(50)(49)/2 = 1225$

14. You want to create a mileage grid showing the distance between every pair of the 10 Canadian provincial and territorial capitals. How many numbers will you have to compute?
    Ans: $(10)(9)/2 = 45$

15. The local cafe offers three different entrees, 10 different vegetables, and four different salads. A "blue plate special" includes an entree, a vegetable, and a salad. How many different ways can a special be constructed?
    Ans: 120

16. A nearby ice cream shop offers 31 different flavors and three different types of cones. How many different single scoop cones can be ordered?
    Ans: 93

17. In some states, license plates use a mixture of letters and numerals. How many possible plates could be constructed using three letters followed by three numerals?
    Ans: $26^3 \cdot 10^3 = 17,576,000$

18. In some states, license plates use a mixture of letters and numerals. How many possible plates could be constructed using two letters followed by four numerals?
    Ans: $26^4 \cdot 10^2 = 6,760,000$

19. What is an advantage of a *heuristic* algorithm?
    Ans: Fast

20. What is a disadvantage of a *heuristic* algorithm?
    Ans: Not always optimal

21. What is *critical* about the *critical path* of an order-requirement digraph?
    Ans: It requires the critical or essential amount of time required to complete the project.

22. Can a graph have an Euler circuit, but not a Hamiltonian circuit? Explain your answer.
    Ans:

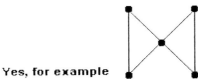

Yes, for example

23. Can a graph have a Hamiltonian circuit, but not an Euler circuit? Explain your answer.
Ans:

Yes, for example

24. Will the nearest-neighbor algorithm ever use the most expensive edge of a graph?
Ans: Yes

25. The route of a neighborhood garbage truck generally follows an Euler circuit. Under what circumstances should it instead follow a Hamiltonian circuit?
Ans: If it only picks up at central locations

26. The route of a delivery truck generally follows a Hamiltonian circuit. Under what circumstances should it instead follow an Euler circuit?
Ans: If it delivers to every house

27. In the graph below, add wiggly edges to indicate a Hamiltonian circuit.

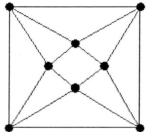

Ans: (bold lines should be squiggly)

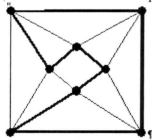

28. In the graph below, add wiggly edges to indicate a Hamiltonian circuit.

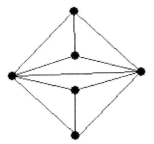

Ans: (bold lines should be squiggly)

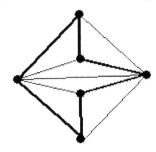

29. Construct an example of a connected graph that does not have a Hamiltonian circuit.
Ans: Answers will vary. One solution is:

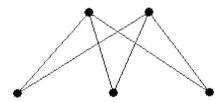

30. Construct an example of a connected graph that has a Hamiltonian circuit but does not have an Euler circuit.
Ans: Answers will vary. One solution is:

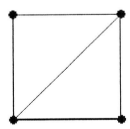

31. A connected graph H has a spanning tree with 50 edges. How many vertices does the spanning tree have? How many vertices does H have? What can one say about the number of edges H has?
Ans: The spanning tree has 51 vertices. H also has 51 vertices. H must have at least 50 edges.

Chapter 3: Multiple-Choice

1. Given the order-requirement digraph below (with time given in minutes) and the priority list T_1, T_2, T_3, T_4, T_5, T_6, apply the list-processing algorithm to construct a schedule using two processors. How much time does the resulting schedule require?

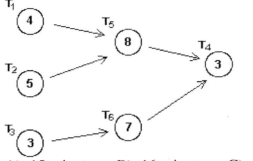

   A) 15 minutes   B) 16 minutes   C) 17 minutes   D) 18 minutes
   Ans: C

2. Given the order-requirement digraph below (with time given in minutes) and the priority list T_1, T_2, T_3, T_4, T_5, T_6, apply the list-processing algorithm to construct a schedule using two processors. How much time does the resulting schedule require?

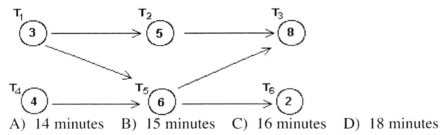

   A) 14 minutes   B) 15 minutes   C) 16 minutes   D) 18 minutes
   Ans: D

3. Given the order-requirement digraph below (with time given in minutes) and the priority list T_1, T_2, T_3, T_4, T_5, T_6, T_7, apply the list-processing algorithm to construct a schedule using two processors. How much time does the resulting schedule require?

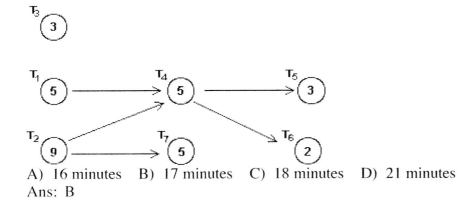

A) 16 minutes   B) 17 minutes   C) 18 minutes   D) 21 minutes
Ans: B

4. Given the order-requirement digraph below (with time given in minutes) and the priority list T_1, T_2, T_3, T_4, T_5, T_6, T_7, T_8, apply the list-processing algorithm to construct a schedule using two processors. How much time does the resulting schedule require?

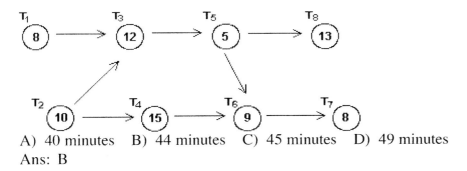

A) 40 minutes   B) 44 minutes   C) 45 minutes   D) 49 minutes
Ans: B

5. Given the order-requirement digraph below (with time given in minutes) and the priority list T_1, T_2, T_3, T_4, T_5, T_6, apply the list-processing algorithm to construct a schedule using two processors. How much time does the resulting schedule require?

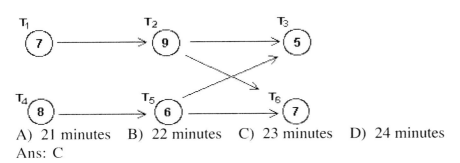

A) 21 minutes   B) 22 minutes   C) 23 minutes   D) 24 minutes
Ans: C

6. Given the order-requirement digraph below (with time given in minutes) and the priority list T₁, T₂, T ₃, T₄, T₅, T₆, apply the critical-path scheduling algorithm to construct a schedule using two processors. How much time does the resulting schedule require?

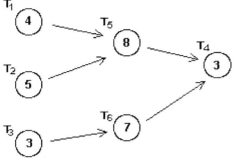

A) 15 minutes   B) 16 minutes   C) 17 minutes   D) 18 minutes
Ans: C

7. Given the order-requirement digraph below (with time given in minutes) and the priority list T₁, T₂, T ₃, T₄, T₅, T₆, apply the critical-path scheduling algorithm to construct a schedule using two processors. How much time does the resulting schedule require?

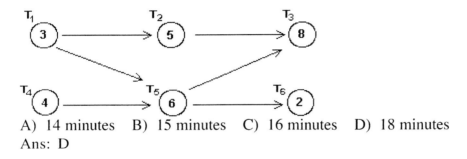

A) 14 minutes   B) 15 minutes   C) 16 minutes   D) 18 minutes
Ans: D

8. Given the order-requirement digraph below (with time given in minutes) and the priority list T₁, T₂, T ₃, T₄, T₅, T₆, T₇, apply the critical-path scheduling algorithm to construct a schedule using two processors. How much time does the resulting schedule require?

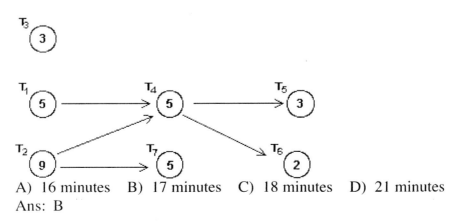

A) 16 minutes   B) 17 minutes   C) 18 minutes   D) 21 minutes
Ans: B

9. Given the order-requirement digraph below (with time given in minutes) and the priority list T_1, T_2, T_3, T_4, T_5, T_6, T_7, T_8, apply the critical-path scheduling algorithm to construct a schedule using two processors. How much time does the resulting schedule require?

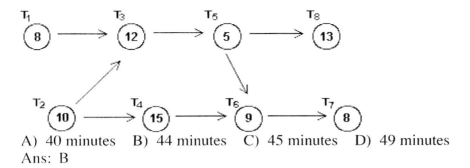

A) 40 minutes   B) 44 minutes   C) 45 minutes   D) 49 minutes

Ans: B

10. Given the order-requirement digraph below (with time given in minutes) and the priority list T_1, T_2, T_3, T_4, T_5, T_6, apply the critical-path scheduling algorithm to construct a schedule using two processors. How much time does the resulting schedule require?

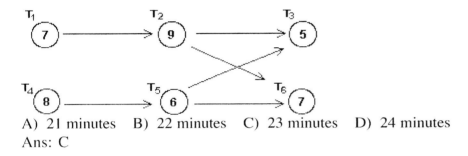

A) 21 minutes   B) 22 minutes   C) 23 minutes   D) 24 minutes

Ans: C

11. What is the minimum time required to complete nine independent tasks on three processors when the sum of all the times of the nine tasks is 72 minutes?
    A) 3 minutes   B) 8 minutes   C) 24 minutes   D) 27 minutes
    Ans: C

12. What is the minimum time required to complete eight independent tasks on two processors when the sum of all the times of the eight tasks is 72 minutes?
    A) 4 minutes   B) 9 minutes   C) 16 minutes   D) 36 minutes
    Ans: D

13. What is the minimum time required to complete 12 independent tasks on two processors when the sum of all the times of the 12 tasks is 84 minutes?
    A) 6 minutes   B) 14 minutes   C) 24 minutes   D) 42 minutes
    Ans: D

14. What is the minimum time required to perform six independent tasks with a total task time of 48 minutes on three machines?
    A) 2 minutes   B) 8 minutes   C) 16 minutes   D) 18 minutes
    Ans: C

15. What is the minimum time required to perform eight independent tasks with a total task time of 48 minutes on four machines?
    A) 2 minutes   B) 6 minutes   C) 12 minutes   D) 24 minutes
    Ans: C

16. Use the decreasing-time-list algorithm to schedule these tasks on two machines:
            4 minutes, 5 minutes, 8 minutes, 3 minutes, 3 minutes, 7 minutes
How much time does the resulting schedule require?
    A) 15 minutes   B) 16 minutes   C) 17 minutes   D) 18 minutes
    Ans: A

17. Use the decreasing-time-list algorithm to schedule these tasks on two machines:
            3 minutes, 5 minutes, 8 minutes, 4 minutes, 6 minutes, 2 minutes
How much time does the resulting schedule require?
    A) 14 minutes   B) 15 minutes   C) 16 minutes   D) 18 minutes
    Ans: A

18. Use the decreasing-time-list algorithm to schedule these tasks on two machines:
            9 minutes, 6 minutes, 3 minutes, 4 minutes, 8 minutes
How much time does the resulting schedule require?
    A) 14 minutes   B) 15 minutes   C) 16 minutes   D) 17 minutes
    Ans: C

19. Use the decreasing-time-list algorithm to schedule these tasks on two machines:
            9 minutes, 2 minutes, 8 minutes, 5 minutes, 4 minutes, 8 minutes
How much time does the resulting schedule require?
    A) 17 minutes   B) 18 minutes   C) 19 minutes   D) 22 minutes
    Ans: B

20. Use the decreasing-time-list algorithm to schedule these tasks on two machines:
            9 minutes, 8 minutes, 7 minutes, 9 minutes, 2 minutes, 5 minutes.
How much time does the resulting schedule require?
    A) 19 minutes   B) 20 minutes   C) 21 minutes   D) 22 minutes
    Ans: C

21. Choose the packing that results from the use of the first fit (FF) bin-packing algorithm to pack the following weights into bins that can hold no more than 8 lbs.

    6 lbs, 2 lbs, 4 lbs, 3 lbs, 5 lbs, 3 lbs, 2 lbs, 4 lbs

a.
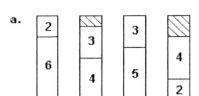
b.
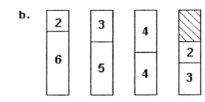

c.
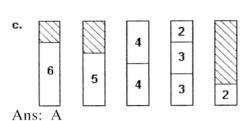
d.
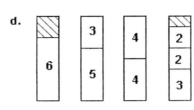

Ans: A

22. Choose the packing that results from the use of the next fit (NF) bin-packing algorithm to pack the following weights into bins that can hold no more than 8 lbs.

    6 lbs, 2 lbs, 4 lbs, 3 lbs, 5 lbs, 3 lbs, 2 lbs, 4 lbs

a.
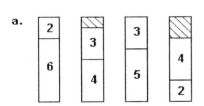
b.
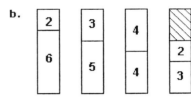

c.
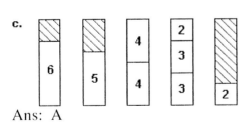
d.
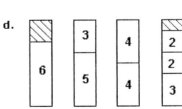

Ans: A

23. Choose the packing that results from the use of the worst fit (WF) bin-packing algorithm to pack the following weights into bins that can hold no more than 8 lbs.
    6 lbs, 2 lbs, 4 lbs, 3 lbs, 5 lbs, 3 lbs, 2 lbs, 4 lbs

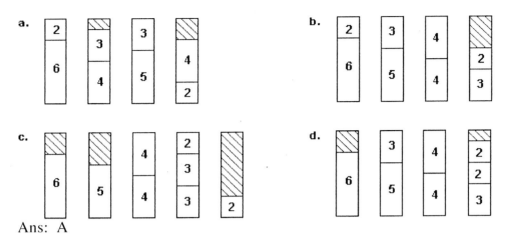

Ans: A

24. Choose the packing that results from the use of the first-fit decreasing (FFD) bin-packing algorithm to pack the following weights into bins that can hold no more than 8 lbs.
    6 lbs, 2 lbs, 4 lbs, 3 lbs, 5 lbs, 3 lbs, 2 lbs, 4 lbs

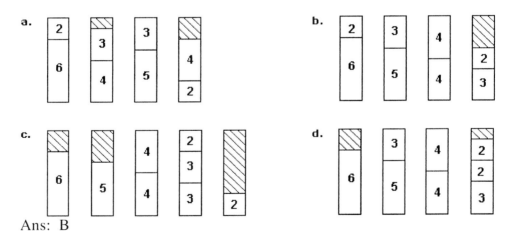

Ans: B

25. Choose the packing that results from the use of the next-fit decreasing (NFD) bin-packing algorithm to pack the following weights into bins that can hold no more than 8 lbs.
6 lbs, 2 lbs, 4 lbs, 3 lbs, 5 lbs, 3 lbs, 2 lbs, 4 lbs

a. 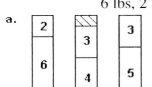 b.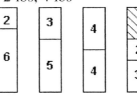

c. 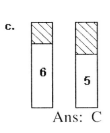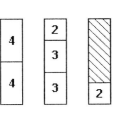 d.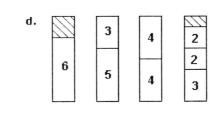

Ans: C

26. Choose the packing that results from the use of the worst-fit decreasing (WFD) bin-packing algorithm to pack the following weights into bins that can hold no more than 8 lbs.
6 lbs, 2 lbs, 4 lbs, 3 lbs, 5 lbs, 3 lbs, 2 lbs, 4 lbs

a. 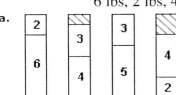 b.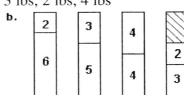

c. 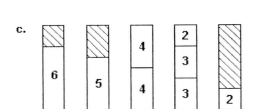 d.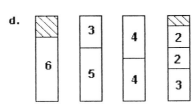

Ans: D

27. Choose the packing that results from the use of the first fit (FF) bin-packing algorithm to pack the following weights into bins that can hold no more than 9 lbs.
    4 lbs, 5 lbs, 3 lbs, 2 lbs, 7 lbs, 6 lbs, 4 lbs, 2 lbs

a.

b.

c.

d. Another packing
Ans: B

28. Choose the packing that results from the use of the next fit (NF) bin-packing algorithm to pack the following weights into bins that can hold no more than 9 lbs.
    4 lbs, 5 lbs, 3 lbs, 2 lbs, 7 lbs, 6 lbs, 4 lbs, 2 lbs

a.

b.

c.

d. Another packing
Ans: D

29. Choose the packing that results from the use of the worst fit (WF) bin-packing algorithm to pack the following weights into bins that can hold no more than 9 lbs.

   4 lbs, 5 lbs, 3 lbs, 2 lbs, 7 lbs, 6 lbs, 4 lbs, 2 lbs

a.     b.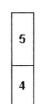

c.

d. Another packing
Ans: C

30. Choose the packing that results from the use of the first-fit decreasing (FFD) bin-packing algorithm to pack the following weights into bins that can hold no more than 9 lbs.

   4 lbs, 5 lbs, 3 lbs, 2 lbs, 7 lbs, 6 lbs, 4 lbs, 2 lbs

a.   b.

c.

d. Another packing
Ans: C

31. Choose the packing that results from the use of the next-fit decreasing (NFD) bin-packing algorithm to pack the following weights into bins that can hold no more than 9 lbs.
    4 lbs, 5 lbs, 3 lbs, 2 lbs, 7 lbs, 6 lbs, 4 lbs, 2 lbs

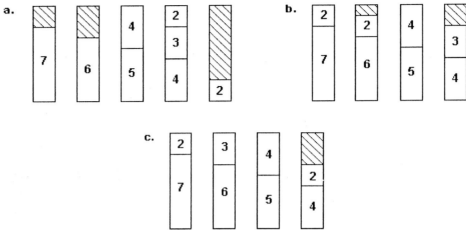

d. Another packing
Ans: A

32. Choose the packing that results from the use of the worst-fit decreasing (WFD) bin-packing algorithm to pack the following weights into bins that can hold no more than 9 lbs.
    4 lbs, 5 lbs, 3 lbs, 2 lbs, 7 lbs, 6 lbs, 4 lbs, 2 lbs

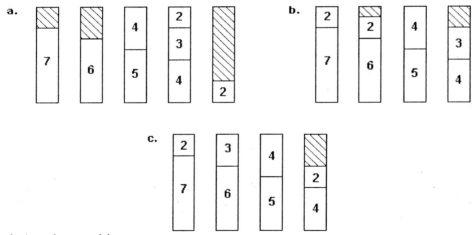

d. Another packing
Ans: B

33. Choose the packing that results from the use of the first fit (FF) bin-packing algorithm to pack the following weights into bins that can hold no more than 8 lbs.
    5 lbs, 7 lbs, 1 lb, 2 lbs, 4 lbs, 5 lbs, 1 lb, 1 lb, 3 lbs, 6 lbs, 2 lbs

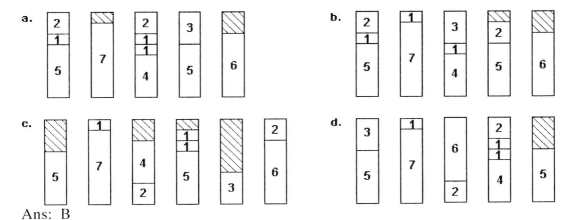

Ans: B

34. Choose the packing that results from the use of the next fit (NF) bin-packing algorithm to pack the following weights into bins that can hold no more than 8 lbs.
    5 lbs, 7 lbs, 1 lb, 2 lbs, 4 lbs, 5 lbs, 1 lb, 1 lb, 3 lbs, 6 lbs, 2 lbs

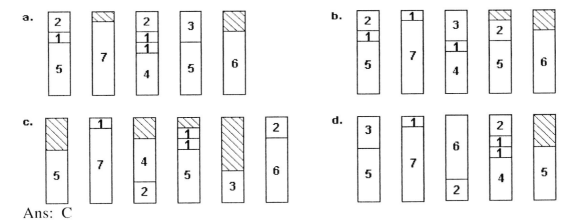

Ans: C

35. Choose the packing that results from the use of the worst fit (WF) bin-packing algorithm to pack the following weights into bins that can hold no more than 8 lbs.

5 lbs, 7 lbs, 1 lb, 2 lbs, 4 lbs, 5 lbs, 1 lb, 1 lb, 3 lbs, 6 lbs, 2 lbs

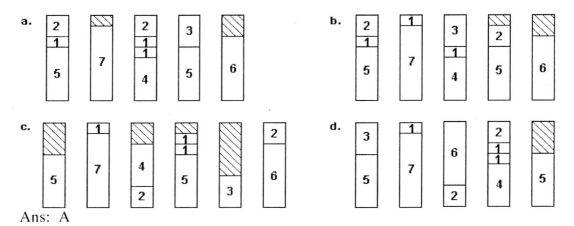

Ans: A

36. Choose the packing that results from the use of the first-fit decreasing (FFD) bin-packing algorithm to pack the following weights into bins that can hold no more than 8 lbs.

5 lbs, 7 lbs, 1 lb, 2 lbs, 4 lbs, 5 lbs, 1 lb, 1 lb, 3 lbs, 6 lbs, 2 lbs, 3 lbs

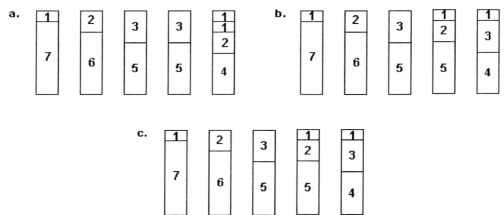

d. Another packing

Ans: A

37. Choose the packing that results from the use of the next-fit decreasing (NFD) bin-packing algorithm to pack the following weights into bins that can hold no more than 8 lbs.
    5 lbs, 7 lbs, 1 lb, 2 lbs, 4 lbs, 5 lbs, 1 lb, 1 lb, 3 lbs, 6 lbs, 2 lbs, 3 lbs

a.

1	2	3	3	1
7	6	5	5	1
				2
				4

b.

1	2	3	1	1
7	6	5	2	3
			5	4

c.

1	2	3	1	1
7	6	5	2	3
			5	4

d. Another packing
Ans: D

38. Choose the packing that results from the use of the worst-fit decreasing (WFD) bin-packing algorithm to pack the following weights into bins that can hold no more than 8 lbs.
    5 lbs, 7 lbs, 1 lb, 2 lbs, 4 lbs, 5 lbs, 1 lb, 1 lb, 3 lbs, 6 lbs, 2 lbs, 3 lbs

a.

1	2	3	3	1
7	6	5	5	1
				2
				4

b.

1	2	3	1	1
7	6	5	2	3
			5	4

c.

1	2	3	1	1
7	6	5	2	3
			5	4

d. Another packing
Ans: B

39. A talent show producer needs to fit 17 acts of varying lengths into three segments. The segments should be as short as possible and are to be separated by intermissions. How many acts will be placed in each segment?
    A)   Either 5 or 6 segment
    B)   At least 5 per segment
    C)   No more than 6 per segment
    D)   The answer will vary, depending on the lengths of the acts
    Ans: D

Use the following to answer questions 40-44:

Suppose that a crew can currently complete in a minimum amount of time the job whose order-requirement digraph is shown below.

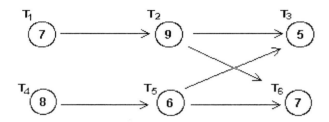

40. If Task T_1 is shortened from 7 minutes to 4 minutes, then what is the maximum amount by which the completion time of the entire job can be shortened?
    A) It cannot be reduced.   B) 1 minute   C) 2 minutes   D) 3 minutes
    Ans: C

41. If Task T_2 is shortened from 9 minutes to 6 minutes, then what is the maximum amount by which the completion time of the entire job can be shortened?
    A) It cannot be reduced.   B) 1 minute   C) 2 minutes   D) 3 minutes
    Ans: C

42. If Task T_4 is shortened from 8 minutes to 5 minutes, then what is the maximum amount by which the completion time of the entire job can be shortened?
    A) It cannot be reduced.   B) 1 minute   C) 2 minutes   D) 3 minutes
    Ans: A

43. If Task T_5 is shortened from 6 minutes to 3 minutes, then what is the maximum amount by which the completion time of the entire job can be shortened?
    A) It cannot be reduced.   B) 1 minute   C) 2 minutes   D) 3 minutes
    Ans: A

44. If Task T_6 is shortened from 7 minutes to 4 minutes, then what is the maximum amount by which the completion time of the entire job can be shortened?
    A) It cannot be reduced.   B) 1 minute   C) 2 minutes   D) 3 minutes
    Ans: C

45. The first fit (FF) algorithm never uses more boxes than the next fit (NF) algorithm.
    A) True   B) False
    Ans: B

46. The worst fit (WF) algorithm never uses more boxes than the first fit (FF) algorithm.
    A) True   B) False
    Ans: B

47. When scheduling tasks using the list-processing algorithm, increasing the number of machines always reduces the completion time.
    A) True   B) False
    Ans: B

48. When scheduling tasks using the list-processing algorithm, decreasing the time of each task always decreases the completion time.
    A) True   B) False
    Ans: B

49. The list-processing algorithm for scheduling tasks is guaranteed to always produce an optimal solution.
    A) True   B) False
    Ans: B

50. The worst-fit decreasing (WFD) algorithm for bin-packing is guaranteed to always produce an optimal solution.
    A) True   B) False
    Ans: B

51. Which of the following is a correct vertex coloring of the given graph? (Capital letters indicate which color the vertex is colored.)

I. 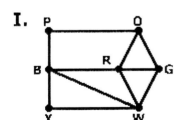   II.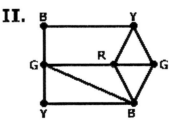

    A) I only   B) II only   C) Both I and II   D) Neither I nor II
    Ans: C

52. Which of the following is a correct vertex coloring of the given graph? (Capital letters indicate which color the vertex is colored.)

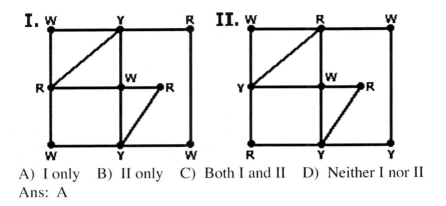

A) I only   B) II only   C) Both I and II   D) Neither I nor II

Ans: A

53. Which of the following is a correct vertex coloring of the given graph? (Capital letters indicate which color the vertex is colored.)

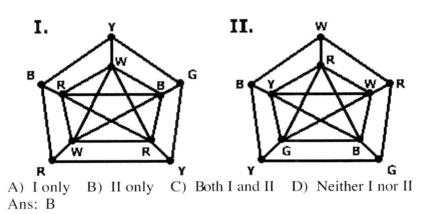

A) I only   B) II only   C) Both I and II   D) Neither I nor II

Ans: B

54. The table below shows chemical compounds that cannot be mixed without causing dangerous reactions. If a graph were used to facilitate scheduling of disposal containers for the compounds, how many edges would it have?

	A	B	C	D	E	F
A		X		X	X	
B	X		X		X	X
C		X		X		
D	X		X			X
E	X	X				
F		X		X		

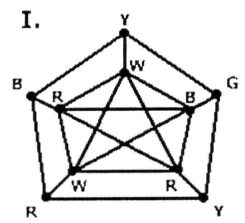
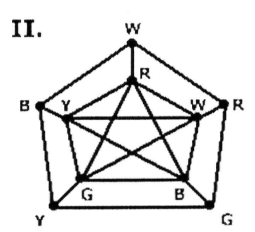

A) I only   B) II only   C) Both I and II   D) Neither I and II
Ans: A

55. Find the chromatic number of the graph below:

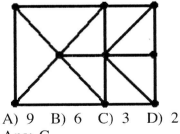

A) 9   B) 6   C) 3   D) 2
Ans: C

56. Find the chromatic number of the graph below:

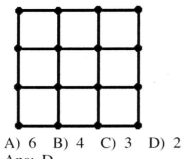

A) 6 B) 4 C) 3 D) 2
Ans: D

57. Find the chromatic number of the graph below:

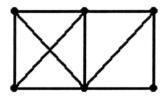

A) 6 B) 4 C) 3 D) 2
Ans: B

58. Assume an order-requirement digraph requires 30 minutes when scheduled on three machines. Based on this information, when the digraph is instead scheduled on two machines, how much time will be required?
A) Exactly 30 minutes   C) Exactly 45 minutes
B) Exactly 40 minutes   D) At least 45 minutes
Ans: D

59. Assume an order-requirement digraph has a critical path with length 40 minutes. Based on this information, when the digraph is scheduled on four machines, how much time will be required?
A) Exactly 10 minutes   C) At least 40 minutes
B) Exactly 30 minutes   D) Exactly 40 minutes
Ans: C

60. Assume a job consists of six independent tasks ranging in time from 3 to 12 minutes and totaling 36 minutes. Efficiently scheduled on four machines, how much time will the job require?
A) Exactly 3 minutes   C) Exactly 12 minutes
B) Exactly 9 minutes   D) More than 12 minutes
Ans: C

61. What is the minimum time required to complete 12 independent tasks on 4 processors when the sum of all the times of the 12 tasks is 120 minutes?
    A) 10 minutes   B) 30 minutes   C) 40 minutes   D) 60 minutes
    Ans: B

62. What is the minimum time required to complete eight independent tasks with a total task time of 160 minutes on four machines?
    A) 10 minutes   B) 20 minutes   C) 40 minutes   D) 60 minutes
    Ans: B

Use the following to answer questions 63-66:

Select from choices A) to D) to answer the question(s) below.

A)

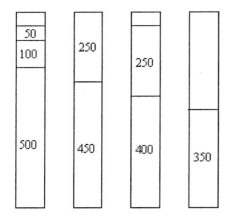

B)

C)

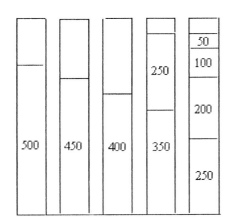

D)

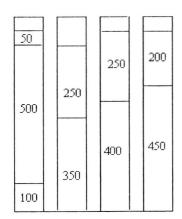

63. Choose the packing that results from the use of the first fit (FF) bin-packing algorithm to pack data files with the following sizes onto compact discs that can hold no more than 700 MB.

    100 MB, 500 MB, 250 MB, 350 MB, 400 MB, 250 MB, 450 MB, 200 MB, 50 MB
    A) A   B) B   C) C   D) D
    Ans: D

64. Choose the packing that results from the use of the next fit (NF) bin-packing algorithm to pack data files with the following sizes onto compact discs that can hold no more than 700 MB.

    100 MB, 500 MB, 250 MB, 350 MB, 400 MB, 250 MB, 450 MB, 200 MB, 50 MB
    A) A   B) B   C) C   D) D
    Ans: B

65. Choose the packing that results from the use of the first-fit decreasing (FFD) bin-packing algorithm to pack data files with the following sizes onto compact discs that can hold no more than 700 MB.

   100 MB, 500 MB, 250 MB, 350 MB, 400 MB, 250 MB, 450 MB, 200 MB, 50 MB
   A) A   B) B   C) C   D) D
   Ans: A

66. Choose the packing that results from the use of the next-fit decreasing (NFD) bin-packing algorithm to pack data files with the following sizes onto compact discs that can hold no more than 700 MB.

   100 MB, 500 MB, 250 MB, 350 MB, 400 MB, 250 MB, 450 MB, 200 MB, 50 MB
   A) A   B) B   C) C   D) D
   Ans: C

Chapter 3: Free-Response

1. Which of the algorithms—first fit (FF), next fit (NF), or worst fit (WF)—would be most preferable when filling boxes on an assembly line? Why?
   Ans: NF. One doesn't have to go back.

2. Which of the algorithms—first fit (FF), next fit (NF), or worst fit (WF)—would be most preferable when packing cloth dolls? Why?
   Ans: FF. One can pack as tightly as needed.

3. Which of the algorithms—first fit (FF), next fit (NF), or worst fit (WF)—would be most preferable when packing china dishes? Why?
   Ans: WF. There can be equal room in each box.

4. Which of the algorithms—first fit (FF), next fit (NF), or worst fit (WF)—would be most preferable when cutting wooden shelves from planks? Why?
   Ans: WF. This allows for some "error" or sawdust scraps.

5. Which of the algorithms—first fit (FF), next fit (NF), or worst fit (WF)—would be most preferable when cutting quilt pieces? Why?
   Ans: FF. This keeps scraps large if possible.

6. Use the first fit (FF) bin-packing algorithm to pack the following weights into bins that can hold no more than 9 lbs.
   5 lbs, 7 lbs, 1 lb, 2 lbs, 4 lbs, 5 lbs, 1 lb, 1 lb, 3 lbs, 6 lbs, 2 lbs

   Ans: 1
        2
       1 1 5 6
       5 7 4 3 2

7. Use the next fit (NF) bin-packing algorithm to pack the following weights into bins that can hold no more than 9 lbs.
   5 lbs, 7 lbs, 1 lb, 2 lbs, 4 lbs, 5 lbs, 1 lb, 1 lb, 3 lbs, 6 lbs, 2 lbs

   Ans:

           1
        1 4 1 6
      5 7 2 5 3 2

8. Use the worst fit (WF) bin-packing algorithm to pack the following weights into bins that can hold no more than 9 lbs.

5 lbs, 7 lbs, 1 lb, 2 lbs, 4 lbs, 5 lbs, 1 lb, 1 lb, 3 lbs, 6 lbs, 2 lbs

Ans: 1
2
1 1 5 6
5 7 4 3 2

9. Use the first-fit decreasing (FFD) bin-packing algorithm to pack the following weights into bins that can hold no more than 9 lbs.

5 lbs, 7 lbs, 1 lb, 2 lbs, 4 lbs, 5 lbs, 1 lb, 1 lb, 3 lbs, 6 lbs, 2 lbs

Ans:

```
                1
                1
   2  3  4  2
   7  6  5  5  1
```

10. Use the next-fit decreasing (NFD) bin-packing algorithm to pack the following weights into bins that can hold no more than 9 lbs.

5 lbs, 7 lbs, 1 lb, 2 lbs, 4 lbs, 5 lbs, 1 lb, 1 lb, 3 lbs, 6 lbs, 2 lbs

Ans:

```
                     1
                     1
                     2
              4  2
   7  6  5  5  3  1
```

11. Use the worst-fit decreasing (WFD) bin-packing algorithm to pack the following weights into bins that can hold no more than 9 lbs.

5 lbs, 7 lbs, 1 lb, 2 lbs, 4 lbs, 5 lbs, 1 lb, 1 lb, 3 lbs, 6 lbs, 2 lbs

Ans:

```
      1     1
   2  2  4  3
   7  6  5  5  1
```

12. A talent show producer needs to fit 17 acts of varying lengths into three segments. The segments should be as short as possible and are to be separated by intermissions. This problem could be solved by using
Ans: the list-processing algorithm for independent tasks.

Use the following to answer questions 13-16:

Use the order-requirement digraph below (with time given in minutes) and the priority list T_1, T_2, T_3, T_4, T_5, T_6 to answer the question(s) below.

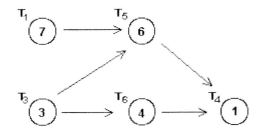

13. Apply the list-processing algorithm to construct a schedule using two processors.
    Ans:

		7	13	14
T1			T5	T4
T2	T3	T6	\\\\\\\	

    2   5   9

14. Apply the list-processing algorithm to construct a schedule using three processors.
    Ans:

	7	13	14
T1		T5	T4
T2	\\	T6	\\\\\\\\\\\\
T3	\\\\\\\\\\\\\\\\\\\\		

    3

15. Apply the critical-path scheduling algorithm to construct a schedule using two processors.
    Ans:

		7	13	14
T1			T5	T4
T3	T6	T2	\\\\\\\\	

    3   7   9

16. Apply the critical-path scheduling algorithm to construct a schedule using three processors.
    Ans:

		7	13	14

T1		T5	T4
T3	T6	\\\\\\\\\\\\
T2	\\\\\\\\\\\\\\\\\\\\\\\	

    3   7

17. What is the minimum time required to complete 12 independent tasks on three processors when the sum of all the times of the 12 tasks is 60 minutes?
    Ans: 20 minutes

18. What is the minimum time required to complete eight independent tasks on two processors when the sum of the times of the eight tasks is 64 minutes?
    Ans: 32 minutes

19. Give an example of an order-requirement digraph with six tasks $T_1, T_2, T_3, T_4, T_5, T_6$ for which the critical-path is T_1, T_3, T_4.
    Ans: For example,

    $$T_1 (5) \to T_3 (6) \to T_4 (5)$$

    $$T_2 (1) \to T_5 (1) \to T_6 (1)$$

20. Give an example of an order-requirement digraph with six tasks $T_1, T_2, T_3, T_4, T_5, T_6$ that requires 10 minutes when scheduled on two processors.
    Ans:

    For example, $T_1 (3) \to T_2 (3) \to T_3 (4)$
    $T_4 (2)$ $T_5 (6)$ $T_2 (1)$

21. Give an example in which six independent tasks require 12 minutes when scheduled on three processors.
    Ans: For example, 6,6,6,6,6,6.

22. Give an example in which the first fit (FF) and next fit (NF) bin-packing algorithms produce the same packing.
    Ans: For example, when the capacity is 10 lbs. The weights are 7 lbs, 6 lbs, 5 lbs, and 5 lbs.

23. Give an example in which the first-fit decreasing (FFD) and worst-fit decreasing (WFD) bin-packing algorithms produce the same packing.
    Ans: For example, when the capacity is 10 lbs. The weights are 7 lbs, 6 lbs, 5 lbs, and 5 lbs.

24. Why are there several different algorithms for the bin-packing problem?
    Ans: There are different situations and no best algorithm.

25. When scheduling independent tasks, why does the decreasing-time-list algorithm generally produce good schedules? Does it always produce an optimal schedule?
    Ans: It produces good schedules because the bigger tasks are done early, allowing for smaller tasks to fill in the remaining time.

26. When scheduling tasks using an order-requirement digraph, why does the critical-path scheduling algorithm generally produce good schedules? Does it always produce an optimal schedule?
    Ans: It completes "prerequisite" tasks early, but this is not always an optimal schedule.

27. Find the chromatic number of the graph below:

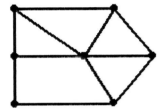

    Ans: The chromatic number is 3.

28. Find the chromatic number of the graph below:

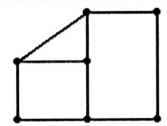

    Ans: The chromatic number is 3.

29. The table below represents species of plants that have competing light or water requirements. Draw the graph that would be useful in determining the minimum number of different habitats that would be needed to display all these plants in a garden.

	A	B	C	D	E
A		X		X	X
B	X		X		
C		X		X	
D	X		X		X
E	X			X	

Ans: Answers may vary. One solution is given by the graph below:

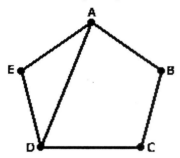

30. Use the decreasing-time list algorithm to schedule these tasks on three machines:
7, 2, 5, 3, 9, 1, 6, 5, 3, 7
How much time does the resulting schedule require?
Ans: 16 minutes

Use the following to answer questions 31-34:

Use the order requirement digraph below (with time given in minutes) and the priority list T_1, T_2, T_3, T_4, T_5, T_6, T_7, T_8 to answer the question(s) below.

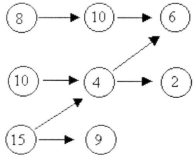

31. Apply the critical-path scheduling algorithm to construct a schedule using two processors.
Ans:

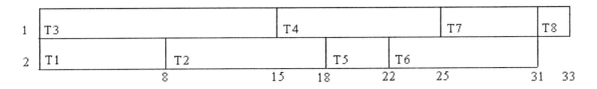

32. Apply the critical-path scheduling algorithm to construct a schedule using three processors.
Ans:

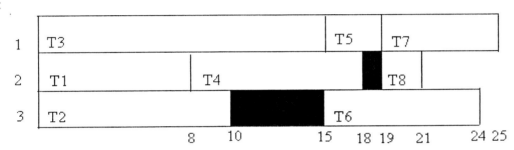

33. Apply the list-processing algorithm to construct a schedule using two processors.
Ans:

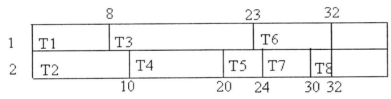

34. Apply the list-processing algorithm to construct a schedule using three processors.
Ans:

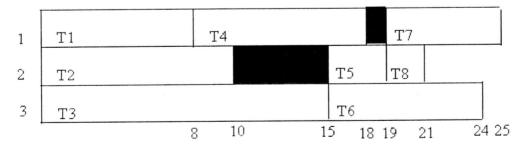

35. What is the minimum time to complete 12 independent tasks on four processors when the sum of all the times of the 12 tasks is 60 minutes?
Ans: 15 minutes

Chapter 4: Multiple-Choice

1. Find the graph of the equation $3x + 5y = 30$.

a.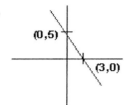
(0,5)
(3,0)

b.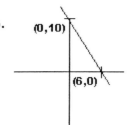
(0,10)
(6,0)

c.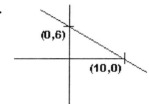
(0,6)
(10,0)

d.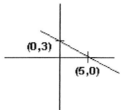
(0,3)
(5,0)

Ans: C

2. Find the graph of the equation $4x + 2y = 12$.

a.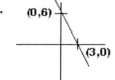
(0,6)
(3,0)

b.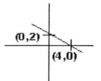
(0,2)
(4,0)

c.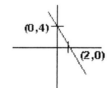
(0,4)
(2,0)

d.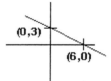
(0,3)
(6,0)

Ans: A

3. Find the graph of the equation $4x + 6y = 18$.

a.

(0,6)
(4,0)

b.
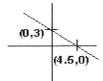
(0,3)
(4.5,0)

c.
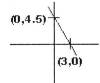
(0,4.5)
(3,0)

d.
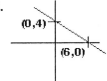
(0,4)
(6,0)

Ans: B

4. Find the graph of the equation $5x + 2y = 15$.

a.
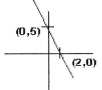
(0,5)
(2,0)

b.
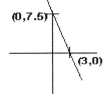
(0,7.5)
(3,0)

c.
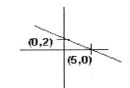
(0,2)
(5,0)

d.
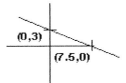
(0,3)
(7.5,0)

Ans: B

5. Find the graph of the inequality $3x + 4y \le 12$.

a.

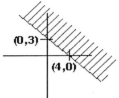

b.

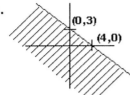

c.

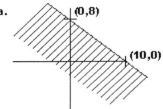

d.

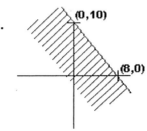

Ans: D

6. Find the graph of the inequality $4x + 5y \le 40$.

a.

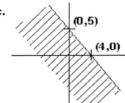

b.

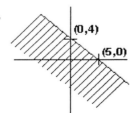

c.

d.

Ans: A

7. Find the graph of the inequality $6x + 4y \le 48$.

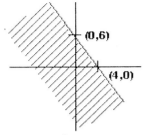

a.

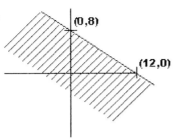

b.

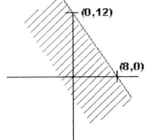

c.

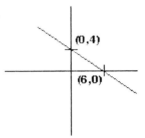

d.

Ans: C

8. Find the graph of the inequality $3x + 7y \le 21$.

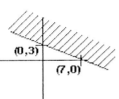

a.

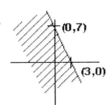

b.

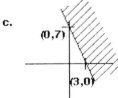

c.

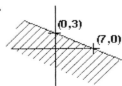

d.

Ans: D

9. Find the point of intersection of the lines whose equations are $2x + 3y = 12$ and $1x + 5y = 13$.
   A) (2, 3)   B) (3, 2)   C) (6, 0)   D) (–2, 3)
   Ans: B

10. Find the point of intersection of the lines whose equations are $4x + 2y = 12$ and $3x + 9y = 39$.
    A) (5, –4)   B) (10, 1)   C) (1, 4)   D) (2, 2)
    Ans: C

11. Find the point of intersection of the lines whose equations are $3x + 2y = 21$ and $2x + 1y = 13$.
    A) $(5, 3)$ B) $(29, 45)$ C) $(8, -3)$ D) $(3, 5)$
    Ans: A

12. Find the point of intersection of the lines whose equations are $2x + 5y = 6$ and $3x + 2y = 9$.
    A) $(3, 0)$ B) $(2, 1)$ C) $(-3, 0)$ D) $(1, 2)$
    Ans: A

13. Graph the constraint inequalities for a linear programming problem shown below. Which feasible region shown is correct?
    $$2x + 3y \leq 12$$
    $$x \geq 0, y \geq 0$$

    a. 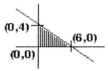   b.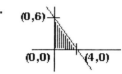

    c. 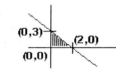   d.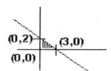

    Ans: A

14. Graph the constraint inequalities for a linear programming problem shown below. Which feasible region shown is correct?
    $$4x + 3y \leq 24$$
    $$x \geq 0, y \geq 0$$

    a.   b.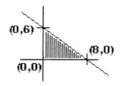

    c. 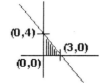   d.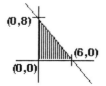

    Ans: D

15. Graph the constraint inequalities for a linear programming problem shown below. Which feasible region shown is correct?

$$6x + 4y \leq 12$$
$$x \geq 0, y \geq 0$$

a.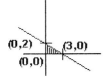

b.

c.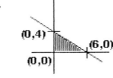

d.

Ans: B

16. Graph the constraint inequalities for a linear programming problem shown below. Which feasible region shown is correct?

$$1x + 4y \leq 8$$
$$x \geq 0, y \geq 0$$

a.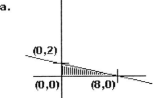

b.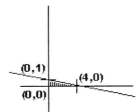

c.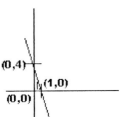

d.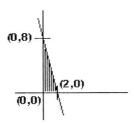

Ans: A

17. Write a resource constraint for this situation: a lawn service company has 40 hours of worker time available. Mowing a lawn (x) takes 3 hours and trimming (y) takes 2 hours. The profit from mowing is $15 and the profit from trimming is $10.

A) $3x + 2y \leq 40$

B) $(40/3)x + 10y \leq 40$

C) $15x + 10y \leq 40$

D) $5x + 5y \leq 40$

Ans: A

18. Write a resource constraint for this situation: producing a plastic ruler (x) requires 10 grams of plastic while producing a pencil box (y) requires 30 grams of plastic. There are 2000 grams of plastic available.
    A) $200x + (2000/30)y \le 2000$
    C) $10x + 30y \le 2000$
    B) $30x + 10y \le 2000$
    D) $x + y \le 2000$
    Ans: C

19. Write the constraint inequalities for this situation: Kim and Lynn produce pottery vases and bowls. A vase requires 35 oz. of clay and 5 oz. of glaze. A bowl requires 20 oz. of clay and 10 oz. of glaze. There are 500 oz. of clay available and 200 oz. of glaze available. The profit on one vase is $5 and the profit on one bowl is $4.
    A) $35x + 5y \le 5, 20x + 10y \le 4, x \ge 0, y \ge 0$
    B) $35x + 5y \le 500, 20x + 10y \le 200, x \ge 0, y \ge 0$
    C) $35x + 20y \le 500, 5x + 10y \le 200, x \ge 0, y \ge 0$
    D) $35x + 20y \le \$5, 5x + 10y \le \$4, x \ge 0, y \ge 0$
    Ans: C

20. Write the constraint inequalities for this situation: a cheeseburger requires 5 oz. of meat and 0.7 oz. of cheese while a superburger requires 7 oz. of meat and 0.6 oz. of cheese. The burger stand has 350 oz. of meat and 42 oz. of cheese available. The profit on a cheeseburger is 10 cents and the profit on a superburger is 40 cents.
    A) $5x + 7y \le 350, 0.7x + 0.6y \le 42, x \ge 0, y \ge 0$
    B) $5x + 0.7y \le 10, 7x + 0.6y \le 40, x \ge 0, y \ge 0$
    C) $5x + 7y \le 10, 0.7x + 0.6y \le 40, x \ge 0, y \ge 0$
    D) $70x + 50y \le 350, 60x + 70y \le 42, x \ge 0, y \ge 0$
    Ans: A

21. Write the resource constraints for this situation: a small stereo manufacturer makes a receiver and a CD player. Each receiver takes eight hours to assemble and one hour to test and ship. Each CD player takes 15 hours to assemble and two hours to test and ship. The profit on each receiver is $30 and the profit on each CD player is $50. There are 160 hours available in the assembly department and 22 hours available in the testing and shipping department.
    A) $8x + 1y \le 30, 15x + 2y \le 50, x \ge 0, y \ge 0$
    B) $8x + 1y \le 160, 15x + 2y \le 22, x \ge 0, y \ge 0$
    C) $8x + 15y \le 30, 1x + 2y \le 50, x \ge 0, y \ge 0$
    D) $8x + 15y \le 160, 1x + 2y \le 22, x \ge 0, y \ge 0$
    Ans: D

22. Write the resource constraints for this situation: Kim and Lynn produce tables and chairs. Each piece is assembled, sanded, and stained. A table requires 2 hours to assemble, 3 hours to sand, and 3 hours to stain. A chair requires 4 hours to assemble, 2 hours to sand, and 3 hours to stain. The profit earned on each table is $20 and on each chair is $12. Together Kim and Lynn spend at most 16 hours assembling, 10 hours sanding, and 13 hours staining.
    A) $2x + 4y \leq 16, 3x + 2y \leq 10, 3x + 3y \leq 13, x \geq 0, y \geq 0$
    B) $2x + 3y + 3z \leq 20, 4x + 2y + 3z \leq 12, x \geq 0, y \geq 0, z \geq 0$
    C) $16x + 10y + 13z \leq 0, 2x + 3y + 3z \leq 20, 4x + 2y + 3z \leq 12, x \geq 0, y \geq 0, z \geq 0$
    D) $8x + 4y \leq 16, (10/3)x + 5y \leq 10, (13/3)x + (13/3)y \leq 13, x \geq 0, y \geq 0$
    Ans: A

23. Write the resource constraints for this situation: a company manufactures patio chairs and rockers. Each piece is made of wood, plastic, and aluminum. A chair requires 1 unit of wood, 1 unit of plastic, and 2 units of aluminum. A rocker requires 1 unit of wood, 2 units of plastic, and 5 units of aluminum. The company's profit on a chair is $7 and on a rocker is $12. The company has available 400 units of wood, 500 units of plastic, and 1450 units of aluminum.
    A) $1x + 1y + 2z \leq 7, 1x + 2y + 5z \leq 12, x \geq 0, y \geq 0, z \geq 0$
    B) $1x + 1y \leq 400, 1x + 2y \leq 500, 2x + 5y \leq 1450, x \geq 0, y \geq 0$
    C) $400x + 500y + 1450z \leq 0, 1x + 1y + 2z \leq 7, 1x + 2y + 5z \leq 12, x \geq 0, y \geq 0, z \geq 0$
    D) $7x + 12y \leq 400, 2x + 5y \leq 1450, x \geq 0, y \geq 0$
    Ans: B

24. Graph the feasible region identified by the inequalities:

$$2x + 3y \le 12$$
$$1x + 5y \le 10$$
$$x \ge 0, y \ge 0$$

a.

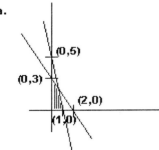

b.

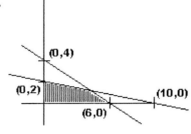

c.

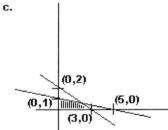

d.

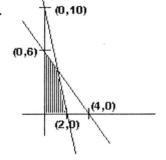

Ans: B

25. Graph the feasible region identified by the inequalities:

$$4x + 1y \le 12$$
$$2x + 7y \le 28$$
$$x \ge 0, y \ge 0$$

a.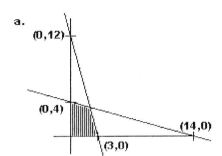

b.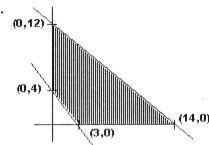

c.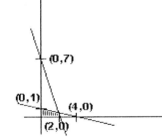

d.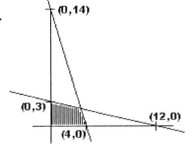

Ans: A

26. Graph the feasible region identified by the inequalities:

$$5x + 1y \le 10$$
$$3x + 3y \le 18$$
$$x \ge 0, y \ge 0$$

a.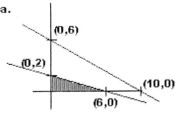

b.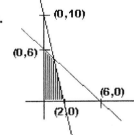

c.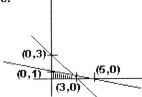

d.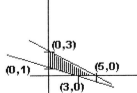

Ans: B

27. Graph the feasible region identified by the inequalities:

$$4x + 3y \le 12$$
$$3x + 3y \le 18$$
$$x \ge 0, y \ge 0$$

a.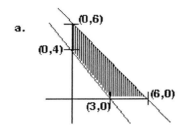

b.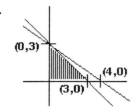

c.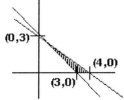

d.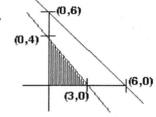

Ans: D

28. Given below is the sketch of the feasible region in a linear programming problem. Which point is *not* in the feasible region?

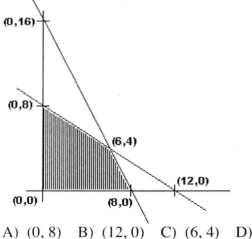

A) (0, 8)   B) (12, 0)   C) (6, 4)   D) (2, 2)
Ans: B

29. Given below is the sketch of the feasible region in a linear programming problem. Which point is *not* in the feasible region?

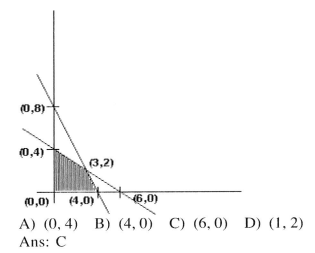

A) $(0, 4)$ B) $(4, 0)$ C) $(6, 0)$ D) $(1, 2)$
Ans: C

30. Given below is the sketch of the feasible region in a linear programming problem. Which point is *not* in the feasible region?

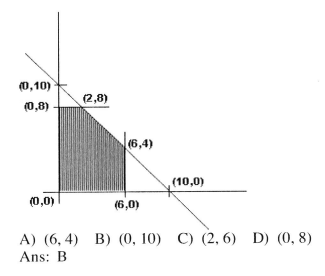

A) $(6, 4)$ B) $(0, 10)$ C) $(2, 6)$ D) $(0, 8)$
Ans: B

31. Given below is the sketch of the feasible region in a linear programming problem. Which point is *not* in the feasible region?

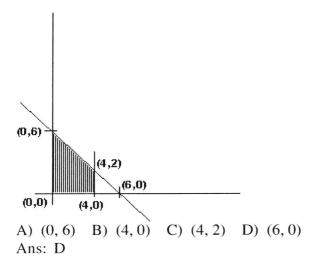

A) (0, 6) B) (4, 0) C) (4, 2) D) (6, 0)
Ans: D

32. Given below is the sketch of the feasible region in a linear programming problem. Which point is *not* in the feasible region?

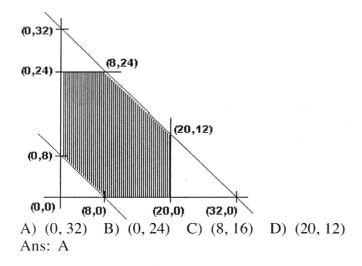

A) (0, 32) B) (0, 24) C) (8, 16) D) (20, 12)
Ans: A

33. Write a profit formula for this mixture problem: Kim and Lynn produce pottery vases and bowls. A vase requires 35 oz. of clay and 5 oz. of glaze. A bowl requires 20 oz. of clay and 10 oz. of glaze. There are 500 oz. of clay available and 200 oz. of glaze available. The profit on one vase is $5 and the profit on one bowl is $4.
A) $P = 500x + 200y$ B) $P = 35x + 20y$ C) $P = 5x + 4y$ D) $P = 5x + 10y$
Ans: C

34. Write a profit formula for this mixture problem: a small stereo manufacturer makes a receiver and a CD player. Each receiver takes eight hours to assemble, one hour to test and ship, and earns a profit of $30. Each CD player takes 15 hours to assemble, two hours to test and ship, and earns a profit of $50. There are 160 hours available in the assembly department and 22 hours available in the testing and shipping department.
    A) $P = 8x + 1y$ B) $P = 160x + 22y$ C) $P = 15x + 2y$ D) $P = 30x + 50y$
    Ans: D

35. Write a profit formula for this mixture problem: Kim and Lynn produce tables and chairs. Each piece is assembled, sanded, and stained. A table requires two hours to assemble, three hours to sand, and three hours to stain. A chair requires four hours to assemble, two hours to sand, and three hours to stain. The profit earned on each table is $20 and on each chair is $12. Together Kim and Lynn spend at most 16 hours assembling, 10 hours sanding, and 13 hours staining.
    A) $P = 20x + 12y$ C) $P = 16x + 10y + 13z$
    B) $P = 2x + 3y + 3z$ D) $P = 8x + 9y$
    Ans: A

36. Write a profit formula for this mixture problem: A company manufactures patio chairs and rockers. Each piece is made of wood, plastic, and aluminum. A chair requires one unit of wood, one unit of plastic, and two units of aluminum. A rocker requires one unit of wood, two units of plastic, and five units of aluminum. The company's profit on a chair is $7 and on a rocker is $12. The company has available 400 units of wood, 500 units of plastic, and 1450 units of aluminum.
    A) $P = 400x + 500y + 1450z$ C) $P = 7x + 12y$
    B) $P = 4x + 8y$ D) $P = 1x + 2y + 5z$
    Ans: C

37. The graph of the feasible region for a mixture problem is shown below. Find the point that maximizes the profit function $P = 2x + y$.

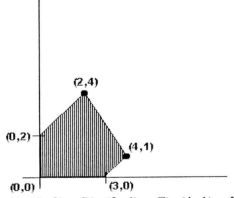

    A) (0, 2)   B) (2, 4)   C) (4, 1)   D) (3, 0)
    Ans: C

38. The graph of the feasible region for a mixture problem is shown below. Find the point that maximizes the profit function P = *x* + *4y*.

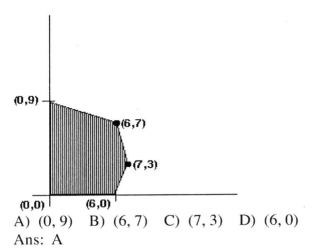

A) (0, 9) B) (6, 7) C) (7, 3) D) (6, 0)
Ans: A

39. The graph of the feasible region for a mixture problem is shown below. Find the point that maximizes the profit function P = 2*x* + 5*y*.

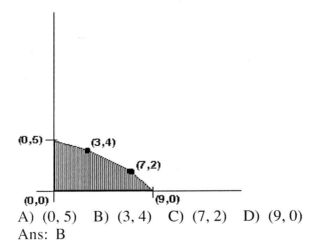

A) (0, 5) B) (3, 4) C) (7, 2) D) (9, 0)
Ans: B

40. The graph of the feasible region for a mixture problem is shown below. Find the point that maximizes the profit function P = 3x + 6y.

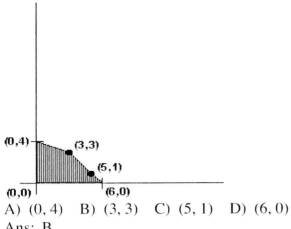

A) (0, 4)   B) (3, 3)   C) (5, 1)   D) (6, 0)
Ans: B

41. The graph of the feasible region for a mixture problem is shown below. Find the point that maximizes the profit function P = 3x + 6y.

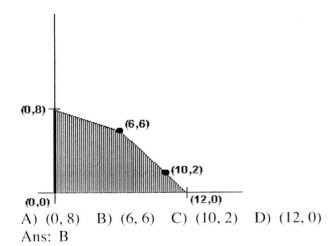

A) (0, 8)   B) (6, 6)   C) (10, 2)   D) (12, 0)
Ans: B

42. The graph of the feasible region for a mixture problem is shown below. Find the point that maximizes the profit function $P = 3x + y$.

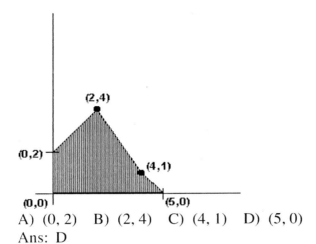

A) (0, 2)   B) (2, 4)   C) (4, 1)   D) (5, 0)
Ans: D

43. The simplex algorithm always gives optimal solutions to linear programming problems.
A) True   B) False
Ans: A

44. An optimal solution for a linear programming problem will always occur at a corner point of the feasible region.
A) True   B) False
Ans: A

45. Any linear programming problem has at most two products.
A) True   B) False
Ans: B

46. An optimal production policy for a linear programming mixture problem may eliminate one product.
A) True   B) False
Ans: A

47. The graph of the inequality $2x + 7y \leq 10$ is a straight line.
A) True   B) False
Ans: B

48. The ordered pair (200, 400) satisfies the inequality $x + 2y \leq 1500$.
A) True   B) False
Ans: A

49. The feasible region for a linear programming mixture problem may have holes in it.
    A) True   B) False
    Ans: B

50. The feasible region for a linear programming mixture problem with two products is in the first quadrant of the Cartesian plane.
    A) True   B) False
    Ans: A

51. Suppose the feasible region has four corners at these points: (0, 0), (5, 0), (0, 4), and (2, 3). If the profit formula is $2x + $3y, what is the maximum profit possible?
    A) $12   B) $13   C) $14   D) $15
    Ans: B

52. Suppose the feasible region has four corners at these points: (0, 0), (8, 0), (0, 12), and (4, 8). If the profit formula is $2x + $4y, what is the maximum profit possible?
    A) $16   B) $40   C) $48   D) $54
    Ans: C

53. Suppose the feasible region has five corners at these points: (1, 1), (1, 7), (5, 7), (5, 5), and (4, 3). If the profit formula is $10x + $5y, which point maximizes the profit?
    A) (1, 7)   B) (5, 7)   C) (5, 5)   D) (4, 3)
    Ans: B

54. Suppose the feasible region has five corners, at these points: (1, 1), (1, 7), (5, 7), (5, 5), and (4, 3). If the profit formula is $5x − $2y, which point maximizes the profit?
    A) (1, 7)   B) (5, 7)   C) (5, 5)   D) (4, 3)
    Ans: C

55. Find the graph of the equation $3x + 2y = 6$.

A)

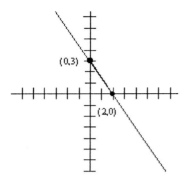

B)

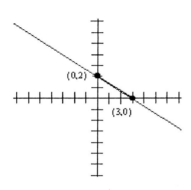

C)

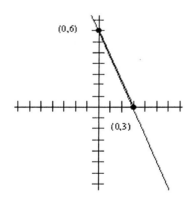

D)

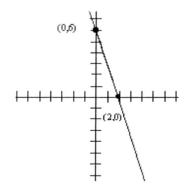

Ans: A

56. Find the graph of the inequality $2x + 6y \leq 18$.
    A)

    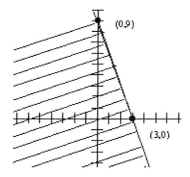

    B)

    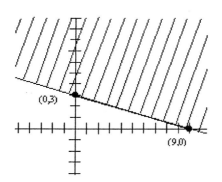

    C)

    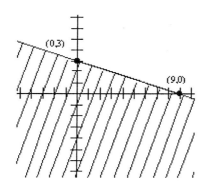

    D)

    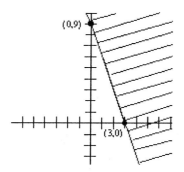

    Ans: C

57. Find the point of intersection of the lines whose equations are x + 3y = 18 and 2x + y = 11.
    A) (3, 5)   B) (5, 3)   C) (2, 3)   D) (3, 2)
    Ans: A

58. Suppose the feasible region has four corners, at these points: (0, 0), (5, 0), (0, 4), and (2, 3). For which of these profit formulae is the profit maximized, producing a mix of products?
    A) $4x + $3y   B) $3x + $4y   C) $x – $y   D) $2x – $y
    Ans: B

59. Suppose the feasible region has four corners, at these points: (0, 0), (8, 0), (0, 12), and (4, 8). For which of these profit formulae is the profit maximized, producing a mix of products?
    A) $5x + $2y   B) $2x + $5y   C) $x – $y   D) $2x – $y
    Ans: A

60. Consider the feasible region identified by the inequalities below.

    $x \geq 0; y \geq 0; x + y \leq 4; x + 3y \leq 6$

    Which point is *not* a corner of the region?
    A) (0, 2)   B) (0, 4)   C) (3, 1)   D) (4, 0)
    Ans: B

61. Which of these methods for the transportation problem produces a feasible solution?
    A)   Stepping Stone Method (SSM)   C)   Both SSM and NCR
    B)   Northwest Corner Rule (NCR)   D)   Neither SSM nor NCR
    Ans: C

62. Which of these methods for the transportation problem produces an improved solution?
    A)   Stepping Stone Method (SSM)   C)   Both SSM and NCR
    B)   Northwest Corner Rule (NCR)   D)   Neither SSM nor NCR
    Ans: A

Chapter 4: Free-Response

1. Sketch the graph of the equation $3x + 5y = 30$.
   Ans:

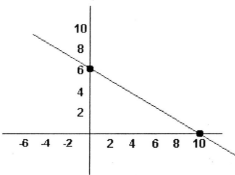

2. Sketch the graph of the equation $4x + 3y = 24$.
   Ans:

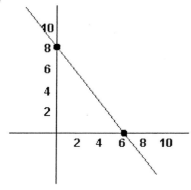

3. Sketch the graph of the equation $x + 3y = 9$.
   Ans:

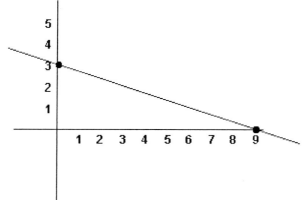

4. Sketch the graph of the inequality $2x + 4y \le 12$.
   Ans:

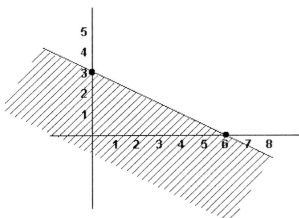

5. Sketch the graph of the inequality $5x + y \le 15$.
   Ans:

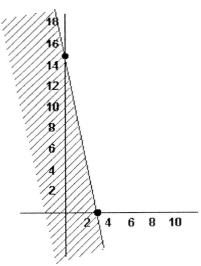

6. Sketch the graph of the inequality $4x + 6y \leq 12$.
   Ans:

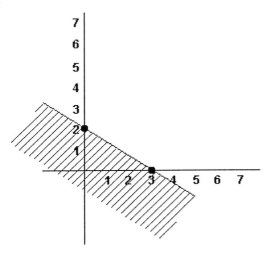

7. Find the point of intersection for the lines represented by the equations $2x + 4y = 12$ and $3x + y = 13$.
   Ans: $(4, 1)$

8. Find the point of intersection for the lines represented by the equations $x + 5y = 28$ and $4x + 3y = 27$.
   Ans: $(3, 5)$

9. Find the point of intersection for the lines represented by the equations $3x + 2y = 14$ and $4x + 5y = 28$.
   Ans: $(2, 4)$

10. Find the point of intersection for the lines represented by the equations $2x + 7y = 61$ and $3x + 4y = 46$.
    Ans: $(6, 7)$

11. With the given constraints for the following linear programming mixture problem, graph the feasible region.

$$2x + 3y \leq 1800$$
$$x \geq 0$$
$$y \geq 0$$

Ans:

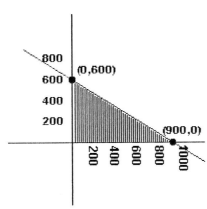

12. With the given constraints for the following linear programming mixture problem, graph the feasible region.

$$x + 6y \leq 110$$
$$x \geq 0$$
$$y \geq 0$$

Ans:

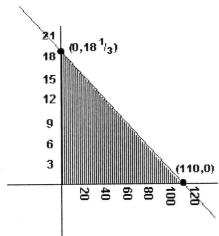

13. With the given constraints for the following linear programming mixture problem, graph the feasible region.

$$2x + 3y \leq 180$$
$$5x + 2y \leq 230$$
$$x \geq 0$$
$$y \geq 0$$

Ans:

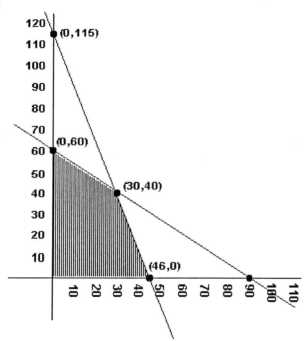

14. With the given constraints for the following linear programming mixture problem, graph the feasible region.

$$x + 6y \leq 1100$$
$$4x + y \leq 2100$$
$$x \geq 0$$
$$y \geq 0$$

Ans:

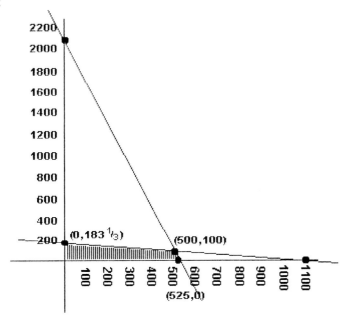

15. With the given constraints for the following linear programming mixture problem, graph the feasible region.

$$x + 3y \le 23$$
$$3x + 7y \le 50$$
$$x \ge 2$$
$$y \ge 4$$

Ans:

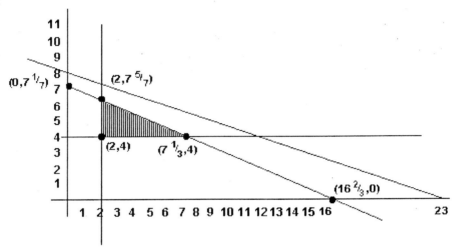

16. Find the constraint inequalities and the profit formula for this linear programming mixture problem: Toni has a small business producing dried floral wreaths and table arrangements. Each wreath takes seven hours to produce, uses 12 stems of flowers, and earns a profit of $23. Each table arrangement takes five hours to produce, uses 20 stems of flowers, and earns a profit of $26. Toni can work no more than 30 hours per week and has a steady supply of 100 stems of dried flowers per week. What should Toni's production schedule be to optimize profit?

Ans: x is the number of wreaths produced and y is the number of table arrangements produced.

Constraint inequalities:
$$7x + 5y \le 30$$
$$2x + 20y \le 100$$
$$x \ge 0$$
$$y \ge 0$$

Profit formula: $23x + 26y = P$

17. Find the constraint inequalities and the profit formula for this linear programming mixture problem: the Acme Construction Company builds two types of houses. Plan A requires 200 man-hours for rough construction and 70 man-hours for finish work. Plan B requires 300 man-hours for rough construction and 50 man-hours for finish work. Acme has carpenters available to provide up to 900 hours of rough construction per month and 260 hours of finish work per month. If Acme clears $7000 profit on a Plan A house and $8000 profit on a Plan B house, how should they schedule production to maximize profit?

Ans: x is the number of Plan A homes produced and y is the number of Plan B homes.

Constraint inequalities: $200x + 300y \leq 900$

$70x + 50y \leq 260$

$x \geq 0$

$y \geq 0$

Profit formula: $P = 7000x + 8000y$

18. Write the constraint inequalities and the profit formula for this linear programming mixture problem: the "Dig-The-Pig" ham shop sells regular and special ham and cheese sandwiches. The regular is made of 5 oz. of meat, 0.7 oz. of cheese, and requires three minutes of preparation time. The special is made of 7 oz. of meat, 0.6 oz. of cheese, and requires 11 minutes of preparation time. The profit on a regular sandwich is 10 cents while the profit on a special sandwich is 40 cents. If "Dig-The-Pig" has 350 oz. of meat, 42 oz. of cheese, and 330 minutes of preparation time available each lunch period, how many of each type of sandwich should they try to sell to maximize profit?

Ans: x is the number of regular sandwiches made and y is the number of special sandwiches made.

Constraint inequalities: $5x + 7y \leq 350$

$.7x + .6y \leq 42$

$3x + 11y \leq 330$

$x \geq 0$

$y \geq 0$

Profit formula: $P = 10x + 40y$

19. Write the constraint inequalities and the profit formula for this linear programming mixture problem: Amazin' Raisin Baking Co. makes both raisin cake and raisin pie. A batch of raisin cakes requires 5 lbs. of flour, 2 lbs. of sugar, and 1 lb. of raisins. A batch of raisin pies requires 2 lbs. of flour, 3 lbs. of sugar, and 4 lbs. of raisins. There are 165 lbs. of flour, 110 lbs. of sugar, and 120 lbs. of raisins available each week. Standing orders require at least 5 batches of raisin cakes and 8 batches of raisin pies per week. If profit on a batch of raisin cakes is $35 and profit on a batch of raisin pies is $40, how many batches of each should be made per week to maximize profit?
    Ans: x is the number of cakes and y is the number of pies.

    Constraint inequalities:
$$5x + 2y \le 165$$
$$2x + 3y \le 110$$
$$1x + 4y \le 120$$
$$x \ge 5$$
$$y \ge 8$$

    Profit formula:
$$P = 35x + 40y$$

20. Solve this linear programming mixture problem: Kim and Lynn produce pottery vases and bowls. A vase requires 25 oz. of clay and 5 oz. of glaze. A bowl requires 20 oz. of clay and 10 oz. of glaze. There are 500 oz. of clay available and 160 oz. of glaze available. The profit on one vase is $5 and the profit on one bowl is $3.
    Ans: x is the number of vases and y is the number of bowls.

    Constraint inequalities:
$$25x + 20y \le 500$$
$$5x + 10y \le 160$$
$$x \ge 0$$
$$y \ge 0$$

    Profit formula:
$$5x + 3y = P$$

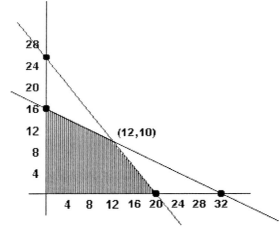

21. Solve this linear programming mixture problem: A small stereo manufacturer makes a receiver and a CD player. Each receiver takes eight hours to assemble, one hour to test and ship, and earns a profit of $30. Each CD player takes fifteen hours to assemble, two hours to test and ship, and earns a profit of $50. There are 160 hours available in the assembly department and 26 hours available in the testing and shipping department. What should the production schedule be to maximize profit?

Ans: x is the number of receivers and y is the number of CD players.

Constraint inequalities: $8x + 15y \leq 160$
$$1x + 2y \leq 26$$
$$x \geq 0$$
$$y \geq 0$$

Profit formula: $P = 30x + 50y$

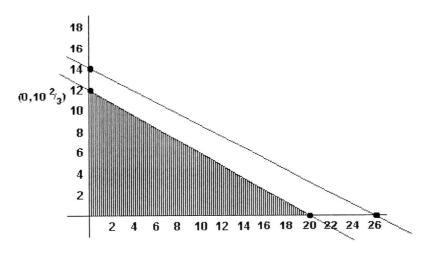

Maximum profit occurs at (20,0). Make 20 receivers and no CD players.

22. Explain what the real world implications are if the optimal production policy for a linear programming mixture problem is represented by a point on the x-axis of the Cartesian plane.

Ans: If the optimal production policy for a linear programming problem is represented by a point on the x-axis, it means that profit is optimized by making only one type of product. In order to maximize profit, the company needs to drop from its product line the item represented by the variable y.

23. Describe the shape of the feasible region for linear programming mixture problems with two products.

Ans: A linear programming mixture problem with two products has a feasible region which is represented by a convex polygon in Quadrant I of the Cartesian plane.

24. Name two alternatives to the graphical approach for solving linear programming problems.

    Ans: Two alternatives to the graphical approach are the simplex algorithm and Karmarkar's algorithm.

25. Explain why a linear programming mixture problem might have minimum constraints other than zero.

    Ans: Answers may vary. A linear programming problem might have minimum constraints other than zero if the company had standing orders for some number of its products which must be filled and cannot be canceled.

26. Explain why the feasible region for a linear programming mixture problem must be in the first quadrant of the Cartesian plane.

    Ans: In a linear programming mixture problem, x and y represent the number of two different products to be made. Since it is impossible to produce negative numbers of products, the feasible region must be in Quadrant I.

27. Graph the feasible region identified by the inequalities:

    $x + y \leq 5$
    $x + 2y \leq 8$
    $x \geq 0, y \geq 0$
    Ans:

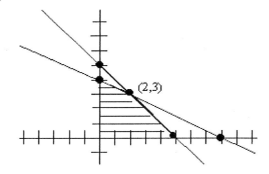

28. Graph the feasible region identified by the inequalities:

$2x + 5y \le 70$
$5x + y \le 60$
$x \ge 0, y \ge 0$

Ans:

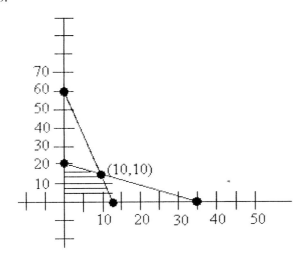

29. Find the maximum value of P, where P = 10x + 100y subject to the constraints:

$x \ge 0; y \ge 0 ; 2x + 5y \le 20; 2x + y \le 12$
Ans: The maximum occurs at the point (6, 0), where P = 600.

30. Find the maximum value of P, where P = 3x + 4y subject to the constraints:

$x \ge 0; y \ge 0 ; x + 2y \le 8; x + y \le 5$
Ans: The maximum occurs at the point (2, 3), where P = 18.

31. Find the point of intersection of the lines whose equations are 6x + 5y = 80 and 2x + y = 20.
Ans: (5, 10)

32. What type of solution does the Northwest Corner Rule produce for the transportation problem?
Ans: Feasible, but probably not optimal

33. What type of solution does the Stepping Stone Method produce for the transportation problem?
Ans: Feasible, more efficient, but possibly not optimal

34. A solution for the transportation problem is optimal when the empty cells have what property?
    Ans: Every empty cell's indicator value is positive or zero

Chapter 5: Multiple-Choice

1. Below are listed the ages (in months) of children at a home day care. Choose the correct stemplot of the data.

    18, 24, 25, 35, 37, 42, 47, 48, 48, 58

    a.
    ```
    1 | 8
    2 | 45
    3 | 57
    4 | 278
    5 | 8
    ```
    b.
    ```
    1 | 8
    2 | 45
    3 | 57
    4 | 2788
    5 | 8
    ```
    c.
    ```
    1 | 1
    2 | 2
    3 | 2
    4 | 4
    5 | 1
    ```
    d.
    ```
    1 | 18
    2 | 24, 25
    3 | 35, 37
    4 | 42, 47, 48
    5 | 58
    ```
    A) A   B) B   C) C   D) D
    Ans: B

2. Below are listed the numbers of children in the classrooms of a small elementary school. Choose the correct stemplot of the data.

    12, 14, 20, 21, 21, 25, 27, 30, 30, 30

    a.
    ```
    1 | 12,14
    2 | 20,21,27
    3 | 30
    ```
    b.
    ```
    1 | 2
    2 | 5
    3 | 3
    ```
    c.
    ```
    1 | 24
    2 | 01157
    3 | 000
    ```
    d.
    ```
    1 | 24
    2 | 0157
    3 | 0
    ```
    A) A   B) B   C) C   D) D
    Ans: C

3. Given the stemplot below, which description is true?

    ```
    2 | 9
    3 | 267
    4 | 12
    5 | 0
    6 |
    7 | 5
    ```
    A)   There are no outliers on the stemplot.
    B)   The numbers 29 and 75 are outliers on the stemplot.
    C)   The number 75 is the only outlier on the stemplot.
    D)   The number 60 is the only outlier on the stemplot.
    Ans: C

4. Given the stemplot below, which description is true?

```
2 | 9
3 | 267
4 | 12
5 | 0259
6 | 258
7 | 05
```

A)   There are no outliers on the stemplot.
B)   The number 29 is the only outlier on the stemplot.
C)   The numbers 29 and 75 are the only outliers on the stemplot.
D)   The number 75 is the only outlier on the stemplot.
Ans: A

5. Given the stemplot below, which description is true?

```
0 | 9
1 | 89
2 | 12
3 | 0259
4 | 258
5 | 0
```

A)   There are no outliers on the stemplot.
B)   The number 9 is the only outlier on the stemplot.
C)   The numbers 9 and 50 are the only outliers on the stemplot.
D)   The number 50 is the only outlier on the stemplot.
Ans: B

Use the following to answer questions 6-8:

Use the following histogram of waiting times for patients at a health clinic to answer the question(s) below.

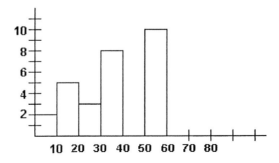

6. How many patients waited between 20 and 29 minutes?
A) 2   B) 3   C) 6   D) 8
Ans: B

7. Based on the histogram, which statement must be true?
   A)   There are no gaps in the histogram.
   B)   Eight patients waited exactly 35 minutes.
   C)   Two patients were seen immediately on arrival at the clinic.
   D)   More patients waited longer than one half-hour than waited less than one half-hour.
   Ans: D

8. Based on the histogram, which statement is true?
   A)   The histogram is roughly symmetric.
   B)   The class from 50 to 59 minutes represents 10 outliers.
   C)   There is a gap in the histogram.
   D)   The histogram is skewed to the right.
   Ans: C

9. Below is a histogram of the ages of people attending a concert. Which statement is true?

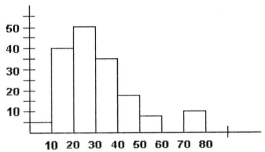

   A)   The histogram is roughly symmetric.
   B)   There is a gap in the histogram.
   C)   The histogram is skewed to the left.
   D)   The center of the distribution is at about age 50.
   Ans: B

10. Given the histogram below, which statement is true?

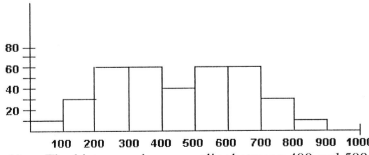

   A)   The histogram has an outlier between 400 and 500.
   B)   The histogram is skewed to the right.
   C)   The histogram is symmetric.
   D)   The histogram has a gap between 400 and 500.
   Ans: C

11. Given the histogram below, which statement is true?

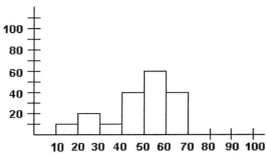

A)   The histogram has a gap.   C)   The histogram is skewed to the left.
B)   There is an outlier at 100.   D)   The histogram is roughly symmetric.
Ans: C

Use the following to answer questions 12-15:

Use the following information to answer the question(s) below.

Below are the ages of 15 students in a college class.

    27, 50, 33, 25, 86, 25, 85, 31, 37, 44, 20, 36, 59, 34, 28

12. What is the median age?
    A) 34   B) 31   C) 41.3   D) 20.6
    Ans: A

13. What is the mean age?
    A) 34   B) 31   C) 41.3   D) 20.6
    Ans: C

14. What is the standard deviation of the ages?
    A) 26.4   B) 20.6   C) 19.9   D) 4.5
    Ans: B

15. What is the the first quartile of the ages?
    A) 20   B) 25   C) 27   D) 50
    Ans: C

16. Below are the heights (in inches) of students in a third-grade class. Find the mean height.

    39, 37, 48, 49, 40, 42, 48, 53, 47, 42, 49, 51, 52, 45, 47, 48

    A) 47.5   B) 50   C) 46.0625   D) 47
    Ans: C

17. Below are the heights (in inches) of students in a third-grade class. Find the median height.

    39, 37, 48, 49, 40, 42, 48, 53, 47, 42, 49, 51, 52, 45, 47, 48

    A) 47.5   B) 50   C) 46.0625   D) 47
    Ans: A

Use the following to answer questions 18-23:

Use the following information to answer the question(s) below.

Below is a list of the number of dogs owned by families in a particular neighborhood:

4, 3, 7, 1, 5, 1, 2, 9, 0, 3

18. What is the mean number of dogs owned?
    A) 2.7   B) 3   C) 3.5   D) 3.9
    Ans: C

19. What is the median number of dogs owned?
    A) 2.7   B) 3   C) 3.5   D) 3.9
    Ans: B

20. What is the standard deviation for this data?
    A) 2.8   B) 5.6   C) 7.3   D) 8.1
    Ans: A

21. What is the first quartile for this data?
    A) 0   B) 1   C) 1.5   D) 2
    Ans: B

22. What is the third quartile for this data?
    A) 5   B) 6   C) 7   D) 9
    Ans: A

23. What is the range for this data?
    A) 1   B) 3   C) 7   D) 9
    Ans: D

Use the following to answer questions 24-27:

Use the following information to answer the question(s) below.

Below are the number of errors made by a typist on various pages of typing.

   14, 6, 12, 19, 2, 35, 5, 4, 3, 7, 5, 8

24. Find the mean number of errors.
   A) 6.5   B) 7   C) 9.583   D) 10
   Ans: D

25. Find the median number of errors.
   A) 6.5   B) 7   C) 9.583   D) 10
   Ans: A

26. Find the third quartile for the number of errors.
   A) 5   B) 13   C) 15.5   D) 4.5
   Ans: B

27. Find the first quartile for the number of errors.
   A) 5   B) 13   C) 15.5   D) 4.5
   Ans: D

28. Given the set of data below, find the mean.

      2, 4, 4, 5, 6, 9

   A) 4.5   B) 5   C) 7   D) 30
   Ans: B

29. Given the set of data below, find the median.

      2, 4, 4, 5, 6, 9

   A) 4.5   B) 5   C) 7   D) 30
   Ans: A

30. Given the set of data below, find the range.

      2, 4, 4, 5, 6, 9

   A) 2   B) 4   C) 7   D) 9
   Ans: C

31. Given the set of data below, find the standard deviation.

    2, 4, 4, 5, 6, 9

    A) 2.37   B) 4.5   C) 4.74   D) 5.6
    Ans: A

32. Given the set of data below, find the mean.

    25, 16, 50, 19, 42, 37

    A) 34.5   B) 31   C) 31.5   D) 50
    Ans: C

33. Given the set of data below, find the median.

    25, 16, 50, 19, 42, 37

    A) 34.5   B) 31   C) 31.5   D) 50
    Ans: B

34. Given the set of data below, find the range.

    25, 16, 50, 19, 42, 37

    A) 12   B) 34   C) 50   D) 66
    Ans: B

35. Given the set of data below, find the standard deviation.

    25, 16, 50, 19, 42, 37

    A) 6.07   B) 13.58   C) 184.3   D) 921.5
    Ans: B

Use the following to answer questions 36-39:

Use the following information to answer the question(s) below.

Below are the numbers of pages in seven chapters of a textbook.

    14, 14, 20, 38, 47, 48, 57

36. What is the mean number of pages?
    A) 34   B) 38   C) 37.33   D) 42.5
    Ans: A

37. What is the median number of pages?
    A) 34   B) 38   C) 37.33   D) 42.5
    Ans: B

38. What is the range?
    A) 14   B) 38   C) 43   D) 71
    Ans: C

39. What is the standard deviation?
    A) 18.52   B) 18   C) 17.82   D) 17.67
    Ans: C

40. Below are the lengths (in minutes) of phone calls made on an 800 line to a business on one day. Find the five-number summary for this data.

    14, 6, 12, 19, 2, 35, 5, 4, 3, 7, 5, 8

    A)   5, 8, 14, 15.5, 20   C)   2, 4, 6, 12, 19
    B)   2, 4, 7, 14, 35   D)   2, 4.5, 6.5, 13, 35
    Ans: D

41. Below are the numbers of accidents occurring at a certain corner on 15 consecutive days. Find the five-number summary of the data.

    0, 1, 3, 4, 5, 2, 2, 6, 7, 2, 0, 1, 3, 6, 3

    A) 0, 1.5, 3.5, 5.5, 7   B) 0, 1, 3, 5, 7   C) 0, 4, 6, 1, 3   D) 0, 1.5, 3, 5.5, 7
    Ans: B

42. Below are the scores of 21 students on a history exam. Find the five-number summary of the scores.

    50, 60, 60, 60, 65, 65, 70, 75, 75, 75, 75, 80, 80, 80, 85, 85, 90, 95, 95, 95, 100

    A)   50, 65, 75, 85, 100   C)   50, 65, 76.9, 87.5, 100
    B)   50, 65, 75, 87.5, 100   D)   50, 65, 77.5, 90, 100
    Ans: B

43. Which of the following statements about measures of the center of a distribution of data is true?
    A)   Neither the mean nor the median is strongly affected by an outlier in the data.
    B)   The mean is strongly affected by an outlier in the data but the median is not.
    C)   The median is strongly affected by an outlier in the data but the mean is not.
    D)   Both the mean and the median are strongly affected by an outlier in the data.
    Ans: B

44. Which of the following statements about measures of the spread of data is true?
    A)   Neither the quartiles nor the standard deviation is strongly affected by an outlier in the data.
    B)   The quartiles are strongly affected by an outlier in the data but the standard deviation is not.
    C)   The standard deviation is strongly affected by an outlier in the data but the quartiles are not.
    D)   Both the quartiles and the standard deviation are strongly affected by an outlier in the data.
    Ans: C

45. Given the histogram below for a set of data, which of the following statements is true?

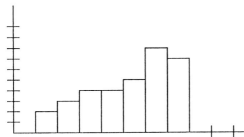

    A)   The five-number summary would describe the data better than the mean and standard deviation.
    B)   The mean and standard deviation would describe the data better than the five-number summary.
    C)   Either the mean and standard deviation or the five-number summary would be equally good to describe the data.
    D)   Neither the mean and standard deviation nor the five-number summary could be used to describe the data.
    Ans: A

46. Given the histogram below for a set of data, which statement is true?

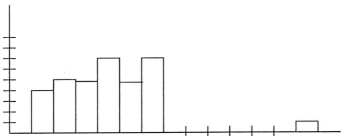

A)   Either the mean or the median would describe the center of the data well.
B)   The mean would be a better measure of the center of the data than the median.
C)   The median would be a better measure of the center of the data than the mean.
D)   Neither the mean nor the median would be a good measure of the center of the data.

Ans: C

47. Given the histogram below for a set of data, which statement is true?

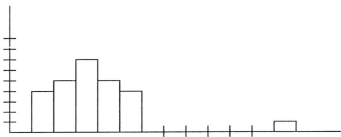

A)   For the set of data shown, the mean and the median are about equal.
B)   For the set of data shown, the mean is greater than the median.
C)   For the set of data shown, the median is greater than the mean.
D)   For the set of data shown, the relationship between the mean and the median cannot be determined.

Ans: B

48. Given the histogram below for a set of data, which statement is true?

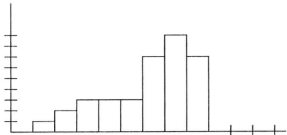

A)   For the set of data shown, the mean and the median are about equal.
B)   For the set of data shown, the mean is greater than the median.
C)   For the set of data shown, the median is greater than the mean.
D)   For the set of data shown, the relationship between the mean and the median cannot be determined.

Ans: C

49. Given the histogram below for a set of data, which statement is true?

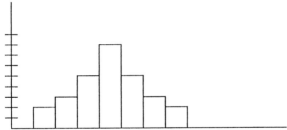

A)   For the set of data shown, the mean and the median are about equal.
B)   For the set of data shown, the mean is greater than the median.
C)   For the set of data shown, the median is greater than the mean.
D)   For the set of data shown, the relationship between the mean and the median cannot be determined.

Ans: A

50. Below is a list of gas mileage ratings for selected passenger cars in miles per gallon:

    53, 43, 89, 41, 85, 86, 91, 92, 95, 94, 86, 102, 114, 30, 123

    Choose the correct histogram of the data.
    A)

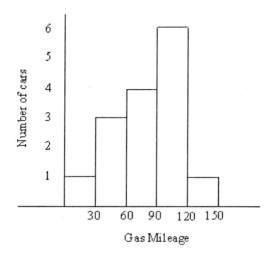

    B)

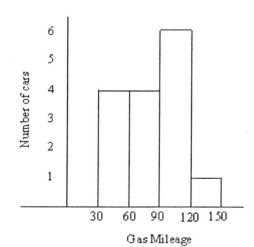

    C)

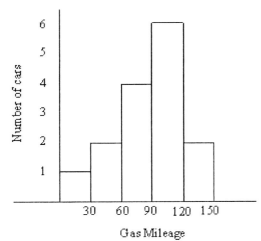

D)

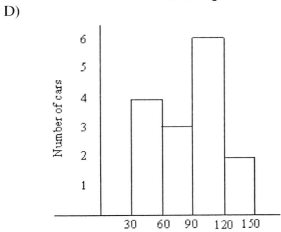

Ans: B

51. Below is a list of gas mileage ratings for selected passenger cars in miles per gallon:

53, 43, 89, 41, 85, 86, 91, 92, 95, 94, 86, 102, 114, 30, 123

Choose the correct stemplot of the data.

A)
```
 3 | 0
 4 | 3 1
 5 | 3
 6 |
 7 |
 8 | 9 5 6 6
 9 | 1 2 5 4
10 | 2
11 | 4
12 | 3
```

B)
```
 3 | 0
 4 | 1 3
 5 | 3
 6 | 0
 7 | 0
 8 | 5 6 6 9
 9 | 1 2 4 5
10 | 2
11 | 4
12 | 3
```

C)
```
 3 | 0
 4 | 1 3
 5 | 3
 6 |
 7 |
 8 | 5 6 6 9
 9 | 1 2 4 5
10 | 2
11 | 4
12 | 3
```

D)

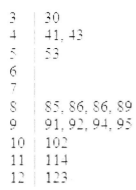

Ans: C

52. The shelf life of a battery produced by one major company is known to be normally distributed, with a mean life of 3.5 years and a standard deviation of 0.75 years. What is the upper quartile of battery shelf life?
A) 4. years   B) 4.25 years   C) 4.17 years   D) 5.25 years
Ans: A

53. The length of students' college careers at Anytown University is known to be normally distributed, with a mean length of 5.5 years and a standard deviation of 1.75 years. What is the lower quartile for the length of students' careers at Anytown University?
A) 4.83 years   B) 3.75 years   C) 4.33 years   D) 2.75 years
Ans: C

54. The scores of students on standardized test form a normal distribution with a mean of 300 and a standard deviation of 40. What are the lower and upper quartile scores for this test?
A) 280 and 320   B) 273 and 327   C) 260 and 340   D) 150 and 450
Ans: B

55. The mean length of time, per week, that students at a certain school spend on their homework is 24.3 hours, with a standard deviation of 1.2 hours. Assuming the distribution of study times is normal, what percent of students spend more than 25.1 hours per week on homework?
A) 16.5%   B) 5%   C) 12.5%   D) 25%
Ans: D

56. The scores of students on a standardized test are normally distributed with a mean of 300 and a standard deviation of 40. What is the probability that a randomly chosen student scores below 273 on the test?
A)   approximately 0.025   C)   approximately 0.165
B)   approximately 0.25   D)   approximately 0.125
Ans: B

57. The annual income of residents in a county is $42,000 with a standard deviation of $10,000. Between what two values do 95% of the incomes of county residents lie?
    A) $40,000 and $44,000   C) $32,000 and $52,000
    B) $22,000 and $62,000   D) $30,000 and $50,000
    Ans: B

58. The shelf life of a battery produced by one major company is known to be normally distributed, with a mean life of 3.5 years and a standard deviation of 0.75 years. What range of years contains 68% of all battery shelf lives?
    A) 2 to 5 years   B) 2.5 to 4.5 years   C) 2.83 to 4.17 years   D) 2.75 to 4.25
    Ans: D

59. The scores of students on a standardized test are normally distributed with a mean of 300 and a standard deviation of 40. Between what two values do 99.7% of the test scores lie?
    A) 260 to 340   B) 220 to 380   C) 297 to 303   D) 180 to 420
    Ans: D

60. The mean length of time, per week, that students at a certain school spend on their homework is 24.3 hours, with a standard deviation of 1.4 hours. Assuming the distribution of study times is normal, what percent of students study between 22.9 and 25.7 hours?
    A) 99.7%   B) 95%   C) 68%   D) 50%
    Ans: C

61. The length of students' college careers at Anytown University is known to be normally distributed, with a mean length of 5.5 years and a standard deviation of 1.75 years. What percent of students have college careers lasting between 2 and 9 years?
    A) 50%   B) 99.75%   C) 68%   D) 95%
    Ans: D

62. The shelf life of a battery produced by one major company is known to be normally distributed, with a mean life of 3.5 years and a standard deviation of 0.75 years. What percent of batteries last between 1.25 and 5.75 years?
    A) 99.7%   B) 95%   C) 68%   D) 50%
    Ans: A

63. The annual income of residents in a certain county is normally distributed, with a mean of $42,000 and a standard deviation of $10,000. What is the probability that a randomly chosen resident has income over $52,000?
    A) 16%   B) 32%   C) 50%   D) 68%
    Ans: A

64. The weight of potato chip bags filled by a machine at a packaging plant is normally distributed, with a mean of 15.0 ounces and a standard deviation of 0.2 ounces. What is the probability that a randomly chosen bag will weigh less than 14.6 ounces?
A) 50%   B) 5%   C) 2.5%   D) 2%
Ans: C

65. The weight of potato chip bags filled by a machine at a packaging plant is normally distributed, with a mean of 15.0 ounces and a standard deviation of 0.2 ounces. What is the probability that a randomly chosen bag will weigh more than 15.6 ounces?
A) 5%   B) 2.5%   C) 0.3%   D) 0.15%
Ans: D

66. The distribution of home prices in Nirvana is skewed to the left. The median price is $167,900. The mean is:
A)   lower than $167,900.
B)   greater than $167,900.
C) $167,900.
D)   unable to be determined with this information.
Ans: A

67. Bruce is considering relocating to a new city. His options are Altuna, Boundary Valley, and Collie Creek. All other living expenses seem to be equal for the three choices, but Bruce is worried about his heating and cooling bill. The only information he has at his disposal is the following table:

City	Mean daily temperature	Standard deviation for the daily temperature
Altuna	64	15
Boundary Valley	64	16
Collie Creek	64	5

Which city is likely to have the least expensive heating and cooling costs?
A)   Altuna
B)   Boundary Valley
C)   Collie Creek
D)   Unable to be determined with this information
Ans: C

Chapter 5: Free-Response

1. Below are family income figures (in thousands of dollars) for fifteen residents of a neighborhood. Make a stemplot of the income data.

17	31	25	30	21
25	28	19	32	25
32	27	21	26	21

   Ans:

   ```
   1 | 79
   2 | 111555678
   3 | 0123
   ```

2. The data below represent the numbers of auto accidents at a certain intersection each month for a year. Make a stemplot of the data.

   0, 1, 3, 4, 5, 2, 2, 6, 7, 2, 0, 1

   Ans: 0|001122234567

3. The fifty measurements given below represent the weights, in ounces, of zucchini grown in a garden one summer. Make a histogram of the weights using classes of width of 5 oz. Does the distribution appear to be symmetric?

12	8	23	14	25	22	16	28	35	26
27	26	30	18	37	26	31	37	20	28
42	21	27	7	25	18	23	11	23	32
30	29	36	22	38	32	26	6	17	33
28	11	20	32	24	28	12	32	19	38

   Ans:

   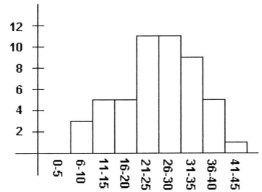

   The distribution is not quite symmetric.

4. Below are exam scores for 26 students in an English course. Make a histogram of the scores.

84	77	67	94	90	77	79
81	56	89	77	88	72	93
74	76	28	80	58	94	
66	77	89	81	78	93	

Ans:

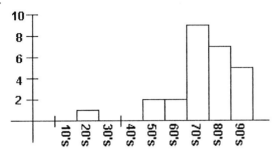

5. Below are exam scores for 26 students in an English course. Find the median exam score.

84	77	67	94	90	77	79
81	56	89	77	88	72	93
74	76	28	80	58	94	
66	77	89	81	78	93	

Ans: The median score is 73.

6. Below are family income figures (in thousands of dollars) for fifteen residents of a neighborhood. Find the median family income.

17	31	25	30	21
25	28	19	32	25
32	27	21	26	21

Ans: The median income is $25,000.

7. Find the mean of the following set of data

23, 45, 26, 18, 11, 42, 35, 16, 32
Ans: The mean is 27.56.

8. Below are the ages of students attending an art exhibit. Find the mean age of the students.

    11, 11, 12, 12, 13, 1 3, 13, 13, 13, 14, 14, 15, 15, 15, 16, 16, 17, 17, 18
    Ans: The mean age is 14.11 years.

9. Below are the ages of students attending an art exhibit. Find the first and third quartiles of the data.

    11, 11, 12, 12, 13, 1 3, 13, 13, 13, 14, 14, 15, 15, 15, 16, 16, 17, 17, 18

    Ans: The first quartile is 13 years. The third quartile is 16 years.

10. A linguist is studying the lengths of paragraphs in a given text. The number of words in 20 paragraphs are given below. Find the five-number summary for the data.

42	88	37	75	98	93	73	62	96	80
52	76	66	54	73	69	83	62	53	79

    Ans: The five number summary is: 37, 58, 73, 81.5, 98.

11. Find the five-number summary for the following set of data:

2	11	6	4	18
1	9	2	2	15
8	16	12	11	17

    Ans: The five number summary is: 1, 2, 9, 15, 18.

12. Below are the exam scores of thirty students. Make a boxplot of this data.

24	31	38	49	51	55	56	59	62	63
65	66	69	72	72	74	76	81	84	84
86	86	86	88	88	88	91	91	92	99

Ans:

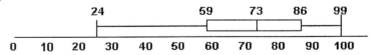

13. Below are the ages of thirty people who died in a city hospital in one month. Make a boxplot of this data.

7	22	25	31	37	38	41	48	49	50
55	58	62	62	64	65	66	66	72	75
76	76	76	85	86	88	88	88	92	94

Ans:

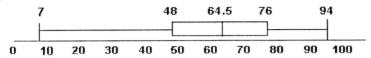

14. Find the standard deviation of the following set of data:

    5, 7, 17, 31, 45, 47, 68, 85, 96, 99

Ans: The standard devaition is 35.63.

15. Below are the ages of 6 patients seen by a pediatrician on one day. Find the standard deviation of the ages.

    3, 6, 7, 9, 15, 20

Ans: The standard deviation is 6.32.

16. Two towns both have a mean income for their residents of $30,000. The standard deviation of incomes of residents in town A is $2600 and the standard deviation of incomes of residents in town B is $25,000. Explain what this says about the difference in the distribution of incomes in the two towns.
    Ans: In town A, the mean income is $30,000 and almost all residents earn between $20,000 and $40,000. The standard deviation of $2600 says incomes do not vary much among residents of the town. In town B, since the standard deviation is $25,000, we know that there are very poor residents and very rich residents even though the mean income is also $30,000.

17. Below are the ages of six patients seen by a pediatrician on one day. Find the standard deviation of the ages.

    3, 6, 7, 9, 15, 20

Ans: The standard deviation is 6.32.

18. Find the standard deviation of the following set of measurements.

    4, 7, 9, 11, 13, 22

    Ans: The standard deviation is 6.23.

19. After computing the standard deviation for a set of measurements, you notice your answer is negative. Is this possible?
    Ans: No. The standard deviation is never less than zero.

20. Could it be possible that the standard deviation is less than one?
    Ans: Yes. If the data is very close, the standard deviation will be small.

21. Below is a histogram of car prices on a used car lot. An advertisement for the lot says the average price of a car for sale is $12,000. Could the advertisement be true? Why or why not?

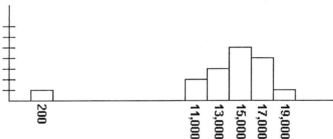

    Ans: Yes, the advertisement could be true. The presence of a car or cars with a sale price of $200 (the outlier(s) on the histogram) could lower the mean sale price to $12,000.

22. Below is a histogram for a set of data. Would you use the five-number summary or the mean and standard deviation to describe these data? Why?

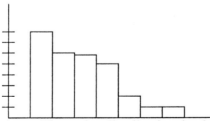

    Ans: Since the distribution is skewed, the five-number summary would be the better choice to describe the data shown in the histogram.

23. In the list of five measurements shown below, one is blurred. What *must* this value be, if the mean of the five measurements is 7?

           8   5   10   3   #

    Ans: The missing number must be 9.

24. In the list of five measurements shown below, one is blurred. What *must* this value be, if the mean of the five measurements is 6?

           8   5   10   3   #

    Ans: The missing number must be 4.

25. In the list of five measurements shown below, one is blurred. Supply a fifth value that would make the median 8.

           8   5   10   3   #

    Ans: Answers may vary. Any value greater than or equal to 8 would be correct.

26. In the list of five measurements shown below, one is blurred. Supply a fifth value that would make the median 5.

           8   5   10   3   #

    Ans: Answers may vary. Any value less than or equal to 5 would be correct.

27. Create a set of five positive numbers that have median 6 and mean 10.
    Ans: Answers may vary. One possibility is { 2, 2, 6, 20, 20}.

28. Create a set of five positive numbers that have median 8 and mean 6.
    Ans: Answers may vary. One possibility is { 3, 3, 8, 8, 8}.

29. Below is a list of gas mileage ratings for selected passenger cars in miles per gallon:

53, 43, 89, 41, 85, 86, 91, 92, 95, 94, 86, 102, 114, 30, 123

Make a boxplot to represent this data.
Ans:

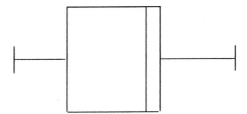

30. The scores of students on a standardized test form a normal distribution with a mean score of 500 and a standard deviation of 100. Between what two values do the middle 50% of scores lie?
Ans: The middle 50% of all scores lie between 433 and 567.

31. The average length of time, per week, that students at a certain university spend on homework is normally distributed with a mean of 24.3 hours and a standard deviation of 1.4 hours. Jane tells her parents she spends more time studying than 75% of the students on campus. How many hours per week must Jane spend on homework for this to be true?
Ans: Jane must study more than 25 1/4 hours.

32. The scores of students on a standardized test form a normal distribution with a mean of 300 and a standard deviation of 40. Two thousand students took the test. Find the number of students who score above 380.
Ans: 50

33. The distribution of the scores on a standardized exam is approximately normal with mean 400 and standard deviation 35. What percentage of scores lie between 435 and 470?
Ans: 13.5%

34. The distribution of the scores on a standardized exam is approximately normal with mean 400 and standard deviation 35. Between what two values do the middle 50% of scores lie?
Ans: Between 377 and 423

Chapter 6: Multiple-Choice

1. An outlier is an individual value that:
   A) extends the pattern.
   B) deviates from the pattern.
   C) determines the strength of the relationship.
   D) outlines the general form of the data.
   Ans: B

2. If two variables are negatively associated, then above-average values of one tend to accompany:
   A) below average values of the other.   C) oppositely signed values of the other.
   B) above average values of the other.   D) negatively signed values of the other.
   Ans: A

3. If two variables are both positive, and tend to be linked so that growth of one variable tends to indicate growth in the other variable, then:
   A) the variables are positively associated.
   B) the variables are negatively associated.
   C) the variables have no association with each other.
   Ans: A

4. If a regression line for two variables has a small positive slope, then:
   A) the variables are positively associated.
   B) the variables are negatively associated.
   C) the association of the variables cannot be determined.
   D) the variables have no association with each other.
   Ans: A

5. If two variables are negatively associated, then the regression line:
   A) has a negative intercept.   C) has negative coefficients.
   B) has a negative slope.   D) is valid for only negative values.
   Ans: B

6. If two variables are positively associated, then the regression line:
   A) is horizontal.   C) has a positive slope.
   B) has a positive intercept.   D) has a positive y-intercept.
   Ans: C

7. If the regression line is $y = 4 - 3x$, then the variables:
   A) have a positive association.
   B) have a negative association.
   C) have an association that is sometimes positive and sometimes negative.
   Ans: B

8. If the regression line is 2x + 4y = 10, then the variables:
   A)   have a positive association.
   B)   have a negative association.
   C)   have an association that is sometimes positive and sometimes negative.
   Ans: B

9. If the regression line is x = 5y − 2, then the variables:
   A)   have a positive association.
   B)   have a negative association.
   C)   have an association that is sometimes positive and sometimes negative.
   Ans: A

10. If the variables have a negative association, then their correlation:
    A)   must be less than −1.   C)   must be between 0 and 1.
    B)   must be between −1 and 0.   D)   must be greater than 1.
    Ans: B

11. If the correlation between two variables is 1, then the points of their scatterplot:
    A)   all lay within 1 unit of the regression line.
    B)   all lay within ½ unit of the regression line.
    C)   all lay on the regression line.
    D)   lay so that exactly half of the points are on each side of the regression line.
    Ans: C

12. If the correlation between two variables is −1, then the points of their scatterplot:
    A)   all lay within 1 unit of the regression line.
    B)   all lay within ½ unit of the regression line.
    C)   all lay on the regression line.
    D)   lay so that exactly half of the points are on each side of the regression line.
    Ans: C

13. If the points of a scatterplot lie on a straight line, then the correlation
    A) must be 1.   B) must be positive.   C) must be 0.   D) must be either 1 or −1.
    Ans: D

14. If the units of measurement change to larger units, then the correlation:
    A) becomes larger.   B) becomes smaller.   C) does not change.
    Ans: C

15. How does an outlier effect the correlation?
    A)   A single outlier has no effect.
    B)   A single outlier has minimal effect.
    C)   A single outlier can change the value of the correlation, but not its sign.
    D)   A single outlier can change the value and the sign of the correlation.
    Ans: D

16. The least-squares regression line minimizes the sum of:
    A)   the squares of the shortest distance from each scatterplot point to the regression line.
    B)   the squares of the shortest vertical distance from each scatterplot point to the regression line.
    C)   the squares of the shortest horizontal distance from each scatterplot point to the regression line.
    D)   none of these.
    Ans: B

17. The slope of the least-squares regression line is:
    A)   the correlation between the variables.
    B)   the same sign as the correlation between the variables.
    C)   the opposite of the correlation between the variables.
    D)   the opposite sign of the correlation between the variables.
    Ans: B

18. The intercept of the least-squares regression line is
    A)   the mean of the y values.
    B)   the mean of the x values.
    C)   the mean of the y values minus the mean of the x values.
    D)   none of these.
    Ans: D

19. If two variables have a strong positive association, then:
    A)   increasing x will cause y to increase.
    B)   making x positive will make y positive.
    C)   doubling x will cause y to double.
    D)   changes in x do not necessarily cause changes in y.
    Ans: D

20. Standardizing an observational value involves:
    A)   subtracting the mean.
    B)   dividing by the mean.
    C)   dividing by the number of samples.
    D)   dividing by one less than the number of samples.
    Ans: A

21. If the least-squares regression line is $y = 3x - 5$, then for $y = 2$, the predicted value for x is:
    A) 1.   B) 3.   C) 2 1/3.   D) 6.
    Ans: C

22. If the least-squares regression line is y = 5x – 3, then for x = 3, the predicted value for y is:
    A) 2.   B) 0.   C) 1 1/5.   D) 12.
    Ans: D

Use the following to answer questions 23-25:

Use the following scatterplot to answer the question(s) below.

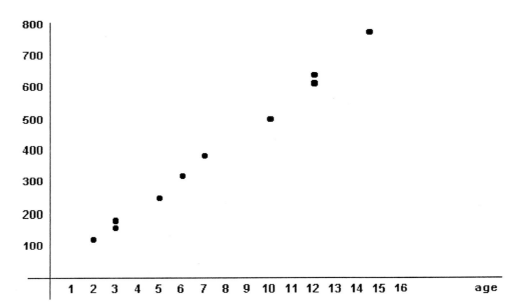

23. For the scatterplot shown below, what can you say about the least-squares regression line?
    A)   Its slope is positive.   C)   It stops at y = 800
    B)   It passes through the point (0,0)   D)   None of these
    Ans: A

24. For the scatterplot shown below, what can you say about the correlation?
    A)   It is almost 0.   C)   It is exactly 1.
    B)   It is between 0 and 1.   D)   It is greater than 1.
    Ans: B

25. For the scatterplot shown below, what y value would you expect to be paired with x = 9?
    A)   About 500
    B)   About 450
    C)   About 400
    D)   It's not possible to answer this question based on the data.
    Ans: B

Use the following to answer questions 26-28:

Use the following scatterplot to answer the question(s) below.

26. What can you say about the correlation of the data?
    A)   The correlation is nearly 1.   C)   The correlation is nearly 0.
    B)   The correlation is nearly −1.   D)   The data has no correlation.
    Ans: C

27. What can you say about the association of the variables?
    A)   The variables are positively correlated.
    B)   The variables are negatively correlated.
    C)   The variables are not correlated.
    D)   The variables are not linearly correlated.
    Ans: D

28. What can you say about outliers in the data set?
    A)   There are no apparent outliers.   C)   There are only two outliers.
    B)   There is only one outlier.   D)   There are many outliers.
    Ans: A

Use the following to answer questions 29-31:

Use the following scatterplot to answer the question(s) below.

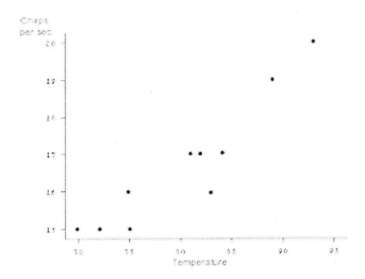

29. What can you say about the slope of the least-squares regression line?
    A)   The slope is zero.   C)   The slope is negative.
    B)   The slope is positive.   D)   The slope varies.
    Ans: B

30. What conclusions can you reach if you hear 18 chirps a minute?
    A)   The temperature is about 87.
    B)   The temperature is about 90.
    C)   This is not a valid answer; 18 is not possible.
    D)   The data of the scatterplot are not valid.
    Ans: A

31. What can you say about the correlation?
    A)   The correlation is greater than 1.   C)   The correlation is between 0 and 1.
    B)   The correlation is exactly 1.   D)   The correlation is negative.
    Ans: C

32. Suppose the points of a scatterplot lie close to the line $3x + 2y = 6$. The slope of this line is:
    A) 3.   B) 2/3.   C) 3/2.   D) –3/2.
    Ans: D

33. Suppose the points of a scatterplot lie close to the line $y = 3 – 2x$. The slope of this line is:
    A) 3.   B) –2.   C) 3/2.   D) –2/3.
    Ans: B

34. Suppose you are taking a survey of young children. If you measure their height and their weight, what do you expect to determine about this data?
    A)   There is no correlation between the data.
    B)   There is a positive correlation between the data.
    C)   There is a negative correlation between the data.
    Ans: B

35. For professional baseball players, one would expect a negative correlation between:
    A)   batting average and salary.   C)   number of home runs and salary.
    B)   years of play and salary.   D)   number of errors and salary.
    Ans: D

36. For professional golfers, one would expect a positive correlation between:
    A)   average score and number of endorsements.
    B)   age and number of endorsements.
    C)   average score and number of years as a pro.
    D)   none of these.
    Ans: D

37. A typing service keeps data on the number of pages in a manuscript and the length of time (in hours) it takes to complete the typing. The least squares regression line for the data is given by $y = 20 + 0.273x$. Use this to predict the length of time needed to type a 40-page manuscript.
    A) 810.92   B) 60.273   C) 30.92   D) 16.38
    Ans: C

38. An airline has determined that the relationship between the number of passengers on a flight and the total weight (in pounds) of luggage stored in the baggage compartment can be estimated by the least squares regression equation $y = 250 + 27x$. Predict the weight of luggage for a flight with 125 passengers.
    A) 402   B) 3625   C) 10,125   D) 34,625
    Ans: B

39. The least squares regression equation $y = 50 + 0.1x$ gives the yield in bushels per acre of corn when x pounds of fertilizer are applied. Predict the yield for a farmer who plans to use 320 pounds of fertilizer.
    A) 82   B) 16,032   C) 37   D) 50.32
    Ans: A

40. A bank collects data on the savings and incomes of families to predict an expected increase in certificate of deposit accounts due to a 10% increase in salaries of employees at a local company. Which variable, savings or income, would be the explanatory variable?
    A) Family savings   B) Family income
    Ans: B

41. A university admissions counselor wishes to predict the performance of freshmen by considering their SAT scores. Which variable, freshman GPA or SAT score, would be the explanatory variable in a least squares regression equation?
A) Freshman GPA   B) SAT score
Ans: B

42. To choose advertising media, a marketing analyst studies the relationship between a consumer's income and the amount spent on restaurant dining. Which variable, consumer's income or dining expenditures, would be the response variable for a least squares regression equation?
A) Consumer's income   B) Dining expenditures
Ans: B

43. To determine the effectiveness of group study sessions, a college instructor gathers data on hours of attendance and exam scores for students in the class. Which variable, hours of attendance or exam scores, would be the response variable for a least-squares regression equation?
A) Hours of attendance   B) Exam scores
Ans: B

44. Max is collecting baseball cards. He has 65 that his aunt gave him for his birthday, and he buys 20 more each week. The total number y of cards that Max has after x weeks is given by which of the following equations?
A) $y = 20 + 65x$ B) $y = 65 + 20x$ C) $y = 20 + x$ D) $y = 85x$
Ans: B

45. A computer store purchases advertising time on local television stations. For the variables representing the number of advertisements purchased and the number of computers sold, you would expect
A)   a substantial negative correlation.   C)   a small correlation.
B)   a substantial positive correlation.   D)   no correlation.
Ans: B

46. A shopping mall is having trouble with shoplifting in several of its stores. For the variables representing the number of security guards on patrol and the number of shoplifting incidents, you would expect
A)   a substantial negative correlation.   C)   a small correlation.
B)   a substantial positive correlation.   D)   no correlation.
Ans: A

Use the following to answer questions 47-50:

Use the table below to answer the question(s) below.

Temperature in degrees F (y)	70	72	74	75	81	82	83	84	89	93
Chirps per second (x)	15	15	15	16	17	17	16	17	19	20

47. Let x = number of chirps per second and y = temperature. What is the slope of the regression line?
A) About 4   B) About 11   C) About 70   D) None of these
Ans: A

48. Let x = number of chirps per second and y = temperature. What is the intercept of the regression line?
A) About 4   B) About 11   C) About −11   D) About 70
Ans: B

49. What is the correlation between the variables?
A) About 0.99   B) About 0.94   C) About 0.70   D) About 0.50
Ans: B

50. Let x = number of chirps per second and y = temperature. How many points are above the regression line?
A) 4   B) 5   C) 6   D) None of these
Ans: A

Use the following to answer questions 51-56:

Use the following data to answer the question(s) below.

Let x = time spent studying and y = test score.

Time spent studying (hours)	1	2	5	4	6	7	8	5	2	4	3	5
Test score (percentage)	49	57	80	70	88	91	98	80	57	72	65	82

51. What is the slope of the regression line?
A) About 2   B) About 7   C) About 43   D) Nnone of these
Ans: B

52. What is the intercept of the regression line?
A) About 70   B) About 48   C) About 43   D) None of these
Ans: C

53. What is the correlation?
    A) About 0.99   B) About 0.90   C) About 0.80   D) About 0.70
    Ans: A

54. What is the expected test score if three hours are spent studying?
    A) About 63   B) About 65   C) About 67   D) About 70
    Ans: B

55. Each additional hour of studying adds, on average, how many test points?
    A) About 1   B) About 5   C) About 7   D) About 10
    Ans: C

56. If you do not study, on average what test score would you expect?
    A) About 43   B) About 46   C) About 48   D) None of these
    Ans: A

57. If the x and y coordinates of a scatterplot are exchanged, the slope of the regression line:
    A)   remains unchanged.   C)   changes to its negative reciprocal.
    B)   changes to its reciprocal.   D)   none of these.
    Ans: D

58. If the x and y coordinates of a scatterplot are exchanged, the correlation of the variables:
    A)   remains unchanged.   C)   changes to its negative reciprocal.
    B)   changes to its reciprocal.   D)   none of these.
    Ans: A

59. If the x and y coordinates of a scatterplot are exchanged, intercept of the regression line:
    A)   remains unchanged.   C)   changes to its reciprocal.
    B)   changes to its opposite.   D)   none of these.
    Ans: D

60. If the x and y coordinates of a scatterplot are exchanged, variables which were previously positively associated:
    A)   remain positively associated. C)   are no longer associated.
    B)   are now negatively associated.
    Ans: A

Chapter 6: Free-Response

1. Suppose the children of a primary school are surveyed. What type of association would you expect between their ages and their height?
   Ans: The variables are most likely positively associated.

2. Suppose the babies in a nursery are surveyed. What type of association would you expect between a child's age and the average number of hours the child sleeps in a day?
   Ans: The variables are most likely negatively associated.

3. What are two variables associated with professional baseball players that are most likely positively associated?
   Ans: Answers will vary. For example, batting average and salary

4. What are two variables associated with professional baseball players that are most likely negatively associated?
   Ans: Answers will vary. For example, number of hits allowed and salary for pitchers

5. Suppose the regression line for a scatterplot passes through the points (0, 10) and (5, 20). What y value is predicted to be related to the value x = 2?
   Ans: 14

6. Suppose the regression line for a scatterplot passes through the points (0, 30) and (5, 20). What y value is predicted to be related to the value x = 2?
   Ans: 26

7. Suppose the regression line for a scatterplot passes through the points (0, 10) and (5, 20). What type of association exists between the variables?
   Ans: A positive association

8. Suppose the regression line for a scatterplot passes through the points (0, 30) and (5, 20). What type of association exists between the variables?
   Ans: A negative association

9. Suppose the equation for a regression line is y = 4x + 6. If x = 5, what is the predicted corresponding value for y?
   Ans: 26

10. Suppose the equation for a regression line is y = 4x + 6. If y = 12, what is the predicted corresponding value for x?
    Ans: 3

11. Suppose the equation for a regression line is y = 18 − 3x. If x = 4, what is the predicted corresponding value for y?
    Ans: 6

12. Suppose the equation for a regression line is $y = 18 - 3x$. If $y = 9$, what is the predicted corresponding value for x?
    Ans: 3

13. Suppose the equation for a regression line has a positive slope. What type of association exists between the variables?
    Ans: A positive association

14. What can you say about the slope of a regression line for variables that are negatively associated?
    Ans: The slope is negative.

15. If all the points of a scatterplot lie on a straight line, what can you say about the correlation of the data?
    Ans: $r = 1$ or $r = -1$.

16. When the units of measurement are changed, what happens to the correlation of the data?
    Ans: The correlation does not change.

17. Is it possible for the correlation for a scatterplot to change dramatically when a single point is moved?
    Ans: It is possible to change the value from positive to negative by moving a single outlier.

18. If there is an association between two variables, is it reasonable to presume that changes in one variable will cause changes in the other variable?
    Ans: No. Association does not imply causation.

19. Below are data on the age of ten cars and the amount spent on auto repairs in one year. Make a scatterplot of the data.

Age (years)	Auto repairs ($)
2	120
3	175
3	160
5	250
6	325
7	380
10	500
12	615
12	630
15	770

Ans:

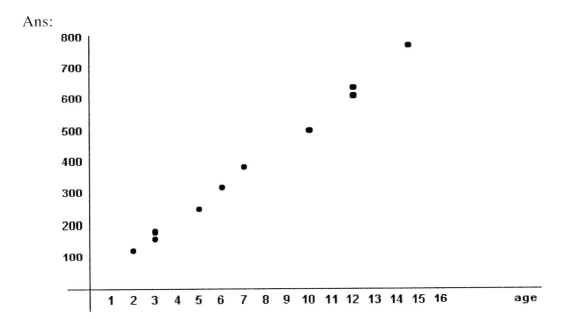

20. Below are data on two related variables. Make a scatterplot of the data.

X	Y
118	66
99	50
120	73
121	69
123	72
108	65
111	62

Ans:

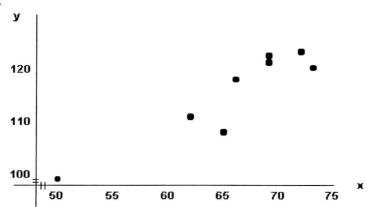

21. Suppose that age and amount of time slept per day are gathered from people at a mall. According to this data, young children and older adults tend to sleep more than older children and younger adults. How could you describe the resulting scatterplot of this data, where x represents ages and y represents the amount of sleep per day?
Ans: The points follow a general "U" shape, higher at the ends and lower in the middle.

22. Suppose the points of a scatterplot tend to follow the bell-shaped curve of the normal distribution. What can you say about the feasibility of using a least-squares regression line to describe this data?
Ans: This will not be effective, as the data does not consistently show a linear relationship among the variables.

23. Below is the scatterplot for data collected on two variables. Would a least squares regression equation be useful in describing the relationship between the variables? Why or why not?

Ans: The least squares regression line would not be useful to describe the relationship between the variables. While there does appear to be a strong relationship between the variables, the relationship does not appear to be linear.

Use the following to answer questions 24-25:

Use the following scatteplot to answer the question(s) below.

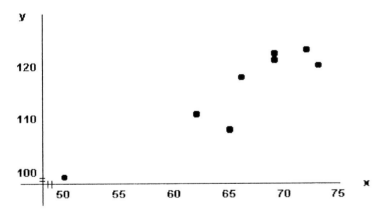

24. What type of association exists between the variables on the scatterplot?
    Ans: A positive correlation

25. Does the scatterplot have an outlier?
    Ans: The point (50, 100) appears to be an outlier.

26. A little league manager keeps a record book showing the statistics for his players. The first few lines of the record book show:

Player	At Bats	Hits	Average
Brett	142	37	.261
Mike	128	32	.250
Carlos	128	35	.273
John	123	36	.293

What are the individuals and the variables in these data?
Ans: The individuals are the players. The variables are at-bats, hits, and average.

27. The least-squares regression line is the "best" line in that it minimizes a certain sum. What is this sum?
Ans: The sum of the squares of the vertical distances from each data point to the line.

28. Can outliers significantly impact the least-squares regression line?
Ans: Yes. The removal or repositioning of a single outlier can dramatically change the least-squares regression line.

29. Ten crickets were observed under various temperatures and the number of chirps each cricket made per second was recorded. The results are shown in the table below.

Temperature in degrees F	70	72	74	75	81	82	83	84	89	93
Chirps per second	15	15	15	16	17	17	16	17	19	20

Make a scatterplot. Is the association between these variables positive or negative?

Ans: The association is positive.

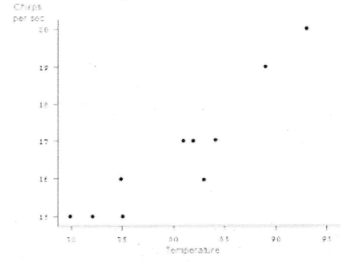

30. Describe the form, direction, and strength of the relationship.

Time spent studying (hours)	1	2	5	4	6	7	8	5	2	4	3	5
Test score (percentage)	49	57	80	70	88	91	98	80	57	72	65	82

Ans: The form is a straight-line pattern. The direction is positive: as study time increases, test scores increase. The relationship is strong, since the points all lie close to a line.

Chapter 7: Multiple-Choice

1. A polling company conducted a survey of voters to obtain data for a political campaign. They selected 3500 voters randomly from the 168,000 names on the voter registration lists of the county and found that 1372 intended to vote for candidate Doe. The 3500 voters represent:
   A) the population.   B) the sample.
   Ans: B

2. A polling company conducted a survey of voters to obtain data for a political campaign. They selected 3500 voters randomly from the 168,000 names on the voter registration lists of the county and found that 1372 intended to vote for candidate Doe. The 168,000 names represent:
   A) the population.   B) the sample.
   Ans: A

3. A marketing company conducted a survey of college students to obtain data for an advertising campaign. They selected 1421 students randomly from campus directories of 132 colleges and universities. The 1421 students represent:
   A) the population.   B) the sample.
   Ans: B

4. A marketing company conducted a survey of college students to obtain data for an advertising campaign. They selected 1421 students randomly from campus directories of 132 colleges and universities. The students in the directories at the 132 colleges and universities represent:
   A) the population.   B) the sample.
   Ans: A

5. To determine the proportion of voters who favor a certain candidate for governor, the campaign staff phones 2500 residents of the state chosen from the state property tax rolls. The 2500 residents represent:
   A) the population.   B) the sample.
   Ans: B

6. To determine the proportion of voters who favor a certain candidate for governor, the campaign staff phones 2500 residents of the state chosen from the state property tax rolls. All property owners in the state represent:
   A) the population.   B) the sample.
   Ans: A

7. In order to determine the mean weight of bags of chips filled by its packing machines, a company inspects 50 bags per day and weighs them. In this example, the population is:
   A)   the 50 bags inspected each day.
   B)   all potato chips produced by the company.
   C)   all bags of chips produced by the company.
   D)   the weight of the 50 bags inspected.
   Ans: C

8. To estimate the proportion of voters in a town likely to favor a tax increase for road repair, a random sample of people chosen from the voter registration list is surveyed and the proportion who favor the increase is found to be 43%. The actual proportion in the town is 40%. This difference is most likely an example of sampling:
   A) bias.   B) variability.
   Ans: B

9. To determine the proportion of students at a university who favor the construction of a parking garage, a sample of people driving through the student center parking lot is surveyed and it is found that 45% favor the garage. The actual proportion of the student body who favor the garage is 40%. This difference is most likely an example of sampling:
   A) bias.   B) variability.
   Ans: A

10. To determine the proportion of students at a university who favor the construction of a parking garage, a sample of people on the current enrollment list is surveyed and it is found that 45% favor the garage. The actual proportion of the student body who favor the garage is 40%. This difference is most likely an example of sampling:
    A) bias.   B) variability.
    Ans: B

11. To estimate the mean income of all residents in a town, a sample of people chosen from the telephone directory is surveyed and the mean is found to be $43,000. The actual mean income in the town is $40,000. This difference is most likely an example of sampling:
    A) bias.   B) variability.
    Ans: A

12. A polling company surveys 200 people outside a county courthouse concerning tighter restrictions on smoking in public buildings. Their results indicate that 34% of those surveyed favor tighter restrictions. The actual proportion of county residents who favor tighter restrictions is 65%. The difference is most likely due to:
    A)   variability in sampling.
    B)   bias due to the use of a convenience sample.
    C)   confounding variables in the survey.
    D)   the wording of the survey.
    Ans: B

13. You wish to survey the students at your college to determine their feelings about the quality of services in the student center. Which of the following sampling designs is best for avoiding bias?
    A)   Place an ad in the student newspaper asking all readers to mail in their opinions.
    B)   Obtain a list of student names from the registrar and select 250 names to contact.
    C)   Air an announcement on the campus radio station asking all listeners to phone in their opinions.
    D)   Survey every tenth student who enters the student center.
    Ans: B

14. To determine the proportion of students at a university who favor the construction of a parking garage, a student senate member surveys students as they leave the student union. This type of sample is a:
    A)   convenience sample.   C)   multi-stage random sample.
    B)   simple random sample.   D)   voluntary response sample.
    Ans: A

15. In order to determine the proportion of voters in a small town who favor a candidate for mayor, the campaign staff takes out an ad in the paper asking voters to call in their preference for mayor. This type of sample is a:
    A)   convenience sample.   C)   multi-stage random sample.
    B)   simple random sample.   D)   voluntary response sample.
    Ans: D

16. A marketing company conducts a survey of college students to obtain data for a marketing campaign. They randomly select five in-state colleges and then randomly choose 100 students from the registration lists of these colleges. This type of sample is a:
    A)   convenience sample.   C)   multi-stage random sample.
    B)   simple random sample.   D)   voluntary response sample.
    Ans: C

17. To estimate the number of motorists likely to favor a tax increase for road repair, a polling company chooses 1000 names at random from a list of registered car owners provided by the county license office. This type of sample is a:
   A)   convenience sample.   C)   multi-stage random sample.
   B)   simple random sample.   D)   voluntary response sample.
   Ans: B

18. Which of the following sampling techniques is most likely to produce biased results?
   A)   Multi-stage random sampling   C)   Voluntary response sampling
   B)   Sampling using a random digits table   D)   Simple random sampling
   Ans: C

19. A polling company conducted a survey of voters to obtain data for a political campaign. They selected 3500 voters randomly from the 16,800 names on the voter registration lists of the county and found that 1365 intended to vote for candidate Doe. The sample proportion is:
   A) 0.081   B) 0.208   C) 0.39   D) 0.1365
   Ans: C

20. A poll of 80 students selected at random at Midtown University found that 20 were in favor of a fee increase to support extra maintenance of gardens on campus. In the example, the sample proportion is:
   A) 0.2   B) 0.08   C) 0.8   D) 0.25
   Ans: D

21. A sample of 50 people at a local fast-food restaurant found 15 in favor of new fat-free menu items. In this example, the sample proportion is:
   A) 0.15   B) 0.25   C) 0.3   D) 0.5
   Ans: C

22. A poll of 60 students selected at random at State University found that 12 were in favor of higher parking fees to support extra police patrols of parking lots on campus. In this example, the sample proportion is:
   A) 0.2   B) 0.12   C) 0.05   D) 0.6
   Ans: A

23. A random sample of 600 voters in Centralville indicated that 48 of them believed their congressional representative was honest and trustworthy. The sample proportion is:
   A) 0.08   B) 0.125   C) 0.48   D) 0.8
   Ans: A

24. A soft-drink bottler selects 80 cans at random from a production line and finds that 32 are underfilled. The sample proportion of underfilled cans is:
   A) 0.025   B) 0.04   C) 0.32   D) 0.4
   Ans: D

Use the following to answer questions 25-31:

Use the following random digits to answer the question(s) below.

101	01033	08705	42934	79257	89138	21506	26797
102	49105	00755	39242	50772	44036	54518	56865
103	61589	35486	59500	20060	89769	54870	75586
104	08900	87788	73717	19287	69954	45917	80026
105	75029	51052	25648	02523	84300	83093	39852
106	91276	88988	12439	73741	30492	19280	41255
107	74008	72750	70742	67769	72837	27098	07049
108	98406	27011	76385	15212	03806	85928	76385

25. A large group of people are eating dinner at a Chinese restaurant. They are very hungry. The menus are printed in Chinese but no one in the group can read Chinese. Use the portion of the random digits table above, starting at line 105, to choose five dishes from the menu numbered 01 to 50.
A) 2, 5, 7, 9, 10   C) 02, 10, 23, 25, 30
B) 02, 10, 23, 25, 25   D) 02, 05, 09, 25, 30
Ans: C

26. Beginning with line 102 of the random digits table above, select three individuals from the list below to serve on a student affairs committee.

01 Crosby	06 Jones	11 Turner	16 Bush
02 Hunter	07 Smith	12 Baker	17 Thompson
03 Cooper	08 Davis	13 Wilson	18 Goodman
04 Grant	09 Ewing	14 Adams	19 Stevens
05 Riley	10 Doe	15 Hill	20 Williams

A) Cooper, Doe, Smith   C) Doe, Smith, Smith
B) Doe, Ewing, Grant   D) Crosby, Ewing, Grant
Ans: A

27. Beginning with line 104 of the random digits table above, select three individuals to receive a prize in a contest.

01 Anderson	06 Hall	11 Opus	16 Thompson
02 Butts	07 Hunsaker	12 Parson	17 Ubet
03 Calvin	08 Jones	13 Quayle	18 Watson
04 Ernest	09 Miller	14 Riley	19 Wilson
05 Gaynor	10 Norton	15 Stone	20 Ziggy

   A)   Jones, Jones, Ubet   C)   Jones, Ubet, Wilson
   B)   Hunsaker, Jones, Miller   D)   Butts, Jones, Ubet
   Ans: D

28. Use the random digits table above, starting at line 102, to choose five people from a list numbered 001 to 500 to receive a survey.
   A)   491, 050, 075, 242, 403   C)   49, 10, 50, 07, 55
   B)   491, 007, 392, 440, 354   D)   49, 61, 08, 75, 91
   Ans: A

29. Use the random digits table above, starting at line 103, to choose five people from a list numbered 01 to 99 to receive a survey.
   A)   01, 03, 30, 87, 05   C)   61, 58, 93, 54, 86
   B)   10, 36, 15, 89, 35   D)   61, 58, 35, 48, 59
   Ans: C

30. Use the random digits table above, starting at line 104, to choose four people from a list numbered 001 to 500 to call for a poll.
   A)   089, 008, 778, 873   C)   089, 008, 77, 88
   B)   089, 008, 192, 445   D)   089, 192, 459, 256
   Ans: B

31. Use the random digits table above, starting at line 105, to select four people from a list numbered 00 to 99
   A) 75, 02, 95, 10   B) 75, 51, 25, 02   C) 10, 57, 50, 29   D) 01, 00, 05, 07
   Ans: A

32. Random selection of subjects in a survey is used to eliminate variability in results.
   A) True   B) False
   Ans: B

33. Random selection of subjects for surveys is used to avoid:
   A) placebo effects.   B) variability.   C) double-blindness.   D) bias.
   Ans: D

34. A 10-year study of low-birth-weight babies is performed to determine if birth weight affects IQ and performance in elementary school. Children are identified in hospitals at birth and their performance is tracked until they are 10 years old. This type of study is a(n):
    A)   comparative experiment.
    B)   experiment with compounding variables.
    C)   observational study.
    D)   retrospective study.
    Ans: C

35. A group of 200 students is identified. Half took Latin in high school and half did not. The students are compared to see if the students who took Latin received higher SAT verbal scores. This type of study is a(n):
    A)   comparative experiment.
    B)   experiment with compounding variables.
    C)   prospective study.
    D)   simple random sample.
    Ans: C

36. A group of 100 students is randomly chosen and divided into two groups. One group is taught typing using a set of new materials and the other using traditional methods. After instruction, typing speeds are compared to determine if the new materials improve learning. This type of study is a(n):
    A)   comparative experiment.   C)   prospective study.
    B)   observational study.   D)   retrospective study.
    Ans: A

37. Consider the following situation: A group of 300 students is randomly selected at a local high school and required to fill out yearly questionnaires on family income. Students' performances on standardized tests are then followed throughout their high school years to determine if socio-economic status affects SAT scores. This describes an experiment.
    A) True   B) False
    Ans: B

38. Consider the following situation: Doctors identify 500 women, half of whom had mothers with breast cancer and half of whom did not. The medical records of the women are followed for 20 years to determine if heredity plays a role in breast cancer. This describes a prospective study.
    A) True   B) False
    Ans: A

39. Consider the following situation: Doctors question 5000 women who have had breast cancer to determine if there is a genetic factor that increases the likelihood of cancer. Each woman is asked about her family background and incidences of breast or other types of cancer among her relatives. This describes a prospective study.
   A) True   B) False
   Ans: B

40. A prospective study may be used to show cause and effect.
   A) True   B) False
   Ans: B

41. An observational study may be used to show cause and effect.
   A) True   B) False
   Ans: B

42. An experiment may be used to show cause and effect.
   A) True   B) False
   Ans: A

43. A dummy medication (such as a salt tablet) will often help a patient who trusts the doctor who administers the medicine. This is called:
   A)   confidentiality.   C)   confounding variables.
   B)   double-blindness.   D)   the placebo effect.
   Ans: D

44. A study gathered data on 1000 randomly selected students and showed that students who took Latin in high school had much higher scores on a test of verbal English skills than those who did not take Latin. The study *cannot* conclude that taking Latin improves verbal English skills because:
   A)   the study was not an experiment.   C)   of the placebo effect.
   B)   the study was not double-blind.   D)   the verbal English test was faulty.
   Ans: A

45. A survey is sent to 100 employees at a community hospital asking if they support a law requiring motorcycle riders to wear helmets. The results indicate 88% support the law. If the actual proportion of the community's residents who support the law is 72%, the difference is most likely a result of:
   A)   sampling bias.   C)   an insufficient sample size.
   B)   sampling variability.   D)   a poorly worded questionnaire.
   Ans: A

46. A physical education researcher wishes to determine if walking every day affects the health of middle-aged men. The researcher randomly identifies 400 participants in two groups. Members of one group belong to a health club and walk on its track and members of the other do not. After two months, the researcher decides the group who walks daily is healthier and concludes that walking positively affects men's health. This conclusion is of questionable validity because:
    A)   of the placebo effect.   C)   the study is not double-blind.
    B)   of confounding variables in the study. D)   the researcher is not a doctor.
    Ans: B

47. In a medical study that is double-blind, participants do not know whether or not they are taking the experimental drug. This is to avoid:
    A)   selection bias.   C)   having too small a sample.
    B)   the placebo effect.   D)   statistical significance.
    Ans: B

48. In an experiment, an observed effect is called *statistically significant* if:
    A)   the experiment will help a large number of people.
    B)   the study was double-blind.
    C)   the experiment was well designed.
    D)   the effect is too large to attribute to chance.
    Ans: D

49. The type of statistical study that can show cause and effect is:
    A)   an experimental study.   C)   a prospective study.
    B)   an observational study.   D)   a retrospective study.
    Ans: A

50. Nonresponse occurs when:
    A)   all participants surveyed answer "no" to a question.
    B)   a sample for a study is not chosen at random.
    C)   an individual selected for a sample cannot be contacted.
    D)   a study does not produce statistically significant results.
    Ans: C

51. A flashlight manufacturer sets aside a production line for the assembly of 2000 flashlights to fill a special order. Ninety of these flashlights are selected at random from the production line to be tested, and 15 are found to be defective. The population is:
    A)   the 15 defective flashlights.
    B)   the 90 flashlights tested.
    C)   the 2000 flashlights produced for this order.
    D)   all flashlights produced by the manufacturer.
    Ans: C

52. The executives of an accounting firm plan to survey a random sample of clients to determine how satisfied they are with the service they have received. Of the firm's 5412 regular clients, 500 are surveyed and 435 claim to be very satisfied with the service they have received. The sample is:
    A)   the 5412 regular clients.   C)   the 435 satisfied clients.
    B)   the 500 clients surveyed.   D)   the 65 clients that were not satisfied.
    Ans: B

53. The Whitman County Fire Department conducted a survey to determine how the 40,000 residents of the county feel about the fire department's ability to meet their needs. A random sample of 690 citizens was selected, and 627 of them said that they feel confident about the fire department's service. The population is:
    A)   the 627 confident citizens.
    B)   the 690 citizens surveyed.
    C)   the 40,000 residents of Whitman County.
    D)   the employees of the Whitman County Fire Department.
    Ans: C

54. You must choose a simple random sample of 25 of the 314 members of your fly fishing club. How would you label the population in order to use a table of random digits to make your selection?
    A) $1, 2, 3, \ldots, 24, 25$ C) $001, 002, 003, \ldots, 313, 314$
    B) $1, 2, 3, \ldots, 313, 314$ D) $000, 001, 002, \ldots, 313, 314$
    Ans: C

55. A poll asked 956 licensed drivers whether they supported a nationwide lowering of the drunk driving limit to 0.08% BAC (blood alcohol content), and 72% said they did. Estimate a 95% confidence interval for actual percentage among all licensed drivers.
    A) 70.5% to 73.5%   B) 69% to 75%   C) 71.8% to 72.2%   D) 70% to 74%
    Ans: B

56. A national poll asked 1581 adults whether they were satisfied with their jobs, and 54% said they were. Estimate a 95% confidence interval for the actual percentage among all adults.
    A) 53% to 55%   B) 52% to 56%   C) 51.5% to 56.5%   D) 50% to 58%
    Ans: C

57. As part of a research project, a student wishes to survey members of the workforce to determine whether they prefer male or female bosses. Presuming that about half of the workforce prefers female bosses, estimate how many people the student must survey to have a margin of error of 4%.
    A) 25 people   B) 50 people   C) 625 people   D) 1025 people
    Ans: C

58. Five people need to be selected from the list of names below.

Agee	Harris	Jones	Rao
Boyd	Hayes	King	Riggins
Clayton	Herndon	Lewis	Ruse
Dillon	Hogan	Martin	Smith
Genz	Jensen	Millham	Wallace

Use the following portion of a table of random digits.

134 19862 54700 18777 22218 25414 13151 54954 80615
135 96282 11576 59837 27429 60015 40388 39435 94021
136 17463 26715 71680 04853 55725 87792 99907 67156
137 44880 55285 95472 57551 24602 95311 63293 58110

Starting at line 134 and numbering the names beginning with 01, which five people are selected?
A) Boyd, Genz, Martin, Riggins, Ruse
B) Agee, Harris, Millham, Ruse, Smith
C) Agee, Clayton, Genz, Millham, Riggins
D) Boyd, Dillon, Harris, Rao, Ruse
Ans: B

59. Use the following portion of a table of random digits, starting at line 135, to choose five people from a list numbered 001 to 500.

134 19862 54700 18777 22218 25414 13151 54954 80615
135 96282 11576 59837 27429 60015 40388 39435 94021
136 17463 26715 71680 04853 55725 87792 99907 67156
137 44880 55285 95472 57551 24602 95311 63293 58110
A) 080, 098, 172, 256, 298   C) 018, 182, 198, 222, 470
B) 048, 076, 174, 246, 257   D) 001, 157, 274, 296, 388
Ans: D

60. If the confidence interval is determined to be from 56% to 62%, then the margin of error is
A) 6%   B) 3%   C) 1.5%   D) 12%
Ans: B

Chapter 7: Free-Response

1. A polling company working for a candidate for governor surveys a sample of 2500 registered voters in the state to determine if they are in agreement with the candidate's stand on gun control. Describe the population for this study.
   Ans: The population is all registered voters in the state.

2. A biologist draws a sample of 200 fish from a lake to test for mercury levels. She finds that 8% have levels above limits set as healthy. Describe the population for this study.
   Ans: The population is all fish in the lake.

3. In order to determine if students on a college campus are in favor of a tuition hike to pay for expanded parking services, a member of the student senate surveys 25 people in a commuter parking lot. Why is this a poor sampling technique?
   Ans: The students who are being surveyed are commuters who drive to campus and are likely to have different views on parking services than the general student body. This sampling technique would leave out the opinions of students living on campus or others without cars.

4. Convenience samples are said to be highly likely to produce bias in survey results. Explain why this is true.
   Ans: Convenience samples are drawn from individuals who are the most easily available and therefore they are unlikely to draw from all of the target population for a survey.

5. Explain the difference between bias and variability in sampling results.
   Ans: Variability refers to the natural differences in results that occur from one random sample of a population to the next. Variability in sampling results cannot be avoided, but the overall pattern of variability can be described. Bias in sampling results refers to a systematic error caused by poor sampling technique or a poorly worded survey.

6. We wish to know what proportion of students at a major university believe too much emphasis is placed on athletics at the school. Explain how we could choose a sample of 500 students to reduce the possibility of bias in the results.
   Ans: Obtain a list of currently enrolled students from the university registrar. Number the list of students and then use a table of random digits to select 500 numbers corresponding to students on the enrollment list and contact these students.

7. In order to determine what proportion of a town's residents approve of a new plan for trash collection, the town council placed an ad in the newspaper asking residents to phone in their opinions. Explain why the results of this poll may differ from the actual beliefs of all residents in the town.

Ans: The sampling technique described uses self-selection. Only those residents with extreme views on the new plan are likely to respond to the advertisement. A second problem with the poll technique described is that not all residents who will be affected by the new trash collection plan are likely to read the newspaper. The opinions of a large number of residents are therefore unlikely to be included in the results of the poll.

8. Define a *simple random sample*.

Ans: A simple random sample is one in which every group from the population has an equally likely chance of being chosen.

9. Can we eliminate variability in results of sampling? Why or why not?

Ans: We cannot eliminate variability in the results of sampling. Variability refers to the natural differences that occur from one sample to the next in a population.

10. Use the random digits table, beginning at line 103, to choose a sample of four people from the list:

101	01033	08705	42934	79257	89138	21506	26797
102	49105	00755	39242	50772	44036	54518	56865
103	61589	35486	59500	20060	89769	54870	75586
104	08900	87788	73717	19287	69954	45917	80026
105	75029	51052	25648	02523	84300	83093	39852
106	91276	88988	12439	73741	30492	19280	41255
107	74008	72750	70742	67769	72837	27098	07049
108	98406	27011	76385	15212	03806	85928	76385

01 Adams	06 Ford	11 Kramer	16 Post
02 Brown	07 Goodman	12 Loomis	17 Quayle
03 Cook	08 Harris	13 Martin	18 Rogers
04 Davis	09 Inez	14 Norton	19 Stevens
05 Elliot	10 Jones	15 O'Hare	20 Thompson

Ans: Those chosen would be: 02 Brown, 10 Jones, 17 Quayle, and 19 Stevens.

11. We must use a random digits table to choose a sample of eight names from the roster of a club with 100 members. Why can we use two-digit numbers from the table to select our sample?

    Ans: We can number the names on the roster using the labels 00, 01, 02, 03, . . . 96, 97, 98, 99. This list includes 100 distinct labels. (Using this list instead of 001, 002, . . . 098, 099, 100 would result in a more efficient use of the random digits table. Every two-digit portion read from the table would refer to a name on the roster where only 1/10 of the three-digit portions would be useable.)

12. The marketing department of a large national corporation wishes to determine what proportion of the residents of a state may be interested in buying its new product. Describe how the corporation might use a multi-stage random sampling process to choose a sample of the state's residents to survey.

    Ans: Answers may vary. First, the marketing department would break the state up into many contiguous areas, possibly using county borders. They would randomly select several of these counties. Each county selected would be broken up into smaller regions, perhaps neighborhoods. Several neighborhoods in each selected county would be randomly chosen. Within each chosen neighborhood, several individual families would be randomly chosen to be surveyed.

13. A high school principal wishes to determine what proportion of the school's students like the new school mascot. The principal decides to survey every 25th name from the school enrollment records (an alphabetical list of all students at the school). Is this a valid simple random sampling technique? Why or why not?

    Ans: Taking every 25th name from an alphabetical listing of students is not a valid simple random sampling technique since no two students who follow one another on the list could ever be part of the sample. This contradicts the idea that in a simple random sample, every collection of individuals has an equal chance of being chosen.

14. In a poll of 2500 residents of a state, it is found that 480 are in favor of naming the grasshopper the state insect. What is the sample proportion for this poll?

    Ans: 480/2500 = 19.2%
    The sample proportion of residents in favor of naming the grasshopper State Insect is 19.2%.

15. A marketing department surveys 1500 shoppers and finds that 950 would visit a new store more often if it were open Sunday evenings. What is the sample proportion in this survey?

    Ans: 950/1500 = 63.3%
    The sample proportion of the survey of shoppers who would visit a store more frequently if it were open Sunday evenings is 63.3%.

16. Why do opinion polls usually report a "margin of error" with the results of a survey? What does the margin of error mean?

    Ans: The results of an opinion poll are unlikely to match exactly the views of the whole population. Instead, those reporting poll results can be confident that the actual population results fall in an interval around the poll results. The margin of error defines the size of this interval.

17. What is the difference between an observational study and an experiment?

    Ans: An observational study observes individuals and measures some variable of interest, but does not try to change the behavior or conditions of the subjects. In an experiment, the researcher imposes some treatment or condition on some of the individuals in the study and then observes their response.

18. One July, the city council of a small town decides to impose an experimental curfew on all residents under 18 to cut down on loitering in the town square. After four months, the number of teens found in the square after dark has decreased 80%, and the council declares the curfew a success. Explain why this conclusion may not be valid.

    Ans: Answers may vary. In the four months since the curfew began, school would also have started. It is possible that teens are now home doing homework after dark and would have been even without the curfew. It is also possible that the cooler temperatures associated with fall months led to a decline in teens in the square after dark.

19. A farmer believes that exposing chickens to classical music will cause them to produce more eggs. Describe how the farmer may design a randomized comparative experiment to test this theory.

    Ans: Answers may vary. The farmer randomly divides his chickens into two groups. Keeping all other conditions (housing, food, etc.) the same, he plays classical music to one randomly-chosen group. The other group of chickens will be in a coop without music. After two months, the egg production of the two groups of chickens will be compared.

20. A school superintendent believes a new approach to teaching children to read will produce better standardized test scores in the district. Describe how the superintendent may design a randomized comparative experiment to test this theory.

    Ans: Answers may vary. Children in the district will be divided randomly into two groups. This random division will, hopefully, minimize differences between the groups on IQ, parental education level, or other factors the superintendent believes may have an impact on children's test scores. One group is chosen to receive the new approach to reading instruction. The other group is taught reading using traditional methods. (It would be best if the same teacher taught both groups, changing only the instruction method.) The standardized test scores of the two groups are compared at the end of the year.

21. A school principal is concerned with the increasing level of absenteeism in the school. A meeting of parents, teachers, and students is called at which the principal expresses her concern and describes an experimental program that will be instituted to try to curb absenteeism. After two months, absenteeism is down by 15%. Explain how confounding variables may have affected the results of the experiment.

    Ans: The meeting of parents, teachers, and students may have brought to the attention of parents problems associated with absenteeism in the school. Parents may have reacted with measures to increase their children's attendance in ways unrelated to the experimental program.

22. Medical experiments are frequently double-blind. Explain what this means and why medical experiments are designed this way.

    Ans: In a double-blind experiment, neither the participant nor the person collecting the data knows who is taking the experimental treatment and who is taking the placebo. This is done so that when participants report on their health they are not swayed in their own assessments by the thought of being on an experimental treatment. Also, recorders will not unconsciously exaggerate participants' conditions since they do not know which treatment participants are receiving. Running a study as double-blind helps to combat the placebo effect.

23. Describe what is meant by *the placebo effect* in an experiment.

    Ans: The placebo effect refers to the effects of a dummy treatment on the subjects of a study. People who believe they are receiving an experimental treatment designed to make them perform better may actually have a better performance due to the power of suggestion, regardless of the actual effectiveness of the treatment.

24. How does a randomized-comparative experiment control the effects of confounding variables?

    Ans: In a randomized-comparative experiment, subjects are randomly divided into two groups, one of which receives the experimental treatment and the other the traditional treatment. Since the two groups are chosen at random, any possible confounding variables should act equally on both groups. This allows differences in outcomes to more confidently be attributed to the treatment.

25. What does it mean to say that the results of an experiment are *statistically significant*?

    Ans: The results of an experiment are called "statistically significant" if they are greater than one would expect to occur by chance from a group drawn at random from the population of the study.

26. Officials at a university want to determine the percentage of students who favor the allocation of a percentage of tuition funds towards the construction of a new campus parking garage. To find this out, a survey is conducted. One thousand people driving through the administration building parking lot are surveyed, and it is found that 75% of these people favor the garage. Explain why this conclusion might not be valid.

    Ans: Answers may vary. The population of this survey would be all students at the university, and not all of them are likely to be driving through the administration building parking lot, so the population is not well represented. In fact, the sample was taken at a location that is unlikely to include any students at all; generally, people parking at an administration building are likely to be faculty, staff, administrators, or university guests. Also, people who are driving are more likely to favor a parking garage than people who do not drive to campus, so the students who use other modes of transportation would not be represented by this survey even if students did use that parking lot.

27. Officials at a university want to determine the percentage of students who favor the allocation of a percentage of tuition funds towards the construction of a new campus parking garage. To find this out, a survey is conducted. One thousand people driving through the administration building parking lot are surveyed, and it is found that 75% of these people favor the garage. What is the population in this study? What is the sample?

    Ans: The population is all students at this particular university. The sample is the 1000 people actually surveyed.

28. A new stadium is being planned for the local professional football team. One of the proposed funding methods involves the allocation of tax monies to build the stadium. To determine the public opinion of this plan, the first 100 people entering the stadium for a game are surveyed. Explain why the results of this survey might not be valid.

    Ans: Answers may vary. People attending the game are likely to be football fans, and in particular, the first 100 people to arrive are likely to be very eager fans. Fans of the game would be more favorable towards the construction of a new stadium and possibly would not mind this allocation of tax monies, whereas people who do not attend the games at all might oppose this funding method. People who do not attend the games would not be represented in this sample.

29. A recent survey of 536 employees of U.S. corporations determined that 84% of them feel that the executives who run their companies are ethical. Determine the 95% confidence interval for this survey.

    Ans: Approximately the interval between 80.8% and 87.2%.

30. A survey of 127 patients in a particular hospital determined that 54% of them felt that they were receiving excellent care. Determine the 95% confidence interval for this survey.

    Ans: Approximately the interval between 45.2% and 62.8%.

Chapter 8: Multiple-Choice

1. A die is rolled and a coin is flipped simultaneously. The number rolled on the die and whether the coin lands heads or tails is recorded. How many outcomes are in the sample space?
   A) 8   B) 6   C) 10   D) 12
   Ans: D

2. Two coins are flipped at the same time and it is recorded whether each coin lands heads or tails. The sample space for this is:
   A) { H, T}.   B) { HH, HT, TT}.   C) { HH, HT, TH, TT}.   D) { H, H, T, T}.
   Ans: C

3. A spinner numbered 1 through 10 is spun and one die is tossed simultaneously. The number spun and the number rolled are recorded. How many outcomes are in the sample space?
   A) 60   B) 16   C) 10   D) 6
   Ans: A

4. A spinner numbered 1 through 10 is spun and one die is rolled simultaneously. The sum of the number spun and the number rolled is recorded. How many outcomes are in the sample space?
   A) 60   B) 16   C) 15   D) 10
   Ans: C

5. Three dice are tossed. The number rolled on each die is recorded. How many outcomes are in the sample space?
   A) 18   B) 72   C) 216   D) 42
   Ans: C

6. Three dice are tossed. The sum of the numbers rolled is recorded. How many outcomes are in the sample space?
   A) 18   B) 12   C) 16   D) 72
   Ans: C

7. Three dice are rolled and the number rolled on each die is recorded. The outcomes in the sample space are all equally likely.
   A) True   B) False
   Ans: A

8. Three dice are rolled and the sum of the numbers rolled is recorded. The outcomes in the sample space are all equally likely.
   A) True   B) False
   Ans: B

9. Two coins are flipped and the number that landed on heads is recorded. The outcomes in the sample space are all equally likely.
   A) True   B) False
   Ans: B

10. Two coins are flipped and whether each one landed heads or tails is recorded. The outcomes in the sample space are all equally likely.
    A) True   B) False
    Ans: A

11. There are seven blue and six black socks in a drawer. One is pulled out at random. Find the probability that it is black.
    A) 6/13   B) 6/7   C) 1/2   D) 1/6
    Ans: A

12. Two fair dice are rolled and the sum rolled is recorded. Find the probability that the sum is 4.
    A) 1/3   B) 1/12   C) 4/11   D) 1/9
    Ans: B

13. A fair coin is tossed three times. Find the probability of getting exactly 2 heads.
    A) 1/2   B) 1/3   C) 2/3   D) 3/8
    Ans: D

14. If a fair die is rolled once, what is the probability of getting a number less than five?
    A) 1/6   B) 1/2   C) 2/3   D) 5/6
    Ans: C

15. A computer is programmed to randomly print two letters in a row without repeating a letter. What is the probability that the first combination printed is the word "DO"?
    A) 1/650   B) 1/325   C) 2/325   D) 1/26
    Ans: A

16. We need to create three-digit code numbers that must begin with a 7. How many such codes can be made?
    A) 700   B) 107   C) 100   D) 27
    Ans: C

17. We need to create serial numbers that start with one of the letters a, b, c, d, or f followed by three non-repeating digits. How many serial numbers can be created?
    A) 5000   B) 2520   C) 725   D) 3600
    Ans: D

18. We need to create code words that use three letters of the alphabet. Repeating of letters is allowed. How many code words can be created?
    A) 17,576   B) 15,600   C) 78   D) 75
    Ans: A

19. A computer system requires users to have an access code that consists of a three-digit number that is not allowed to start with zero and cannot repeat digits. How many such codes are possible?
    A) 990   B) 648   C) 729   D) 720
    Ans: B

20. The Olympic flag consists of five intertwined circles, one in each of the colors black, blue, green, red, and yellow. What is the probability that a random coloring of the five circles using these colors will produce the exact match of the Olympic symbol?
    A) 1/5   B) 1/3125   C) 5/120   D) 1/120
    Ans: D

21. Either Terry, Chris, or Kim will attend a party. The probability Terry attends is 0.31 and the probability Chris attends is 0.5. What is the probability that Kim attends?
    A) 0.33   B) 0.5   C) 0.81   D) 0.19
    Ans: D

22. If there is a 0.8 probability of rain today, what is the probability it will not rain?
    A) 0.8   B) 0.5   C) 0.2   D) 0.1
    Ans: C

23. A sample space has three outcomes, A, B, and C. The probability of outcome A is 0.39 and the probability of outcome B is 0.25. What is the probability of outcome C?
    A) 0.36   B) 0.33   C) 0.5   D) 0.64
    Ans: A

24. A sample space contains three outcomes, A, B, and C. Which of the following could be a legitimate assignment of probabilities to the outcomes?
    A) $P(A) = 0.2$ $P(B) = 0.4$ $P(C) = 0.6$
    B) $P(A) = 0.2$ $P(B) = 0.2$ $P(C) = 0.6$
    C) $P(A) = 2$ $P(B) = 3$ $P(C) = 1$
    D) $P(A) = 0.3$ $P(B) = 0.3$ $P(C) = 0.3$

    Ans: B

25. A sample space consists of three outcomes, X, Y, and Z. Which of the following could be a legitimate assignment of probabilities to the outcomes?
    A)   P(X) = 0.3   P(Y) = 0.6
    B)   P(X) = 0.3   P(Y) = 0.2
    C)   P(X) = 0.3   P(Y) = 0.3
    D)   P(X) = 0.7   P(Y) = –0.3

    Ans: B

26. A raffle ticket costs $5. First and second prize winners will be drawn at random. The probability of winning the $100 first prize is 1/40 and the probability of winning the $25 second prize is 1/20. What is the mean winnings for one play, taking into account the $5 cost of the ticket?
    A) –1.25   B) –0.875   C) 3.375   D) 3.75
    Ans: A

27. Suppose a game has three outcomes, A, B, and C with probabilities P(A) = 0.2, P(B) = 0.3, and P(C) = 0.5. A player will receive $3 when outcome A occurs, $4 when outcome B occurs, and will have to pay $2 when outcome C occurs. What is the mean value of one trial of the game?
    A) 0.80   B) 1.66   C) 1.00   D) 5.00
    Ans: A

28. At a certain discount store, the number of people in checkout lines varies. The probability model for the number of people in a randomly chosen line is:

Number in line	0	1	2	3	4	5
Probability	0.08	0.15	0.20	0.22	0.15	0.20

    What is the mean number of people in a line?
    A) 2.5   B) 15.92   C) 2.81   D) 2.89
    Ans: C

29. A fair die is rolled. If a number 1 or 2 appears, you will receive $5. If any other number appears, you will pay $2. What is the mean value of one trial of this game?
    A) $1/3   B) $3   C) $3/2   D) –$3
    Ans: A

30. The marketing department of an electronics manufacturer has done research on the number of television sets owned by families in a large town. The probability model for the number of sets owned by a randomly chosen family is given below. What is the mean number of sets per family?

Number of sets	0	1	2	3
Probability	0.04	0.34	0.47	0.15

A) 0.96   B) 1.5   C) 1.77   D) 1.73
Ans: D

31. The shelf life of a battery produced by one major company is known to be normally distributed, with a mean life of 3.5 years and a standard deviation of 0.75 years. What is the upper quartile of battery shelf life?
A) 4.0025 years   B) 4.25 years   C) 4.17 years   D) 5.25 years
Ans: A

32. The length of students' college careers at Anytown University is known to be normally distributed, with a mean length of 5.5 years and a standard deviation of 1.75 years. What is the lower quartile for the length of students' careers at Anytown University?
A) 4.83 years   B) 3.75 years   C) 4.3275 years   D) 2.75 years
Ans: C

33. The scores of students on a standardized test form a normal distribution with a mean of 300 and a standard deviation of 40. What are the lower and upper quartile scores for this test?
A)   299.33 and 300.67   C)   260 and 340
B)   273.2 and 326.8   D)   150 and 450
Ans: B

34. The mean length of time, per week, that students at a certain school spend on their homework is 24.3 hours, with a standard deviation of 1.4 hours. Assuming the distribution of study times is normal, what percent of students spend more than 25.238 hours per week on homework?
A) 16.5%   B) 5%   C) 12.5%   D) 25%
Ans: D

35. The scores of students on a standardized test are normally distributed with a mean of 300 and a standard deviation of 40. What is the probability that a randomly chosen student scores below 273.2 on the test?
A) 0.025   B) 0.25   C) 0.165   D) 0.125
Ans: B

36. The annual income of residents in a county is $42,000 with a standard deviation of $10,000. Between what two values do 95% of the incomes of county residents lie?
    A) $40,000 and $44,000   C) $32,000 and $52,000
    B) $22,000 and $62,000   D) $30,000 and $50,000
    Ans: B

37. The shelf life of a battery produced by one major company is known to be normally distributed, with a mean life of 3.5 years and a standard deviation of 0.75 years. What range of years contains 68% of all battery shelf lives?
    A) 2 to 5 years   C) 2.83 to 4.17 years
    B) 2.5 to 4.5 years   D) 2.75 to 4.25 years
    Ans: D

38. The scores of students on a standardized test are normally distributed with a mean of 300 and a standard deviation of 40. Between what two values do 99.7% of the test scores lie?
    A) 260 to 340   B) 220 to 380   C) 297 to 303   D) 180 to 420
    Ans: D

39. The mean length of time, per week, that students at a certain school spend on their homework is 24.3 hours, with a standard deviation of 1.4 hours. Assuming the distribution of study times is normal, what percent of students study between 22.9 and 25.7 hours?
    A) 99.7%   B) 95%   C) 68%   D) 50%
    Ans: C

40. The length of students' college careers at Anytown University is known to be normally distributed, with a mean length of 5.5 years and a standard deviation of 1.75 years. What percent of students have college careers lasting between 2 and 9 years?
    A) 50%   B) 99.75%   C) 68%   D) 95%
    Ans: D

41. The shelf life of a battery produced by one major company is known to be normally distributed, with a mean life of 3.5 years and a standard deviation of 0.75 years. What percent of batteries last between 1.25 and 5.75 years?
    A) 99.7%   B) 95%   C) 68%   D) 50%
    Ans: A

42. The annual income of residents in a certain county is normally distributed, with a mean of $42,000 and a standard deviation of $10,000. What is the probability that a randomly chosen resident has income over $52,000?
    A) 16%   B) 32%   C) 50%   D) 68%
    Ans: A

43. The weight of potato chip bags filled by a machine at a packaging plant is normally distributed, with a mean of 15.0 ounces and a standard deviation of 0.2 ounces. What is the probability that a randomly chosen bag will weigh less than 14.6 ounces?
    A) 50%   B) 5%   C) 2.5%   D) 2%
    Ans: C

44. The weight of potato chip bags filled by a machine at a packaging plant is normally distributed, with a mean of 15.0 ounces and a standard deviation of 0.2 ounces. What is the probability that a randomly chosen bag will weigh more than 15.6 ounces?
    A) 5%   B) 2.5%   C) 0.3%   D) 0.15%
    Ans: D

45. Using the central limit theorem for a normally distributed variable, how would the standard deviation of the sample mean for a sample of size 200 be related to that of size 3200?
    A)   It would be one-sixteenth as large.   C)   It would be four times as large.
    B)   It would be one-fourth as large.   D)   It would be sixteen times as large.
    Ans: C

46. The weight of bags of potato chips produced by one machine at a packaging plant has a standard deviation of 0.2 ounces. Suppose a sample of 25 bags is drawn from a production run and weighed. What is the standard deviation σ_x of the mean result?
    A) 0.008   B) 0.04   C) 0.2   D) 1.0
    Ans: B

47. A poll of 60 students found that 20% were in favor of raising parking fees to pave two new parking lots. The standard deviation of this poll is about 5.2%. What would be the standard deviation if the sample size was increased from 60 students to 120 students?
    A) 10.4%   B) 7.3%   C) 2.6%   D) 3.68%
    Ans: D

48. The batteries used by a calculator have useful lives that follow a normal distribution, with an average life of 2000 hours and a standard deviation of 200 hours. In the production process, the manufacturer draws random samples of 100 batteries and determines the mean useful life of the sample. What is the standard deviation σ_x of this mean?
    A) 25 hours   B) 100 hours   C) 2 hours   D) 20 hours
    Ans: D

49. A poll of 60 students found that 20% were in favor of raising parking fees to pave two new parking lots. The standard deviation of this poll is about 5.2%. How large a sample would be needed to reduce this standard deviation to 2.6%?
    A) 30   B) 1200   C) 120   D) 240
    Ans: D

50. The weight of bags of potato chips produced by one machine at a packaging plant has a standard deviation of 0.3 ounces. A sample of chip bags is to be drawn and the mean weight calculated. How large must the sample be if the standard deviation of the sampling distribution is to be 0.1 ounce?
    A) 9 bags   B) 3 bags   C) 6 bags   D) 10 bags
    Ans: A

51. You are told that the probability of winning the $3 prize in your state's lottery is 1/137. This means:
    A)   if you buy 137 lottery tickets, you will win the $3 prize exactly once.
    B)   if you buy 137,000 lottery tickets, you will win the $3 prize exactly one thousand times.
    C)   if you buy thousands of lottery tickets, the fraction of tickets that will win the $3 prize will be very close to 1/137.
    D)   you will win the $3 prize when you buy your 138th ticket.
    Ans: C

52. You are told that an event is nearly impossible; it will occur only once in a long sequence of trials. Which of the following probabilities could describe this event?
    A) 0   B) .02   C) .98   D) 1
    Ans: B

53. A game is played with a pair of tetrahedral (four-sided) dice. Each die has faces numbered 1, 2, 3, and 4. To play, roll the two dice and record the sum of the values on the down faces. What is the probability of rolling a sum of 6?
    A) 1/2   B) 1/8   C) 3/8   D) 3/16
    Ans: D

54. Suppose a password must consist of two letters followed by three digits. Repeated characters are allowed. How many such passwords are possible?
    A) 820   B) 468,000   C) 676,000   D) 1,757,600
    Ans: C

55. Suppose a password must consist of two letters followed by three digits. Repeated characters are allowed. A password of this type is chosen at random. What is the probability that the password does not have any vowels?
    A) 0.20   B) 0.44   C) 0.65   D) 0.85
    Ans: C

56. A game consists of rolling a regular die. You pay $5 to play the game, and the $5 is not returned. If you roll a 1 or 2, you win $6. If you roll a 3, 4, 5, or 6, you win nothing. What is the mean value for this game, taking into account the $5 cost of the game?
    A) −$5   B) −$3   C) $1   D) $3
    Ans: B

57. A multiple-choice quiz has three possible answers for each question. You get 4 points for each correct answer, but you lose 3 points for each incorrect answer. No points are gained or lost if you leave the question blank. What is the mean point value of a random guess on the quiz?
A) 1 point   B) 1/3 points   C) −1/3 points   D) −2/3 points
Ans: D

58. The mean volume of a can of Super Soda is 12 ounces, with a standard deviation of 0.6 ounces. If the volumes of all cans of Super Soda are normally distributed, 25% of the cans fall below what volume?
A) 3 ounces   B) 11.4 ounces   C) 11.6 ounces   D) 12.4 ounces
Ans: B

59. The mean volume of a can of Super Soda is 12 ounces, with a standard deviation of 0.6 ounces. The volumes of all cans of Super Soda are normally distributed. What percent of cans of Super Soda contain less than 10.8 ounces?
A) 0.025%   B) 2.5%   C) 0.475%   D) 47.5%
Ans: B

60. A math professor notices that the scores from the most recent exam are normally distributed and decides to grade on a curve. The mean score was 60, with a standard deviation of 15. If the professor wants 16% of the students to get an A, what is the minimum score for an A?
A) 70   B) 75   C) 80   D) 90
Ans: B

Chapter 8: Free-Response

1. A spinner with regions numbered 1 to 4 is spun and a coin is tossed. Both the number spun and whether the coin lands heads or tails is recorded. Write the sample space.
   Ans: {(1,H), (2,H), (3,H), (4,H), (1,T), (2,T), (3,T), (4,T)}

2. Three coins are flipped simultaneously and it is recorded whether each coin lands heads or tails. List the sample space.
   Ans: { HHH, HHT, HTH, THH, HTT, THT, TTH, TTT}

3. A pair of dice is rolled. Sam says there are 36 outcomes in the sample space for this procedure and Sally says there are 11 outcomes in the sample space. Explain how they could both be correct.
   Ans: Sam counts 36 outcomes in the sample space by observing the number rolled on each die. Sally counts 11 outcomes by observing the sum rolled on the die.

4. Exactly one of three contestants will win a game show. The probability that Terry wins is 0.25 and the probability that Chris wins is 0.65. What is the probability that Toni wins?
   Ans: The probability Toni wins is 0.1.

5. If the probability that Kerry gets an "A" in English class is 0.82, what is the probability that Kerry does not get an "A?"
   Ans: The probability Kerry does not get an "A" is 0.18.

6. Suppose three fair coins are tossed and the number of heads that appear is recorded. What is the probability of getting exactly two heads?
   Ans: The probability of getting exactly two heads is 3/8 or 0.375.

7. A pair of fair dice is rolled and the sum of the faces showing is recorded. What is the probability of getting a sum greater than 9?
   Ans: The probability of rolling a sum greater than 9 is 6/36 or 0.167.

8. We wish to make a spinner that will be numbered 1 to 4, but will have the probability of spinning a "1" be 0.5. Draw the face for such a spinner.
   Ans: Answers may vary. Any spinner face which shows half the face labeled "1" is correct.

9. Find the probability of drawing a three or a heart from a regular (bridge) deck of cards. (Such a deck consists of four suits of thirteen cards each. The suits are hearts, spades, diamonds, and clubs. The cards are 1 through 10, Jack, Queen, and King.)
   Ans: The probability of drawing a three or a heart is 16/52 or 0.308.

10. We must create a license plate code that consists of two letters followed by three digits. The letters cannot repeat, but the digits may. How many such license plate codes can be formed?
Ans: 650,000

11. A pizza can be made with any of the following toppings: cheese, pepperoni, sausage, mushrooms, anchovies, green peppers, or olives. How many different three-topping pizzas can be made? Doubling of any topping is not allowed.
Ans: 210

12. A license plate code consists of two letters followed by three digits. The letters cannot repeat, but the digits can. What is the probability that a randomly chosen plate has all three digits the same?
Ans: 6500/650,000 = 1/100 = 0.01

13. A pizza can be made with any of the following toppings: cheese, pepperoni, sausage, mushrooms, anchovies, green peppers, or olives. Doubling of any topping is not allowed. What is the probability that a randomly created three-topping pizza will contain mushrooms?
Ans: 30/210 = 1/7 = 0.143

14. A student is taking a five-question True/False test. If the student chooses answers at random, what is the probability of getting all questions correct?
Ans: 1/32 = 0.03125

15. Below is a probability model for the number of automobiles owned by a randomly chosen family in a large town. What is the mean number of automobiles owned?

Number of automobiles	0	1	2	3
Probability	0.15	0.20	0.55	0.10

Ans: The mean number of automobiles owned is 1.6.

16. Suppose a game has four outcomes, A, B, C, and D. The probability of outcome A is 0.4, the probabilities of each of the other outcomes is 0.2. A player receives $2 if outcome A occurs, $3 if outcome B occurs, $1 if outcome C occurs, and must pay $5 if outcome D occurs. What is the mean value of one trial of this game?
Ans: The mean value of one trial is $0.60.

17. The mean value of one trial of a carnival game is –$.05. Explain what this means.
Ans: The mean value gives the win or loss after a very large number of trials. In this case, a player would lose an average of 5 cents for each trial.

18. Suppose a trial consists of rolling a single die and reporting the number that is rolled. What are the possible outcomes? Are they equally likely?
Ans: Possible outcomes are 1, 2, 3, 4, 5, 6. They are equally likely.

19. Suppose a trial consists of rolling two dice and reporting the sum of the numbers rolled. What are the possible outcomes? Are they equally likely?
Ans: Possible outcomes are 2, 3, 4, 5, 6, 7, 8, 9, 10, 11, 12. They are not equally likely.

20. Suppose a trial consists of rolling two dice and and reporting the smaller of the two numbers rolled? What are the possible outcomes? Are they equally likely?
Ans: Possible outcomes are 1, 2, 3, 4, 5, 6. They are not equally likely.

21. The mean weight of a collection of potatoes in a shipment to a fruit market is 1.3 lbs, with a standard deviation of 0.35 lbs. The distribution of weights is approximately normal. What is the probability that one potato chosen at random will weigh more than 1.65 lbs?
Ans: 0.16

22. The mean weight of a collection of potatoes in a shipment to a fruit market is 1.3 lbs, with a standard deviation of 0.35 lbs. The distribution of weights is approximately normal. What fraction of the potatoes in the shipment will weigh between 0.25 and 2.35 lbs?
Ans: 99.7%

23. In the manufacturing process for ball bearings, the mean diameter is 5 mm with a standard deviation of 0.002 mm. Between what two measurements will 95% of all diameters of ball bearings be found?
Ans: 95% of all diameters will be between 4.996 and 5.004 mm.

24. In the manufacturing process for ball bearings, the mean diameter is 5 mm with a standard deviation of 0.002 mm. Each hour a sample of 20 bearings is drawn, measured, and the mean diameter of the sample found. What is the standard deviation σ_x of the sample mean?
Ans: 0.000447

25. A publisher wishes to know what percent of book pages will need graphics editing. A random sample of 25 pages in a textbook finds that 58% of the pages had drawings or figures on them. The standard deviation for this percent is 9.9%. If the publisher wishes to reduce the standard deviation to 3.3%, how many pages should the publisher sample?
Ans: 225 pages

26. A game consists of tossing a coin and rolling a six-sided die. The results can be recorded easily; for example, if heads shows on the coin and a 4 shows on the die, record this as H4. List the sample space for the results of this game.
Ans: H1, H2, H3, H4, H5, H6, T1, T2, T3, T4, T5, T6

27. A game consists of tossing three coins. Find the probability model for the number of coins showing heads.
Ans:

Number of heads	0	1	2	3
Probability	1/8 or .125	3/8 or .375	3/8 or .375	1/8 or .125

28. A football stadium snack bar conducted a survey and found that 30 customers bought one item, 52 customers bought two items, 21 customers bought three items, and 12 customers bought four items. What is the mean number of items purchased per customer? Round your answer to the nearest tenth.
Ans: 2.1 items

29. Suppose you use a spinner to choose a random number between 0 and 1. Which is more likely—choosing a number between 1/3 and 2/3, or between 1/2 and 3/4?
Ans: Choosing a number between 1/3 and 2/3

30. According to the central limit theorem, how does the standard deviation of averages over four observations compare to the standard deviation of individual observations?
Ans: The standard deviation of the averages is half that of the individual observations.

Chapter 9: Multiple-Choice

1. Majority rule is a good way to choose between two alternatives.
   A) True   B) False
   Ans: A

2. Majority rule is a good way to choose between three alternatives.
   A) True   B) False
   Ans: B

3. Every set of voters' preference lists produces a Condorcet winner.
   A) True   B) False
   Ans: B

4. For a given set of voters' preference lists, different voting procedures may produce different winners.
   A) True   B) False
   Ans: A

5. For a given set of voters' preference lists, different agendas for sequential pairwise voting may produce different winners.
   A) True   B) False
   Ans: A

6. The Borda count method of voting satisfies the independence of irrelevant alternatives criterion.
   A) True   B) False
   Ans: B

7. Sequential pairwise voting satisfies the Condorcet criterion.
   A) True   B) False
   Ans: A

8. How many votes are needed for a majority winner if there are 20 voters?
   A) 10   B) 11   C) 15   D) 20
   Ans: B

9. How many votes are needed for a majority winner if there are 25 voters?
   A) 12   B) 12.5   C) 13   D) 25
   Ans: C

10. In how many ways can a voter rank five candidates, without allowing ties?
    A) 5   B) 32   C) 60   D) 120
    Ans: D

11. In how many ways can a voter rank three candidates, without allowing ties?
    A) 3   B) 6   C) 8   D) 12
    Ans: B

12. A group of 12 students have to decide among three types of pizza: Sausage (S), Mushroom (M), and Beef (B). Their preference rankings are shown below. Which choice will the group make if they use majority rule?

	Number of Students				
	3	3	2	2	2
First choice	B	M	S	B	S
Second choice	M	B	M	S	B
Third choice	S	S	B	M	M

    A) S   B) M   C) B   D) No winner can be chosen.
    Ans: D

13. A group of 12 students have to decide among three types of pizza: Sausage (S), Mushroom (M), and Beef (B). Their preference rankings are shown below. Which choice will the group make if they use plurality voting?

	Number of Students				
	3	3	2	2	2
First choice	B	M	S	B	S
Second choice	M	S	M	S	B
Third choice	S	B	B	M	M

    A) S   B) M   C) B   D) No winner can be chosen.
    Ans: C

14. A group of 12 students have to decide among three types of pizza: Sausage (S), Mushroom (M), and Beef (B). Their preference rankings are shown below. Which choice will the group make if they use the plurality runoff voting method?

	Number of Students				
	3	3	2	2	2
First choice	B	M	S	B	S
Second choice	M	S	M	S	B
Third choice	S	B	B	M	M

    A) S   B) M   C) B   D) No winner can be chosen.
    Ans: A

15. A group of 12 students have to decide among three types of pizza: Sausage (S), Mushroom (M), and Beef (B). Their preference rankings are shown below. Which choice will the group make if they use the Borda count?

	Number of Students				
	3	3	2	2	2
First choice	B	M	S	B	S
Second choice	M	B	M	S	B
Third choice	S	S	B	M	M

A) S   B) M   C) B   D) No winner can be chosen.
Ans: C

16. A group of 12 students have to decide among three types of pizza: Sausage (S), Mushroom (M), and Beef (B). Their preference rankings are shown below. Which choice will the group make if they use the Hare system?

	Number of Students				
	3	3	2	2	2
First choice	B	M	S	B	S
Second choice	M	B	M	S	B
Third choice	S	S	B	M	M

A) S   B) M   C) B   D) No winner can be chosen.
Ans: C

17. A group of 12 students have to decide among three types of pizza: Sausage (S), Mushroom (M), and Beef (B). Their preference rankings are shown below. Which choice will the group make if they use sequential pairwise voting with agenda B, M, S?

	Number of Students				
	3	3	2	2	2
First choice	B	M	S	B	S
Second choice	M	B	M	S	B
Third choice	S	S	B	M	M

A) S   B) M   C) B   D) No winner can be chosen.
Ans: C

18. A group of 12 students have to decide among three types of pizza: Sausage (S), Mushroom (M), and Beef (B). Their preference rankings are shown below. Is there a Condorcet winner among the pizza types?

	Number of Students				
	3	3	2	2	2
First choice	B	M	S	B	S
Second choice	M	B	M	S	B
Third choice	S	S	B	M	M

A) S B) M C) B D) No winner can be chosen.
Ans: C

Use the following to answer questions 19-21:

Use the following information to answer the question(s) below.

Thirty board members must vote on five candidates: X, Y, Z, U, and V. Their preference rankings are summarized in the table below.

	Number of Members		
	12	10	8
First choice	X	Y	Z
Second choice	U	Z	U
Third choice	Y	X	X
Fourth choice	Z	U	V
Fifth choice	V	V	Y

19. Find the winner using the Borda count.
A) X   B) Y   C) Z   D) No winner is chosen.
Ans: A

20. Find the winner using the Hare system.
A) X   B) Y   C) Z   D) No winner is chosen.
Ans: A

21. Find the winner using sequential pairwise voting with the agenda X, Y, Z, U, V.
A) X   B) Z   C) U   D) V
Ans: B

Use the following to answer questions 22-26:

Use the following information to answer the question(s) below.

Fifty voters who elect one of the five candidates A, B, C, D, or E have the preference schedule shown below.

	Number of Voters			
	20	14	10	6
First choice	A	B	B	C
Second choice	C	A	A	D
Third choice	E	D	C	B
Fourth choice	B	C	D	A
Fifth choice	D	E	E	E

22. Which candidate will be elected using plurality voting?
    A) A   B) B   C) C   D) No winner is determined.
    Ans: B

23. Which candidate will be elected using the Borda count?
    A) A   B) B   C) C   D) No winner is determined.
    Ans: A

24. Which candidate will be elected using the Hare system?
    A) A   B) B   C) C   D) No winner is determined.
    Ans: B

25. Which candidate will be elected using sequential pairwise voting with the agenda A, B, C, D, E?
    A) A   B) B   C) C   D) No winner is determined.
    Ans: C

26. Which candidate will be elected using the plurality runoff voting method?
    A) A   B) B   C) C   D) No winner is determined.
    Ans: B

Use the following to answer questions 27-30:

Use the following information to answer the question(s) below.

Suppose that a nine-member committee needs to elect one of the four alternatives A, B, C, or D. Their preference schedule is shown below.

	Number of Members		
	4	3	2
First choice	A	B	C
Second choice	B	D	D
Third choice	C	A	A
Fourth choice	D	C	B

27. Which alternative wins using the Borda count?
    A) A B) B C) C D) No winner is determined.
    Ans: D

28. Which alternative wins using sequential pairwise voting with the agenda A, B, C, D?
    A) A B) B C) C D) D
    Ans: D

29. Is there a Condorcet winner?
    A) B wins B) C wins C) D wins D) No Condorcet winner is determined.
    Ans: D

30. Which alternative wins using the Hare system?
    A) A B) B C) C D) D
    Ans: A

Use the following to answer questions 31-32:

Use the following information to answer the question(s) below.

Consider a 13-person committee that is considering three applicants, A, B, and C, for an opening. The individual rankings are summarized in the table below.

	Number of Members			
	5	4	2	2
First choice	B	C	A	A
Second choice	C	A	B	C
Third choice	A	B	C	A

31. Which applicant would be accepted if the committee used the plurality method?
A) A   B) B   C) C   D) There is no plurality winner.
Ans: B

32. Which applicant would be accepted if the committee used the plurality runoff method?
A) A   B) B   C) C   D) There is no plurality runoff winner.
Ans: A

33. Consider a 13-person committee that is considering three applicants, A, B, and C, for an opening. The individual rankings are summarized in the table below. Which applicant would be accepted if the committee used the Borda count?

	Number of Members			
	5	4	2	2
First choice	B	C	A	A
Second choice	C	B	B	C
Third choice	A	A	C	B

A) A   B) B   C) C   D) There is no Borda count winner.
Ans: B

34. Twenty-nine voters must choose from among three alternatives: A, B, and C. The voters' preference schedules are shown below. C wins in a Borda count. Is the outcome different in a rank system that assigns 5 points for first choice, 2 points for second, and 1 point for third?

	Number of Voters			
	12	8	6	3
First choice	B	C	A	C
Second choice	C	A	B	B
Third choice	A	B	C	A

A)   No, C still wins   C)   Yes, B now wins
B)   Yes, A now wins   D)   Yes, now there is no winner
Ans: C

35. Twenty-nine voters must choose from among three alternatives: A, B, and C. The voters' preference schedules are shown below. Which alternative wins using the Hare system?

	Number of Voters			
	12	8	6	3
First choice	B	C	A	C
Second choice	C	A	B	B
Third choice	A	B	C	A

A) A   B) B   C) C   D) No winner is determined.
Ans: B

Use the following to answer questions 36-41:

Use the following information to answer the question(s) below.

A group of 22 young people must decide whether to go to the beach (B), the mountain (M), or the zoo (Z) on a field trip. Their preference rankings are summarized in the table below.

	Number of Voters		
	10	8	4
First choice	B	M	Z
Second choice	M	B	M
Third choice	Z	Z	B

36. Which choice wins using plurality voting?
    A) M   B) B   C) Z   D) No winner is determined.
    Ans: B

37. Which choice wins using the plurality runoff voting method?
    A) M   B) B   C) Z   D) No winner is determined.
    Ans: A

38. Which choice wins using the Borda count?
    A) M   B) B   C) Z   D) No winner is determined.
    Ans: A

39. Which choice wins using the Hare system?
    A) M   B) B   C) Z   D) No winner is determined.
    Ans: A

40. Which choice wins using sequential pairwise voting with the agenda Z, B, M?
    A) M   B) B   C) Z   D) No winner is determined.
    Ans: A

41. Is there a Condorcet winner?
    A) M   B) B   C) Z   D) No winner is determined.
    Ans: A

Use the following to answer questions 42-45:

Use the following information to answer the question(s) below.

One hundred voters are to elect one of the four candidates A, B, C, or D. Their preference schedule is shown below.

	Number of Voters			
	40	32	18	10
First choice	A	B	D	C
Second choice	C	C	C	D
Third choice	B	A	B	A
Fourth choice	D	D	A	B

42. Which candidate wins using the Hare system?
    A) A wins.   B) B wins.   C) D wins.   D) No winner is determined.
    Ans: D

43. Is there a Condorcet winner?
    A)   Yes, A wins.   C)   Yes, C wins.
    B)   Yes, B wins.   D)   No winner is determined.
    Ans: D

44. Is there a winner using the plurality runoff method?
    A)   Yes, A wins.   C)   Yes, C wins.
    B)   Yes, B wins.   D)   No winner is determined.
    Ans: D

45. Which candidate wins using sequential pairwise voting with the agenda A, C, B, D?
    A) A wins.   B) B wins.   C) C wins.   D) D wins.
    Ans: C

Use the following to answer questions 46-47:

Use the following information to answer the question(s) below.

Eight board members vote by approval voting on four candidates, A, B, C, and D, for new positions on their board as indicated in the following table. An "X" indicates an approval vote.

	Voters							
	1	2	3	4	5	6	7	8
A	X	X	X	X		X	X	X
B		X	X		X	X		X
C		X			X	X	X	X
D	X		X	X	X	X	X	

46. Which candidate will be chosen for the board if just one of them is to be elected?
A) A   B) B   C) C   D) D
Ans: A

47. Which candidate(s) is (are) elected if 80% approval is necessary and at most two are elected?
A)   No candidates are elected.   C)   Only candidate D is elected.
B)   Only candidate A is elected.   D)   Both candidates A and D are elected.
Ans: B

Use the following to answer questions 48-50:

Use the following information to answer the question(s) below.

A five-member evaluating committee votes by approval voting on 10 faculty members for a promotion as indicated in the table below. An "X" indicates an approval vote.

	Voters				
Candidates	1	2	3	4	5
A	X		X	X	X
B	X	X	X	X	X
C			X		X
D		X	X	X	
E	X		X		X
F	X				X
G		X	X	X	
H		X		X	
I	X		X	X	
J		X	X	X	X

48. Which faculty member is chosen for the promotion if just one of them is to be selected?
    A) A B) B C) F D) J
    Ans: B

49. Which candidate(s) receive a promotion if 80% approval is needed?
    A) B only.   C) All except C, F, and H.
    B) A, B, and J.   D) No candidate receives a promotion.
    Ans: B

50. Which faculty member(s) is (are) chosen if 60% approval is necessary and at most three are to be selected?
    A) B only.   C) All except C, F, and H.
    B) A, B, and J.   D) None will be promoted.
    Ans: C

51. How many votes are needed for a majority winner if there are 30 voters?
    A) 10 B) 15 C) 16 D) 30
    Ans: C

52. In how many ways can a voter rank four candidates, without allowing ties?
    A) 48 B) 24 C) 12 D) 8
    Ans: B

Use the following to answer questions 53-59:

Use the following information to answer the question(s) below.

Your fly fishing club is attempting to decide where to go for the next day trip. The choices are Alder River (A), Boulder Pond (B), or Collie Creek (C). The preference rankings of the members are shown below.

	Number of members			
	6	12	15	11
First choice	A	C	B	A
Second choice	B	B	A	C
Third choice	C	A	C	B

53. Which location will be chosen if majority rule is used?
    A) Alder River   C) Collie Creek
    B) Boulder Pond   D) No winner can be chosen.
    Ans: D

54. Which location will be chosen if plurality voting is used?
    A) Alder River   C) Collie Creek
    B) Boulder Pond   D) No winner can be chosen.
    Ans: A

55. Which location will be chosen if the Borda count is used?
    A) Alder River   C) Collie Creek
    B) Boulder Pond   D) No winner can be chosen.
    Ans: A

56. Which location will be chosen if the Hare system is used?
    A) Alder River   C) Collie Creek
    B) Boulder Pond   D) No winner can be chosen.
    Ans: B

57. Which location will be chosen if sequential pairwise voting with agenda B, A, C is used?
    A) Alder River   C) Collie Creek
    B) Boulder Pond   D) No winner can be chosen.
    Ans: C

58. Which location, if any, is the Condorcet winner?
    A) Alder River   C) Collie Creek
    B) Boulder Pond   D) No winner can be chosen.
    Ans: D

59. Which location will be chosen if plurality runoff voting is used?
    A) Alder River   C) Collie Creek
    B) Boulder Pond   D) No winner can be chosen.
    Ans: B

60. After their star pitcher moved to another town, the eight remaining members of the company baseball team needed to select a new pitcher. They used approval voting on the four prospects, and the results are listed below. An "X" indicates an approval vote.

Alan	X			X		X				X
Bob		X		X		X			X	
Chuck		X				X	X			
David	X	X			X		X	X		

    Which pitcher is chosen if just one is to be selected?
    A) Alan   B) Bob   C) Chuck   D) David
    Ans: D

Chapter 9: Free-Response

1. Explain why majority rule is not a good way to choose among four alternatives.
   Ans: Majority rule is not a good way to choose among four alternatives because it is possible that none of the four will get a majority of the vote.

2. Arrow's Impossibility Theorem states that any voting system can give undesirable outcomes. Explain what this means.
   Ans: For any voting system it is possible to find a set of voters' preferences that will cause the voting system to violate a condition deemed desirable for a fair voting system. These conditions may include the Condorcet Winner Criterion and the Independence of Irrelevant Alternatives condition.

3. Explain the Condorcet Winner Criterion.
   Ans: A voting system satisfies the Condorcet Winner Criterion if the winner of an election is also the Condorcet winner, if a Condorcet winner exists.

4. Explain how the plurality runoff voting system might not choose a winner.
   Ans: There could be a tie among the candidates in the runoff.

5. Determine the number of ways it is possible to rank six candidates if no ties are allowed.
   Ans: Six candidates can be ranked in 720 ways if ties are not allowed.

6. Which of the voting procedures, plurality, the Borda count, sequential pairwise voting, or the Hare system, satisfies the Condorcet Winner Criterion?
   Ans: Only Sequential Pairwise voting satisfies the Condorcet Winner Criterion.

7. Which of the voting procedures, plurality, the Borda count, sequential pairwise voting, or the Hare system, satisfies the Pareto condition?
   Ans: Plurality, the Borda count, and the Hare system all satisfy the Pareto condition.

8. Which of the voting procedures, plurality, the Borda count, sequential pairwise voting, or the Hare system, satisfies monotonicity?
   Ans: Plurality, the Borda count, and sequential pairwise voting all satisfy monotonicity.

9. In order to choose which type of music to listen to in a student center music lounge, a Condorcet vote is held by the 15 students present. Below are the preference schedules for the students. Is there a Condorcet winner and if so, which music type?

	Number of Students		
	6	5	4
First choice	classical	rock	rock
Second choice	jazz	jazz	classical
Third choice	rock	classical	jazz

Ans: Rock is the Condorcet winner.

Use the following to answer questions 10-14:

Use the preference schedule of 23 voters shown below to answer the following question(s).

	Number of Voters			
	8	5	6	4
First choice	A	C	B	B
Second choice	C	A	C	A
Third choice	B	B	A	C

10. Which candidate, if any, wins in a majority rule election?
Ans: There is no majority-rule winner.

11. If a rank method is used, which candidate, if any, wins in a straight plurality election?
Ans: B wins in a straight plurality vote.

12. Which candidate, if any, wins if an election is held between A and C and the winner of that race runs against B? Who wins the final election?
Ans: A wins.

13. If a Borda count is used that assigns 3 points for a first place vote, 2 points for a second place vote, and 1 point for a third place vote, who wins the election?
Ans: A wins.

14. Can the four voters in the last column vote strategically to change the outcome of question 13 to one they would like better? Why or why not?
Ans: No. They cannot make B win the election and if they switch any rankings to place C higher, then C would win and this is their least desirable outcome.

Use the following to answer questions 15-16:

Use the following information to answer the question(s) below.

A poll by 15 sports announcers chooses the best basketball team from among three schools: University of Nevada at Las Vegas (LV), University of North Carolina (NC), and Indiana University (IU).

	Number of Announcers			
	5	6	2	2
First choice	LV	NC	IU	NC
Second choice	IU	LV	NC	IU
Third choice	NC	IU	LV	LV

15. If the individual rankings are as summarized in the table, which team wins if they use a rank method that assigns 5, 3, and 1 point(s) to each first, second, and third choice respectively?
    Ans: North Carolina wins with 51 points.

16. If the plurality method is used, who is selected? Who is selected using the plurality runoff method?
    Ans: North Carolina wins both plurality method and plurality runoff method selections.

17. A 17-member committee must elect one of four candidates: R, S, T, or W. Their preference schedule is shown below. Which candidate wins under pairwise sequential voting with the agenda S, T, W, R?

	Number of Members			
	6	4	3	4
First choice	R	S	T	W
Second choice	S	R	S	T
Third choice	T	T	R	S
Fourth choice	W	W	W	R

Ans: S wins.

Use the following to answer questions 18-19:

Use the following information to answer the question(s) below.

Seventeen board members vote on four candidates, A, B, C, or D, for a new position on their board. Their preference schedules are shown below.

	Number of Members		
	7	6	4
First choice	A	D	C
Second choice	B	A	B
Third choice	C	B	D
Fourth choice	D	C	A

18. Which candidate will be selected if they use the Hare system?
    Ans: D wins.

19. Using the Hare system according to the preference schedules shown, what happens if A rejects the offer before the ranking?
    Ans: B wins.

Use the following to answer questions 20-22:

Use the following information to answer the question(s) below.

There are 18 delegates to a political party's convention at which four people, A, B, C, and D, have been nominated as the party's candidate for governor. The delegates' preference schedule is shown below.

	Number of Delegates		
	8	9	4
First choice	A	B	C
Second choice	B	A	B
Third choice	C	D	A
Fourth choice	D	C	D

20. What nominee would be elected if the party uses a Borda count?
    Ans: B wins with 51 points.

21. What nominee would be elected if the party uses a rank system that assigns 5, 4, 1, and 0 point(s) for a first, second, third, and fourth choice, respectively? Is this result different from that which results from a Borda count?
    Ans: With the given rank system, candidate B wins. Under a Borda count, candidate B also wins.

22. Who wins using the plurality method? Do the results change if the plurality runoff method is used?
    Ans: B wins under both plurality and plurality runoff methods.

Use the following to answer questions 23-24:

Use the following information to answer the question(s) below.

An 11-member committee must choose one of the four applicants, K, L, M, and N, for membership on the committee. The committee members have preferences among the applicants as given below.

	Number of Members		
	6	2	3
First choice	K	M	M
Second choice	L	L	N
Third choice	N	K	L
Fourth choice	M	N	K

23. Who wins under the plurality method? Who wins under the plurality runoff method?
    Ans: K wins under both plurality and plurality runoff.

24. Which applicant will be given the position if the members use the Borda count to choose the new member?
    Ans: K is chosen.

25. In how many ways can one rank three candidates if ties are allowed?
    Ans: Three candidates can be ranked in 13 ways if ties are allowed.

26. Consider the following preference table:

	Number of voters		
	3	2	2
First choice	A	B	C
Second choice	B	C	B
Third choice	C	A	A

Which candidate will be chosen if majority rule is used?
Ans: A

27. Consider the following preference table:

	Number of voters			
	6	3	4	2
First choice	A	C	C	B
Second choice	B	B	D	A
Third choice	C	D	A	C
Fourth choice	D	A	B	D

Which candidate will be chosen if plurality voting is used?
Ans: C

28. Consider the following preference table:

	Number of voters			
	4	6	8	4
First choice	D	C	A	B
Second choice	C	B	D	A
Third choice	B	D	C	C
Fourth choice	A	A	B	D

Which candidate will be chosen if the Borda count is used?
Ans: C

29. Consider the following preference table:

	Number of voters		
	3	2	2
First choice	A	B	C
Second choice	B	C	B
Third choice	C	A	A

Which candidate, if any, is the Condorcet winner?
Ans: B

30. After their star pitcher moved to another town, the eight remaining members of the company baseball team needed to select a new pitcher. They used approval voting on the four prospects, and the results are listed below. An "X" indicates an approval vote.

Alan	X	X				X		
Bob	X		X	X	X			X
Chuck		X		X			X	X
David		X	X				X	X

Which pitcher is chosen if just one is to be selected?
Ans: Bob

Chapter 10: Multiple-Choice

1. A vote using Condorcet's method is:
   A) never manipulable.   B) sometimes manipulable.   C) always manipulable.
   Ans: A

2. A vote using majority rule is:
   A) never manipulable.   B) sometimes manipulable.   C) always manipulable.
   Ans: A

3. A vote between two candidates is:
   A) never manipulable.   B) sometimes manipulable.   C) always manipulable.
   Ans: A

4. A vote using the Borda count method is:
   A) never manipulable.   B) sometimes manipulable.   C) always manipulable.
   Ans: B

5. A vote among four or more candidates using the Borda count method is:
   A) never manipulable.   B) sometimes manipulable.   C) always manipulable.
   Ans: B

6. Agenda manipulation is a technique to impact an outcome using:
A)	the Hare method.	C)	the Borda count method.
B)	the plurality runoff method.	D)	the sequential pairwise method.
   Ans: D

7. A vote using plurality is:
   A)   never manipulable.
   B)   manipulable by individuals only.
   C)   manipulable by groups only.
   D)   manipulable by both individuals and groups.
   Ans: C

8. Which of these voting methods never results in a tie?
A)	the Hare method	C)	Condercet method
B)	sequential runoff	D)	plurality runoff
   Ans: C

9. Which of the following is NOT a property of the Condercet method of voting?
A)	Satisfies the Pareto condition	C)	Not a dictatorship
B)	Nonmanipulable	D)	Always produces a winner
   Ans: D

10. After considering all possible one-on-one contests, Copeland's rule chooses as the winner:
    A) the candidate who wins every contest in which he or she participates.
    B) the candidate with the best win-loss record.
    C) the candidate who wins the longest sequence of contests.
    D) the candidate who wins more contests than he or she loses.
    Ans: B

11. The Chair's paradox is the fact that the chair, who can break ties, can:
    A) always end up with his or her preferred candidate.
    B) sometimes end up with his or her preferred candidate.
    C) sometimes end up with his or her least preferred candidate.
    D) never end up with his or her least preferred candidate.
    Ans: C

12. Which of the following is also known as an "insincere ballot"?
    A) A disingenuous ballot   C) A preference ballot
    B) A strategic ballot   D) A dispreference ballot
    Ans: A

13. A person who has tie-breaking power:
    A) always ends up with his or her preferred candidate.
    B) only votes when there is a tie.
    C) may vote twice when there is a tie.
    D) becomes the winning candidate when there is a tie.
    Ans: C

14. One strategy weakly dominates another if it yields an outcome:
    A) that is no worse than the other.   C) that is definitely better than the other.
    B) that is no better than the other.   D) that is definitely worse than the other.
    Ans: A

15. If a voter sincerely prefers A over B over C over D, then he or she will prefer a tie between B and C over:
    A) a tie between B and D.   C) a tie between A and C.
    B) a tie between A and B.
    Ans: A

Use the following to answer questions 16-18:

Use the following information to answer the question(s) below.

Thirty voters with the preference schedules below are to elect a union spokesman from among five candidates: A, B, C, D, and E. If the Borda count is used, candidate B would win.

	Number of Voters		
	12	10	8
First choice	A	B	D
Second choice	D	C	B
Third choice	B	A	A
Fourth choice	C	D	E
Fifth choice	E	E	C

16. Would there be any difference in the result if candidate C withdrew from the race before the ranking?
   A)   No, B still wins.   C)   Yes, now D wins.
   B)   Yes, now A wins.   D)   Yes, now there is no winner.
   Ans: B

17. Would there be any difference in the result if candidate D withdrew from the race before the ranking?
   A)   No, B still wins.   C)   Yes, now C wins.
   B)   Yes, now A wins.   D)   Yes, now there is no winner.
   Ans: A

18. Would there be any difference in the result if candidate A withdrew from the race before the ranking?
   A)   No, B still wins.   C)   Yes, now D wins.
   B)   Yes, now C wins.   D)   Yes, now there is no winner.
   Ans: D

Use the following to answer questions 19-22:

Use the following information to answer the question(s) below.

Consider an 11-member committee that must choose one of three alternatives: X, Y, or Z. Their schedule of preferences is shown below.

	Number of Voters		
	5	4	2
First choice	Z	X	Y
Second choice	Y	Y	X
Third choice	X	Z	Z

19. If the Hare system is used, alternative X wins. Could the voters who most prefer Z vote insincerely in some way to change the outcome in a way that would benefit them?
    A)   Yes, switch ranking of X and Y.   C)   Yes, switch ranking of X and Z.
    B)   Yes, switch ranking of Y and Z.   D)   No, X would always win.
    Ans: B

20. If the Hare system is used, alternative X wins. Could the voters who most prefer Y vote insincerely in some way to change the outcome in a way that would benefit them?
    A)   Yes, switch ranking of X and Y.   C)   Yes, switch ranking of X and Z.
    B)   Yes, switch ranking of Y and Z.   D)   No, X would always win.
    Ans: D

21. Is there an agenda for which X would win under sequential pairwise voting?
    A) Yes, X Y Z   B) Yes, Y Z X   C) Yes, Z Y X   D) No
    Ans: D

22. Is there an agenda for which Z would win under sequential pairwise voting?
    A) Yes, X Y Z   B) Yes, Y Z X   C) Yes, Z Y X   D) No
    Ans: D

Use the following to answer questions 23-26:

Use the following information to answer the question(s) below.

Twenty-nine voters must choose from among three alternatives: A, B, and C. The voters' preference schedules are shown below.

	Number of Voters			
	12	8	6	3
First choice	B	C	A	C
Second choice	C	A	B	B
Third choice	A	B	C	A

23. C wins in a Borda count. Can the six voters in the third column change their preference list to produce an outcome they like better?
    A)   No, C will always win.   C)   Yes, they can rank B, A, C.
    B)   Yes, they can rank A, C, B.   D)   Yes, they can rank C, A, B.
    Ans: C

24. C wins in a Borda count. Can the 12 voters in the first column change their preference list to produce an outcome they like better?
    A)   No, C will always win.   C)   Yes, they can rank B, A, C.
    B)   Yes, they can rank A, C, B.   D)   Yes, they can rank C, A, B.
    Ans: A

25. Using the agenda A, B, C, and sequential pairwise voting, alternative B wins. Is there an agenda that produces C as a winner?
    A)   No, B always wins.   C)   Yes, the agenda C, B, A.
    B)   Yes, the agenda A, C, B.   D)   Yes, the agenda B, A, C.
    Ans: A

26. Using the agenda A, B, C, and sequential pairwise voting, alternative B wins. Is there an agenda that produces A as a winner?
    A)   No, B always wins.   C)   Yes, the agenda C, B, A.
    B)   Yes, the agenda A, C, B.   D)   Yes, the agenda B, A, C.
    Ans: A

Use the following to answer questions 27-29:

Use the following information to answer the question(s) below.

A group of 22 young people must decide whether to go to the beach (B), the mountain (M), or the zoo (Z) on a field trip. Their preference rankings are summarized in the table below, and the decision will be made using a Borda count.

	Number of Voters		
	10	8	4
First choice	B	M	Z
Second choice	M	B	M
Third choice	Z	Z	B

27. Can the four voters in the last column change the results of the vote to their favor by changing their preference rankings?
    A) No B) Yes
    Ans: A

28. Can the 10 voters in the first column change the results of the vote to their favor by changing their preference rankings?
    A) No B) Yes
    Ans: B

29. Can the eight voters in the middle column change the results of the vote to their favor by changing their preference rankings?
    A) No B) Yes
    Ans: A

Use the following to answer questions 30-32:

Use the following preference table to answer the question(s) below.

	Number of voters			
	4	6	8	4
First choice	D	C	A	B
Second choice	C	B	D	A
Third choice	B	D	C	C
Fourth choice	A	A	B	D

30. Using plurality, A wins. Could the four voters who most prefer D (and prefer A least) vote insincerely to change the outcome in a way that would benefit them?
    A)   No, they cannot change the outcome.   C)   Yes, they could get C to win.
    B)   Yes, they could get B to win.   D)   Yes, they could get D to win.
    Ans: C

31. Using plurality, A wins. Could the six voters who most prefer C (and prefer A least) vote insincerely to change the outcome in a way that would benefit them?
    A)   No, they cannot change the outcome.   C)   Yes, they could get C to win.
    B)   Yes, they could get B to win.   D)   Yes, they could get D to win.
    Ans: B

32. Using plurality, A wins. Could the four voters who most prefer B vote insincerely to change the outcome in a way that would benefit them?
    A)   No, they cannot change the outcome.   C)   Yes, they could get C to win.
    B)   Yes, they could get B to win.   D)   Yes, they could get D to win.
    Ans: A

33. Consider the following preference table for two voters:

First choice	D	B
Second choice	C	A
Third choice	B	C
Fourth choice	A	D

    If a Borda count is used, can the voter on the left manipulate the outcome to his or her benefit?
    A) No   B) Yes
    Ans: B

34. Consider the following preference table for two voters:

First choice	D	B
Second choice	C	A
Third choice	B	C
Fourth choice	A	D

    If a Borda count is used, can the voter on the right manipulate the outcome to his or her benefit?
    A) No   B) Yes
    Ans: A

35. Consider the following preference table for two voters:

First choice	C	B
Second choice	B	A
Third choice	D	C
Fourth choice	A	D

If a Borda count is used, can the voter on the left manipulate the outcome to his or her benefit?
A) No   B) Yes
Ans: A

36. Consider the following preference table for two voters:

First choice	C	B
Second choice	B	A
Third choice	D	C
Fourth choice	A	D

If a Borda count is used, can the voter on the right manipulate the outcome to his or her benefit?
A) No   B) Yes
Ans: A

37. Consider the following preference table for two voters:

First choice	C	D
Second choice	B	A
Third choice	D	B
Fourth choice	A	C

If a Borda count is used, can the voter on the left manipulate the outcome to his or her benefit?
A) No   B) Yes
Ans: B

38. Consider the following preference table for two voters:

First choice	C	D
Second choice	B	A
Third choice	D	B
Fourth choice	A	C

If a Borda count is used, can the voter on the right manipulate the outcome to his or her benefit?
A) No   B) Yes
Ans: A

Use the following to answer questions 39-41:

Consider the following preference table for three voters to answer the question(s) below.

First choice	C	D	A
Second choice	B	A	B
Third choice	D	B	D
Fourth choice	A	C	C

39. If a Borda count is used, can the voter on the left manipulate the outcome to his or her benefit?
A) No   B) Yes
Ans: B

40. If a Borda count is used, can the voter on the right manipulate the outcome to his or her benefit?
A) No   B) Yes
Ans: B

41. If a Borda count is used, can the voter in the middle manipulate the outcome to his or her benefit?
A) No   B) Yes
Ans: B

Use the following to answer questions 42-44:

Consider the following preference table for three voters to answer the question(s) below.

First choice	C	D	B
Second choice	B	A	A
Third choice	D	B	D
Fourth choice	A	C	C

42. If a Borda count is used, can the voter on the left manipulate the outcome to his or her benefit?
A) No   B) Yes
Ans: A

43. If a Borda count is used, can the voter on the right manipulate the outcome to his or her benefit?
A) No   B) Yes
Ans: A

44. If a Borda count is used, can the voter on the right manipulate the outcome to his or her benefit?
A) No   B) Yes
Ans: B

45. Consider the following preference table for three voters:

First choice	C	D	D
Second choice	B	B	A
Third choice	D	C	B
Fourth choice	A	A	C

If a Borda count is used, can the voter on the left manipulate the outcome to his or her benefit?
A) No   B) Yes
Ans: B

46. Consider the following preference table for three voters:

First choice	C	D	D
Second choice	B	B	A
Third choice	D	C	B
Fourth choice	A	A	C

If a Borda count is used, can the voter on the right or in the middle manipulate the outcome to his or her benefit?
A)   Neither can
B)   Only the voter on the right can
C)   Only the voter in the middle can
D)   Both can
Ans: A

47. Consider the following preference table for four voters:

First choice	B	D	D	C
Second choice	C	B	A	A
Third choice	A	C	B	B
Fourth choice	D	A	C	D

If a Borda count is used, can the second voter manipulate the outcome so that D wins?
A) No   B) Yes
Ans: A

48. Consider the following preference table for four voters:

First choice	B	D	D	C
Second choice	C	B	A	A
Third choice	A	C	B	B
Fourth choice	D	A	C	D

If a Borda count is used, can the fourth voter manipulate the outcome so that C wins?
A) No   B) Yes
Ans: A

Use the following to answer questions 49-51:

Consider the following preference table for four voters to answer the question(s) below.

First choice	B	D	A	C
Second choice	C	B	D	D
Third choice	A	C	B	B
Fourth choice	D	A	C	A
Fifth choice	E	E	E	E

49. If a Borda count is used, can the first voter manipulate the outcome so that B wins?
    A) No   B) Yes
    Ans: B

50. If a Borda count is used, can the third voter manipulate the outcome so that A wins?
    A) No   B) Yes
    Ans: A

51. If a Borda count is used, can the fourth voter manipulate the outcome so that C wins?
    A) No   B) Yes
    Ans: A

Use the following to answer questions 52-55:

Consider the following preference table for four voters to answer the question(s) below.

First choice	B	D	A	C
Second choice	C	B	C	D
Third choice	A	C	B	B
Fourth choice	D	A	D	A
Fifth choice	E	E	E	E

52. If a Borda count is used, can the first voter manipulate the outcome so that B wins?
    A) No   B) Yes
    Ans: B

53. If a Borda count is used, can the second voter manipulate the outcome so that D wins?
    A) No   B) Yes
    Ans: A

54. If a Borda count is used, can the second voter manipulate the outcome so that B wins?
    A) No   B) Yes
    Ans: B

55. If a Borda count is used, can the third voter manipulate the outcome so that A wins?
    A) No   B) Yes
    Ans: A

Use the following to answer questions 56-58:

Consider the following preference table for three voters to answer the question(s) below.

First choice	B	D	A
Second choice	C	B	C
Third choice	A	C	B
Fourth choice	D	A	D
Fifth choice	E	E	E

56. Is there an agenda for which D would win a sequential pairwise election?
   A) No   B) Yes
   Ans: A

57. Is there an agenda for which A would win a sequential pairwise election?
   A) No   B) Yes
   Ans: A

58. Is there an agenda for which C would win a sequential pairwise election?
   A) No   B) Yes
   Ans: A

Use the following to answer questions 59-62:

Consider the following preference table for three voters to answer the question(s) below.

First choice	C	D	B
Second choice	B	C	D
Third choice	A	A	C
Fourth choice	D	B	A
Fifth choice	E	E	E

59. Is there an agenda for which D would win a sequential pairwise election?
   A) No   B) Yes
   Ans: B

60. Is there an agenda for which C would win a sequential pairwise election?
   A) No   B) Yes
   Ans: B

61. Is there an agenda for which B would win a sequential pairwise election?
   A) No   B) Yes
   Ans: B

62. Is there an agenda for which A would win a sequential pairwise election?
    A) No   B) Yes
    Ans: A

Use the following to answer questions 63-66:

Consider the following preference table for three voters to answer the question(s) below.

First choice	A	D	B
Second choice	D	C	A
Third choice	B	B	D
Fourth choice	C	E	C
Fifth choice	E	A	E

63. Is there an agenda for which A would win a sequential pairwise election?
    A) No   B) Yes
    Ans: B

64. Is there an agenda for which B would win a sequential pairwise election?
    A) No   B) Yes
    Ans: B

65. Is there an agenda for which C would win a sequential pairwise election?
    A) No   B) Yes
    Ans: B

66. Is there an agenda for which D would win a sequential pairwise election?
    A) No   B) Yes
    Ans: B

Chapter 10: Free-Response

1. Explain the difference between sincere and strategic voting.
   Ans: Sincere voting means submitting a ballot that reflects the voter's true preferences. Strategic voting means submitting a ballot that does not reflect the voter's true preferences but will lead to an outcome the voter likes better than would occur if the voter voted sincerely.

2. What is agenda manipulation?
   Ans: The ability to control the winner of an election by the selection of a particular agenda.

3. According to the Chair's Paradox, what surprising situation can befall the tie-breaking chair of a committee?
   Ans: The Chair's least favorite candidate can be elected by the group.

4. If a voting system has three or more alternatives, satisfies the Pareto condition, always produces a unique winner, and is not a dictatorship, what conclusion follows from the GS theorem?
   Ans: The voting method can be manipulated.

5. Are there voting methods that are group manipulable though not individual manipulable?
   Ans: Yes, plurality, for example.

6. Are there voting methods that are never manipulable?
   Ans: Yes, Condorcet's method for example.

7. Are there situations in which the Borda count method is known to be never manipulable?
   Ans: Yes, when there are only two or three candidates, for example.

8. What is purpose of Copeland's Rule with regard to Condorcet's method of voting?
   Ans: It extends Condorcet's method to designating a candidate with the best win-loss record the winner when there is no Condorcet's method winner.

Use the following to answer questions 9-14:

Use the following information to answer the question(s) below.

A seventeen-member committee must elect one of four candidates: R, S, T, or W. See the preference schedule below.

	Number of Members			
	6	4	3	4
First choice	R	S	T	W
Second choice	S	R	S	T
Third choice	T	T	R	S
Fourth choice	W	W	W	R

9. R wins using the plurality method. Could those members who most prefer W vote strategically in some way to change the outcome in a way that will benefit them?
   Ans: Yes. If these four voters ranked candidate T first, T would win with 7 votes. Since the voters prefer T to R, this outcome would be more desirable.

10. R wins using the plurality method. Could those members who most prefer T vote strategically in some way to change the outcome in a way that will benefit them?
    Ans: Yes. If these three voters ranked candidate S first, S would win with 7 votes. Since the voters prefer S to R, this outcome would be more desirable.

11. R wins using the plurality method. Could those members who most prefer S vote strategically in some way to change the outcome in a way that will benefit them?
    Ans: No

12. Is it possible to manipulate the results of a sequential pairwise election?
    Ans: No. S will always win.

13. In a plurality runoff election, candidate S wins. What would happen if the four voters who prefer W insincerely voted for T instead? Is this in their best interests?
    Ans: T and R would face off in the runoff, and R would win. In this case, their least favorite candidate would win instead of a higher ranked alternative.

14. In a plurality runoff election, candidate S wins. What would happen if the four voters who prefer T insincerely voted for S instead? Is this in their best interests?
    Ans: S and R would face off in the runoff, but S would again win. They cannot force a win for their first choice, but they can show allegiance to their second choice and eventual winner.

Use the following to answer questions 15-19:

Use the following information to answer the question(s) below.

An 11-member committee must choose one of the four applicants, K, L, M, and N, for membership on the committee.

	Number of Members		
	6	2	3
First choice	K	M	M
Second choice	L	L	N
Third choice	N	K	L
Fourth choice	M	N	K

15. The committee members have preferences among the applicants as given in the table. If the committee uses pairwise sequential voting with the agenda K, L, M, N, applicant K wins. Can the three voters who least prefer K vote strategically in some way to change the outcome to one they find more favorable? Why or why not?
    Ans: No. The six voters who most prefer applicant K represent a majority of the committee. No matter how the three voters rank the applicants, K will win.

16. The committee members have preferences among the applicants as given in the table. If the committee uses pairwise sequential voting with the agenda K, L, M, N, applicant K wins. Is it possible that another agenda will yield a different winner?
    Ans: No. The six voters who most prefer applicant K represent a majority of the committee. No matter how the voters are ordered, K will win.

17. The committee uses the Borda count method. The committee members have preferences among the applicants as given in the table. Who wins the election? Can the group of three voters favorably impact the results through insincere voting?
    Ans: K currently wins. Yes. For example, by exchanging L and N, L will win instead.

18. The committee uses the Borda count method. The committee members have preferences among the applicants as given in the table. Who wins the election? Can the group of two voters favorably impact the results through insincere voting?
    Ans: K currently wins. Yes. For example, by exchanging L and M, L will win instead.

19. The committee uses the Borda count method. The committee members have preferences among the applicants as given in the table. Suppose the group of six suspect that the group of two intends to insincerely exchange M and L in their rankings. Can the group of six counteract in order to protect K as the winner?
    Ans: Yes. If the group of two exchange M and L and the group of six exchange L and N, K will still win.

20. There are 18 delegates to a political party's convention at which four people, A, B, C, and D, have been nominated as the party's candidate for governor. The delegates' preference schedule is shown below. If the party uses a Borda count, candidate B would be elected. Can the four voters who most prefer C vote strategically in some way to change this outcome to one they would find more favorable? Why or why not?

	Number of Delegates		
	8	9	4
First choice	A	B	C
Second choice	B	A	B
Third choice	C	D	A
Fourth choice	D	C	D

Ans: No. They do not have enough votes to make C win under any possible ranking. Their second choice is B, who is the winner.

Use the following to answer questions 21-23:

Use the following information to answer the question(s) below.

Consider an 11-member committee that must choose one of three alternatives, X, Y, or Z, using the Hare system. Their schedule of preferences is shown below.

	Number of Voters		
	5	4	2
First choice	Z	X	Y
Second choice	Y	Y	X
Third choice	X	Z	Z

21. Who wins? Is it possible for the group of five voters to change the outcome in a way that would benefit them?
    Ans: X wins. If the group of five voters exchange their rankings of Y and Z, then Y wins.

22. Who wins? Is it possible for the group of two voters to change the outcome in a way that would benefit them?
    Ans: X wins. The group of two voters cannot change the outcomes by insincerely changing their preference ordering.

23. The committee suspects that the group of five plans to insincerely reorder their preferences as Y, Z, X. How can the group of four respond?
    Ans: If the group of five exchange Y and Z, then Y wins. The group of four cannot retaliate against this change.

Use the following to answer questions 24-25:

Use the following information to answer the question(s) below.

Twenty-nine voters must choose from among three alternatives, A, B, and C, using the Borda count method. The voters' preference schedules are shown below.

	Number of Voters			
	12	8	6	3
First choice	B	C	A	C
Second choice	C	A	B	B
Third choice	A	B	C	A

24. Who wins Borda count? Can the group of six voters change their preference list to produce an outcome they like better?
    Ans: C wins. If the group of six exchange A and B in their rankings, then B will win instead.

25. Suppose the group of voters anticipate that the group of six plan to insincerely rank B above A. How can the remaining voters respond in their own rankings?
    Ans: B is the winner. The remaining voters are unable to alter their rankings in order to elect a more favored candidate.

Use the following to answer questions 26-27:

Use the following information to answer the question(s) below.

A group of 22 young people must decide whether to go to the beach (B), the mountain (M), or the zoo (Z) on a field trip. Their preference rankings are summarized in the table below, and the decision will be made using a Borda count.

	Number of Voters		
	10	8	4
First choice	B	M	Z
Second choice	M	B	M
Third choice	Z	Z	B

26. Who wins the vote? Can the 4 voters in the last column change the results of the vote to their favor by changing their preference rankings?
    Ans: M wins. No, they cannot change the results through insincere voting.

27. Who wins the vote? Can the 10 voters in the first column change the results of the vote to their favor by changing their preference rankings?
    Ans: M wins. Yes; by exchanging M and Z in their rankings, B would win instead.

Use the following to answer questions 28-30:

Use the following preference table to answer the question(s) below.

	Number of voters			
	4	6	8	4
First choice	D	C	A	B
Second choice	C	B	D	A
Third choice	B	D	C	C
Fourth choice	A	A	B	D

28. Who wins using plurality? Could the four voters who most prefer D vote insincerely to change the outcome in a way that would benefit them?
    Ans: A wins. If the group of four insincerely votes for C instead of D, then C would win.

29. Who wins using plurality? Could the four voters who most prefer B vote insincerely to change the outcome in a way that would benefit them?
    Ans: A wins. No. They cannot force B to win through insincere voting, and A was their second choice.

30. Who wins using plurality? Could the six voters who most prefer C vote insincerely to change the outcome in a way that would benefit them?
    Ans: A wins. If the group of six insincerely votes for B instead of C, then B would win.

Chapter 11: Multiple-Choice

1. What would be the quota for a voting system that has a total of 15 votes and uses a simple majority quota?
   A) 7   B) 8   C) 9   D) 15
   Ans: B

2. What would be the quota for a voting system that has a total of 16 votes and uses a simple majority quota?
   A) 7   B) 8   C) 9   D) 16
   Ans: C

3. What would be the quota for a voting system that has a total of 30 votes and uses a simple majority quota?
   A) 14   B) 15   C) 16   D) 30
   Ans: C

4. Which of the following describe legitimate weighted voting systems?
   I   [16: 13, 8, 6, 4]
   II   [15: 10, 8, 7, 5]

   A) I only   B) II only   C) I and II   D) Neither I nor II
   Ans: A

5. Which of the following describe legitimate weighted voting systems?
   I   [27: 20, 15, 12, 5]
   II   [30: 20, 17, 10, 5]

   A) I only   B) II only   C) I and II   D) Neither I nor II
   Ans: C

6. Which of the following describe legitimate weighted voting systems?
   I   [20: 16, 12, 8]
   II   [24: 20, 15, 10]

   A) I only   B) II only   C) I and II   D) Neither I nor II
   Ans: C

7. Which of the following describe legitimate weighted voting systems?
   I   [20: 30, 10, 6]
   II   [34: 30, 18, 6]

   A) I only   B) II only   C) I and II   D) Neither I nor II
   Ans: D

8. In a weighted voting system, all winning coalitions would become blocking coalitions if each voter switched his/her vote from YES to NO.
A) True   B) False
Ans: A

9. In a weighted voting system, all blocking coalitions would become winning coalitions if each voter switched his/her vote from NO to YES.
A) True   B) False
Ans: B

10. In a weighted voting system, any voter with veto power is a dictator.
A) True   B) False
Ans: B

11. A weighted voting system can have a dictator without dummy voters.
A) True   B) False
Ans: B

12. A weighted voting system can have dummy voters without a dictator.
A) True   B) False
Ans: A

13. In the weighted voting system [9: 10, 5, 3], voter A is a dictator.
A) True   B) False
Ans: A

14. Which voters in the system [30: 20, 17, 10, 5] have veto power?
A) A only   B) A and B   C) A, B, and C   D) None
Ans: D

15. Which voters in the system [38: 20, 15, 12, 5] have veto power?
A) A only   B) A and B   C) A, B, and C   D) None
Ans: B

16. Given the weighted voting system [38: 20, 15, 12, 5], which is a winning coalition?
A) { A, B}   B) { B, C, D}   C) { A, B, D}   D) { A}
Ans: C

17. Given the weighted voting system [38: 20, 15, 12, 5], which of the coalitions listed is/are blocking coalitions?
    I {A}   II {C, D}   III {A, B, C}

A) III only   B) I and II only   C) I, II, and III   D) None
Ans: C

18. Given the weighted voting system [38: 20, 15, 12, 5], which voter(s) is/are dummy voters.
    A) D only B) D and C C) D, C, and B D) There are no dummy voters.
    Ans: D

19. Given the weighted voting system [51: 45, 43, 7, 5], which of the following is a winning coalition?
    A) { A} B) { A, D} C) { A, C} D) { B, D}
    Ans: C

20. Given the weighted voting system [52: 45, 43, 7, 5], which of the following is a minimal winning coalition?
          I {A, B}   II {A, C}   III {A, B, C}

    A) I only B) I and II C) I, II, and III D) None
    Ans: B

21. Given the weighted voting system [51: 45, 43, 7, 5], which of the following is a blocking coalition?
          I {A}   II {B, C}   III {C}

    A) II only B) I and II C) I, II, and III D) None
    Ans: A

22. Given the weighted voting system [9: 6, 4, 2], which of the voters are dummy voters?
    A) C only B) B and C C) B only D) None
    Ans: A

23. Given the weighted voting system [8: 5, 4, 3], which of the coalitions given are minimal winning coalitions?
    A)   { A, B, C}
    B)   { A, B}
    C)   { B, C}
    D)   There are no minimal winning coalitions.
    Ans: B

24. Given the weighted voting system [6: 4, 3, 2, 1], which of the coalitions listed are winning?
          I {A, B}   II {A, C}   III {B, C, D}

    A) I only B) I and II C) I and III D) I, II, and III
    Ans: D

25. Given the weighted voting system [6: 4, 3, 2, 1], which of the coalitions listed are minimal winning coalitions?

    I {A, B} II {A, C} III {B, C, D}

    A) I only   B) I and II   C) II and III   D) I, II, and III
    Ans: D

26. Given the weighted voting system [6: 4, 3, 2, 1], which of the coalitions listed are blocking coalitions?

    I {A, B} II {B, C} III {C, D}

    A) I only   B) I and II   C) II and III   D) I, II, and III
    Ans: B

27. If there are four voters in a weighted voting system, how many distinct coalitions of voters can be formed?
    A) 8   B) 16   C) 24   D) 30
    Ans: B

28. If there are five voters in a weighted voting system, how may different combinations of YES and NO votes can there be?
    A) 10   B) 25   C) 32   D) 120
    Ans: C

29. Calculate $_5C_2$.
    A) 5   B) 10   C) 32   D) 25
    Ans: B

30. Calculate $_{12}C_4$.
    A) 48   B) 20,736   C) 495   D) 11,880
    Ans: C

31. Calculate $_9C_3$.
    A) 27   B) 84   C) 504   D) 729
    Ans: B

32. In a weighted voting system with eight voters, how many coalitions would there be in which exactly five members voted YES?
    A) 32   B) 40   C) 56   D) 256
    Ans: C

33. In a weighted voting system with 20 voters, how many distinct coalitions would there be in which exactly eight members voted YES?
    A) 12   B) 56   C) 160   D) 125,970
    Ans: D

34. Given the weighted voting system [27: 20, 15, 12, 5], calculate the Banzhaf power index.
    A) (8, 8, 8, 0)   B) (8, 6, 6, 2)   C) (6, 6, 6, 1)   D) (8, 6, 6, 0)
    Ans: A

35. Given the weighted voting system [34: 30, 18, 6], calculate the Banzhaf power index.
    A) (6, 4, 2)   B) (6, 2, 2)   C) (6, 6, 6)   D) (6, 4, 0)
    Ans: B

36. Given the weighted voting system [30: 20, 17, 10, 5], calculate the Banzhaf power index.
    A) (10, 6, 6, 0)   B) (8, 6, 6, 2)   C) (10, 6, 6, 2)   D) (8, 4, 4, 0)
    Ans: C

37. In a weighted voting system, the Banzhaf power index of each voter is directly proportional to the weight of the vote.
    A) True   B) False
    Ans: B

38. In a weighted voting system, the Banzhaf power index of a dummy voter is 0.
    A) True   B) False
    Ans: A

39. In the weighted voting system [8: 5, 2, 2, 2, 2, 2], find the Banzhaf power index for voter A.
    A) 8   B) 10   C) 15   D) 40
    Ans: D

40. In the weighted voting system [8: 5, 2, 2, 2, 2, 2], find the Banzhaf power index for voter B.
    A) 2   B) 16   C) 4   D) 20
    Ans: B

41. In the weighted voting system [6: 3, 1, 1, 1, 1, 1, 1], find the Banzhaf power index for voter A.
    A) 6   B) 20   C) 40   D) 82
    Ans: D

42. Are the weighted voting systems [8: 5, 4, 3] and [34: 30, 18, 6] equivalent?
    A) Yes   B) No
    Ans: A

43. Are the weighted voting systems [8: 5, 4, 3] and [11: 10, 9, 2] equivalent?
    A) Yes   B) No
    Ans: B

44. Are the weighted voting systems [18: 10, 9, 8] and [15: 8, 7, 6] equivalent?
    A) Yes B) No
    Ans: B

45. Are the weighted voting systems [11: 10, 9, 2] and [2: 1, 1, 1] equivalent?
    A) Yes B) No
    Ans: A

46. How many permutations of five voters can be made?
    A) 14 B) 25 C) 32 D) 120
    Ans: D

47. Calculate the Shapley-Shubik power index for each voter in the system [8: 5, 4, 3].
    A) (4/6, 1/6, 1/6) B) (3/6, 3/6, 0/6) C) (2/6, 2/6, 2/6) D) (4/6, 2/6, 2/6)
    Ans: A

48. Calculate the Shapley-Shubik power index for each voter in the system [15: 8, 7, 6].
    A) (4/6, 1/6, 1/6) B) (3/6, 3/6, 0/6) C) (2/6, 2/6, 2/6) D) (4/6, 2/6, 2/6)
    Ans: B

49. Calculate the Shapley-Shubik power index for each voter in the weighted voting system
    [8: 5, 2, 2, 2, 2, 2].
    A)   (7/12, 1/12, 1/12, 1/12, 1/12, 1/12)   C)   (5/6, 1/30, 1/30, 1/30, 1/30, 1/30)
    B)   (5/8, 3/40, 3/40, 3/40, 3/40, 3/40)   D)   (1/3, 2/15, 2/15, 2/15, 2/15, 2/15)
    Ans: D

50. Calculate the Shapely-Shubik power index for each voter in the weighted voting system
    [6: 3, 1, 1, 1, 1, 1, 1].
    A)   (3/7, 2/21, 2/21, 2/21, 2/21, 2/21, 2/21)
    B)   (1/2, 1/12, 1/12, 1/12, 1/12, 1/12, 1/12)
    C)   (1/3, 1/9, 1/9, 1/9, 1/9, 1/9, 1/9)
    D)   (2/3, 1/18, 1/18, 1/18, 1/18, 1/18, 1/18)
    Ans: A

51. A committee has four voters and the system [30: 20, 17, 10, 5]. How many extra votes
    does the coalition { A, C, D} have?
    A) 1 B) 5 C) 10 D) 35
    Ans: B

52. A committee has six voters with the system [8: 5, 2, 2, 2, 2, 2]. How many extra votes
    does the coalition { B, C, E, F} have?
    A) 0 B) 1 C) 2 D) 8
    Ans: A

53. A committee has four voters with the system [30: 20, 17, 10, 5]. Which voters are critical in the coalition { A, C, D}?
A) A only   B) A and C   C) C and D   D) D only
Ans: B

54. A committee has six members with the system [8: 5, 2, 2, 2, 2, 2]. Which voters are critical in the coalition { A, C, D}?
A) A only   B) C and D   C) A, C, and D   D) No voter is critical.
Ans: C

55. Calculate C_3^{32} .
A) 10   B) 96   C) 4960   D) 29760
Ans: C

56. What would be the quota for a voting system that has a total of 41 votes and uses a simple majority quota?
A) 20   B) 21   C) 31   D) 41
Ans: B

57. Which of the following describe legitimate weighted voting systems?

I. [10: 5, 4, 3, 8]
II. [9: 5, 8, 3]
A) I only   B) II only   C) I and II   D) Neither I or II
Ans: B

58. Which voters in the system [19: 9, 7, 5, 3, 1] have veto power?
A) A only   B) A and B   C) A, B, and C   D) None
Ans: B

59. Given the weighted voting system [12: 1, 3, 5, 7], which is a winning coalition?
A) { B}   B) { B, C}   C) { B, C, D}   D) { D}
Ans: C

60. Given the weighted voting system [8: 3, 5, 2, 4], which is a blocking coalition?
A) { A, B}   B) { A, C}   C) { A}   D) { B}
Ans: A

61. Given the weighted voting system [19: 9, 7, 5, 3, 1], which of the voters are dummy voters?
A) D only   B) D and E   C) E only   D) None
Ans: C

62. Given the weighted voting system [6: 4, 3, 2, 1], calculate the Banzhaf power index.
    A) (11, 6, 2, 2)   B) (5, 4, 4, 1)   C) (10, 6, 2, 2)   D) (10, 6, 6, 2)
    Ans: D

63. Calculate the Shapley-Shubik power index for each voter in the weighted voting system
    [6: 5, 3, 1].
    A) (1, 0, 0)   B) (2/3, 1/6, 1/6)   C) (1/3, 1/3, 1/3)   D) (1/2, 1/2, 0)
    Ans: B

64. A committee has three members with the system [10: 5, 4, 3, 2, 1]. Which voters are
    critical in the coalition { A, B, C, E}?
    A) A only   B) A and B   C) A and E   D) E only
    Ans: B

Chapter 11: Free-Response

1. Give an example of a weighted voting system that has a dummy voter but no dictator.
   Ans: Answers may vary. One solution is [9: 6, 5, 2].

2. Explain why the weighted voting system [13: 10, 6, 5, 3, 2] is not a legitimate weighted voting system.
   Ans: The system given is not a legitimate weighted voting system since the quota is exactly half of the total vote weight. Two different complementary coalitions exist with vote weight total of 13, (A, D), and (B, C, E).

3. Give an example of a weighted voting system that has a blocking coalition which would not be a winning coalition if all its members voted YES.
   Ans: Answers may vary. One solution is: In the [14: 10, 6, 5, 3, 2], the coalition (A, D) is a blocking coalition since (B, C, E) has only 13 votes. (A, D) would not be a winning coalition by voting YES because (A, D) has only 13 votes.

4. Given the weighted voting system [30: 20, 17, 10, 5], list all winning coalitions.
   Ans: (A, D) (A, C) (B, C, D) (A, B, C) (A, B, D) (A, C, D) (A, B, C, D)

5. Given the weighted voting system [51: 45, 43, 7, 5], list all blocking coalitions.
   Ans: (A, B) (A, C) (A, B, C) (A, B, D) (A, C, D) (A, D) (B, C) (B, C, D) (A, B, C, D)

6. Given the weighted voting system [51: 45, 43, 7, 5], list all minimal winning coalitions.
   Ans: (A, B) (A, C) (B, C, D)

7. Given the weighted voting system [30: 20, 17, 10, 5], list all minimal winning coalitions.
   Ans: (A, B) (A, C) (B, C, D)

8. Given the weighted voting system [30: 20, 17, 10, 5], list all blocking coalitions.
   Ans: (A, B) (A, C) (A, B, C) (A, B, D) (A, C, D) (B, C, D) (A, B, C, D) (A, D) (B, C)

9. A weighted voting system has four voters, A, B, C, and D. List all possible coalitions of these voters. How many such coalitions are there?
   Ans: There are 16 coalitions possible from four voters:
   Ø, (A) (B) (C) (D) (A, B) (A, C) (A, D) (B, C) (B, D) (C, D) (A, B, C) (A, B, D) (A, C, D) (B, C, D) (A, B, C, D)

10. In a weighted voting system, is a voter with veto power the same as a dictator? Explain why or why not.
    Ans: No. A voter with veto power has enough votes to block any measure, but not necessarily enough to pass any issue. A dictator has enough votes to pass any issue on his or her own.

11. A weighted voting system has five voters. How many distinct coalitions are there in which exactly three members vote YES?
    Ans: 10

12. A weighted voting system has 12 members. How many distinct coalitions are there in which exactly seven members vote YES?
    Ans: 792

13. Given the weighted voting system [5: 3, 2, 1, 1, 1], find which voters of the coalition { A, C, D, E} are critical.
    Ans: Since the coalition { A, C, D, E} has one extra vote, the only member who is critical is voter A with weight 3.

14. Given the weighted voting system [8: 5, 4, 3], find the Banzhaf power index for each voter.
    Ans: (6, 2, 2)

15. Given the weighted voting system [14: 10, 6, 5, 3], find the Banzhaf power index for each voter.
    Ans: (10, 6, 6, 2)

16. Given the weighted voting system [7: 4, 1, 1, 1, 1, 1], find the Banzhaf power index for each voter.
    Ans: (32, 20, 20, 20, 20, 20)

17. Suppose a weighted voting system has five members, but that voter E is a dummy voter. Can you find the Banzhaf power index of voter E?
    Ans: The Banzhaf power index of any dummy voter is 0.

18. Give an example of a weighted voting that is equivalent to the [8: 5, 4, 3].
    Ans: Answers may vary. One solution is: [15: 10, 8, 6]

19. Give an example of a weighted voting system that is equivalent to the [15: 8, 7, 6].
    Ans: Answers may vary. One solution is: [32: 20, 15, 10]

20. Is voter C a critical voter in the coalition { A, B, C} of the weighted voting [15: 10, 6, 5, 3, 2]? Why or why not?
    Ans: Yes, A is a critical voter. Without A, the coalition becomes (B, C), which has only 11 votes, no longer enough to win. The number of extra votes of the coalition is six. Voter A has more than this number of votes so voter A is critical.

21. What is the difference between a "critical" voter in a coalition and a "pivotal" voter in a permutation?
    Ans: A critical voter in a winning or blocking coalition is any voter who has sufficient weight so that the coalition would no longer be winning or blocking the remaining vote. The order of voters in the coalition does not matter. There can be more than one critical voter in a coalition. A pivotal voter is the first voter who joins a coalition and gives that coalition enough votes to win. Each permutation has exactly one pivotal voter.

22. Evaluate $_8C_3$.
    Ans: $_8C_3 = \dfrac{8!}{3!5!} = 56$

23. Calculate the Shapley-Shubik power index for the weighted voting system [30: 20, 17, 10, 5].
    Ans: (5/12, 1/4, 1/4, 1/12)

24. Calculate the Shapley-Shubik power index for the weighted voting system [8: 6, 1, 1, 1, 1, 1].
    Ans: (2/3, 1/15, 1/15, 1/15, 1/15, 1/15)

25. There are five distinct three-member voting systems. Give an example of three of the five.
    Ans: Answers may vary. One example of each of the five distinct voting systems is:
    [3: 3, 1, 1]
    [4: 2, 2, 1]
    [2: 1, 1, 1]
    [3: 2, 1, 1]
    [3: 1, 1, 1]

26. A sorority has an executive board consisting of a chair, vice chair, and three other members. Its voting rules indicate that an issue can pass in two ways: if the chair, vice chair, and one other member support the issue or if one of the chair or vice chair and two other members support the issue. Express this as a weighted voting system.
    Ans: Answers may vary. One solution is: [7: 3, 3, 2, 2, 2].

27. Given the weighted voting system [4: 1, 2, 3], list all winning coalitions.
    Ans: { A, C}, {B, C}, {A, B, C}

28. Given the weighted voting system [4: 1, 2, 3], list all blocking coalitions.
    Ans: { C}, {A, B}, {A, C}, {B, C}, {A, B, C}

29. A weighted voting system has 10 members. How many distinct coalitions are there in which exactly six members vote yes?
    Ans: 210

30. Given the weighted voting system [16: 3, 9, 4, 5, 10], calculate the Banzhaf power index for each voter.
Ans: (4, 8, 4, 4, 8)

31. Given the weighted voting system [14: 8, 2, 5, 7, 4], calculate the Shapley-Shubik power index for each voter.
Ans: (7/20, 1/10, 11/60, 4/15, 1/10)

Chapter 12: Multiple-Choice

Use the following to answer questions 1-3:

Use the following distribution of 31 voters at seven different positions over the interval [0, 1] to answer the question(s) below.

Position i	1	2	3	4	5	6	7
Location l_i of position i	0.1	0.2	0.3	0.4	0.5	0.7	0.8
Number of voters at position i	1	4	5	6	5	6	4

1. The equilibrium position is:
   A) 0.3   B) 0.35   C) 0.4   D) 0.47
   Ans: C

2. The mean position is:
   A) 0.3   B) 0.35   C) 0.4   D) 0.47
   Ans: D

3. The median position is:
   A) 0.3   B) 0.35   C) 0.4   D) 0.47
   Ans: C

Use the following to answer questions 4-6:

Use the following distribution of 33 voters at eight different positions over the interval [0, 1] to answer the question(s) below.

Position i	1	2	3	4	5	6	7	8
Location l_i of position i	0.1	0.3	0.4	0.5	0.6	0.7	0.8	0.9
Number of voters at position i	1	4	6	6	6	2	5	3

4. The equilibrium position is:
   A) 0.5   B) 0.55   C) 0.56   D) 0.6
   Ans: A

5. The mean position is:
   A) 0.5   B) 0.55   C) 0.56   D) 0.6
   Ans: C

6. The median position is:
   A) 0.5   B) 0.55   C) 0.56   D) 0.6
   Ans: A

Use the following to answer questions 7-8:

Use the following distribution of 32 voters at eight different positions over the interval [0, 1] to answer the question(s) below.

Position i	1	2	3	4	5	6	7	8
Location l_i of position i	0.1	0.2	0.3	0.5	0.6	0.7	0.8	0.9
Number of voters at position i	6	5	5	3	4	6	2	1

7. The equilibrium position is:
   A) 0.3   B) 0.4   C) 0.5   D) 0.6
   Ans: B

8. The mean position is:
   A) 0.4   B) 0.43   C) 0.47   D) 0.5
   Ans: B

9. The point on the horizontal axis of a voter distribution where half of the voters have attitudes that lie to the left and half of the voters have attitudes that lie to the right is the:
   A) median.   B) mean.   C) mode.   D) maximin position.
   Ans: A

10. The positions of voters on a voter distribution are weighted by the fraction of voters at that position. This is used to find the:
    A) median.   B) mean.   C) mode.   D) maximin position.
    Ans: B

11. A candidate selects a point on the horizontal axis of a voter distribution where no position can guarantee a better outcome, no matter what position another candidate adopts. This position is the:
    A) median.   B) mean.   C) mode.   D) maximin position.
    Ans: D

12. A peak of a voter distribution is a:
    A) median.   B) mean.   C) mode.   D) maximin position.
    Ans: C

13. A poll has identified Candidates A and B as the top two candidates in an election. Candidate A is the Condorcet winner. We know that A will win because of the:
    A)   Condorcet rule.   C)   median-voter theorem.
    B)   poll assumption.   D)   proportional rule.
    Ans: B

14. A distribution of voters is symmetric and unimodal, and the first two candidates have chosen different positions, A and B, that are equidistant from the median. A is below the median and B is above the median. No more than 1/3 of the voters lie between A and B. To win the election, a third candidate should take a position C that lies:
    A) below A.   B) between A and B.   C) above B.   D) nowhere; C cannot win.
    Ans: D

15. A distribution of voters is symmetric and unimodal, and the first two candidates have chosen different positions, A and B, that are equidistant from the median. A is below the median and B is above the median, and 2/3 of the voters lie between A and B. To win the election, a third candidate should take a position C that lies:
    A) below A.   B) between A and B.   C) above B.   D) nowhere; C cannot win.
    Ans: B

Use the following to answer questions 16-18:

Use the following information to answer the question(s) below.

Assume there are four classes of voters that rank four candidates as follows:

I. 7: *A B C D*
II. 5: *B D A C*
III. 3: *C B A D*
IV. 4: *D C B A*

16. Which candidate is the plurality winner?
    A) A   B) B   C) C   D) D
    Ans: A

17. Which candidate is the Condorcet winner?
    A) A   B) B   C) C   D) D
    Ans: B

18. Suppose there is a poll that differentiates the top two candidates. Which candidate will win the election after the poll?
    A) A   B) B   C) C   D) D
    Ans: B

Use the following to answer questions 19-21:

Use the following information to answer the question(s) below.

Assume there are four classes of voters that rank four candidates as follows:

I. 6: *C A B D*
II. 4: *D B A C*
III. 2: *B C A D*
IV. 5: *A D C B*

19. Which candidate is the plurality winner?
    A) A   B) B   C) C   D) D
    Ans: C

20. Which candidate is the Condorcet winner?
    A) A   B) B   C) C   D) D
    Ans: A

21. Suppose there is a poll that differentiates the top two candidates. Which candidate will win the election after the poll?
    A) A   B) B   C) C   D) D
    Ans: A

22. Assume there are three classes of voters that rank four candidates as follows:

    I. 3: *A B C*
    II. 7: *C A B*
    III. 5: *B C A*

    Which candidate is the plurality winner?
    A) A   B) B   C) C   D) There is no plurality winner.
    Ans: C

23. Assume there are three classes of voters that rank four candidates as follows:

    I. 3: *A B C*
    II. 7: *C A B*
    III. 5: *B C A*

    Which candidate is the Condorcet winner?
    A) A   B) B   C) C   D) There is no Condorcet winner.
    Ans: D

24. A distribution of voters is uniform over [0, 1]. Candidates A and B have already entered the election and anticipate a third candidate C to enter the election later. Candidates A and B should choose what positions?
    A)   One at 1/3, the other at 2/3   C)   One at 1/4, the other at 3/4
    B)   Both at 1/2   D)   None of the above
    Ans: C

25. A distribution of voters is uniform over [0, 1]. Candidates A and B have already entered the election and have chosen positions at 1/4 and 3/4, respectively. If C enters at 1/2, who wins the election?
    A) A   B) B   C) C   D) A and B tie.
    Ans: D

26. Assume there are three classes of voters that rank three candidates as follows:

    I. 1: $A B C$
    II. 4: $C B A$
    III. 3: $B A C$

    Which candidate is the Condorcet winner?
    A) A   B) B   C) C   D) There is no Condorcet winner.
    Ans: D

27. Assume there are three classes of voters that rank three candidates as follows:

    I. 1: $A B C$
    II. 4: $C B A$
    III. 3: $B A C$

    According to the poll assumption, which candidate will win?
    A) A   B) B   C) C   D) No conclusion can be made.
    Ans: C

28. Suppose there are three classes of voters that rank four candidates as shown below. For each class of voters, the preferred subset of candidates is enclosed in the first set of parentheses and the non-preferred subset in the second set of parentheses. Thus, the five class I voters prefer A and C, between whom they are indifferent, to B and D, between whom they are also indifferent:

I. 5: $(A\ C)\ (B\ D)$
II. 3: $(B\ C\ D)\ (A)$
III. 4: $(B)\ (A\ C\ D)$

Assuming that each class of voters chooses its dominant strategy, who wins?
A) A   B) B   C) C   D) D
Ans: C

29. Suppose there are three classes of voters that rank four candidates as shown below. For each class of voters, the preferred subset of candidates is enclosed in the first set of parentheses and the non-preferred subset in the second set of parentheses. Thus, the six class I voters prefer A and B, between whom they are indifferent, to C and D, between whom they are also indifferent:

I. 6: $(A\ B)\ (C\ D)$
II. 3: $(B\ C\ D)\ (A)$
III. 4: $(C)\ (A\ B\ D)$

Assuming that each class of voters chooses its dominant strategy, who wins?
A) A   B) B   C) C   D) D
Ans: B

30. Suppose there are four classes of voters that rank four candidates as shown below. For each class of voters, the preferred subset of candidates is enclosed in the first set of parentheses and the non-preferred subset in the second set of parentheses. Thus, the five class I voters prefer B and C, between whom they are indifferent, to A and D, between whom they are also indifferent:

I. 5: $(B\ C)\ (A\ D)$
II. 3: $(A\ B\ C)\ (D)$
III. 3: $(A)\ (B\ C\ D)$
IV. 4: $(C\ D)\ (A\ B)$

Assuming that each class of voters chooses its dominant strategy, who wins?
A) A   B) B   C) C   D) D
Ans: C

31. Suppose there are four classes of voters that rank four candidates as shown below. For each class of voters, the preferred subset of candidates is enclosed in the first set of parentheses and the non-preferred subset in the second set of parentheses. Thus, the seven class I voters prefer C and D, between whom they are indifferent, to A and B, between whom they are also indifferent:

I. 7: $(C\ D)\ (A\ B)$
II. 6: $(A\ C\ D)\ (B)$
III. 1: $(B\ D)\ (A\ C)$
IV. 3: $(B\ C)\ (A\ D)$

Assuming that each class of voters chooses its dominant strategy, who wins?
A) A   B) B   C) C   D) D
Ans: C

32. Suppose there are four classes of voters that rank four candidates as shown below. For each class of voters, the preferred subset of candidates is enclosed in the first set of parentheses and the non-preferred subset in the second set of parentheses. Thus, the four class I voters prefer A and B, between whom they are indifferent, to C and D, between whom they are also indifferent:

I. 4: $(A\ B)\ (C\ D)$
II. 2: $(D)\ (A\ B\ C)$
III. 1: $(A\ B\ C)\ (D)$
IV. 5: $(C\ D)\ (A\ B)$

Assuming that each class of voters chooses its dominant strategy, who wins?
A) A   B) B   C) C   D) D
Ans: D

33. Suppose there are four classes of voters that rank four candidates as shown below. For each class of voters, the preferred subset of candidates is enclosed in the first set of parentheses and the non-preferred subset in the second set of parentheses. Thus, the four class I voters prefer A and B, between whom they are indifferent, to C and D, between whom they are also indifferent:

I. 4: $(A\ B)\ (C\ D)$
II. 5: $(A\ B\ C)\ (D)$
III. 6: $(B\ C\ D)\ (A)$
IV. 5: $(A\ D)\ (B\ C)$

Assuming that each class of voters chooses its dominant strategy, who wins?
A) A   B) B   C) C   D) D
Ans: B

34. Consider the following distribution of 35 voters at eight different positions over the interval [0, 1].

location	0.2	0.3	0.4	0.5	0.6	0.7	0.8	0.9
number of voters	4	7	4	2	3	7	4	4

This distribution of voters is best described as:
A) skewed left.   B) skewed right.   C) symmetric.   D) bimodal.
Ans: D

35. Consider the following distribution of 34 voters at eight different positions over the interval [0, 1].

location	0.2	0.3	0.4	0.5	0.6	0.7	0.8	0.9
number of voters	2	3	3	2	5	7	8	4

This distribution of voters is best described as:
A) skewed left.   B) skewed right.   C) symmetric.   D) bimodal.
Ans: B

36. Consider the following distribution of 34 voters at eight different positions over the interval [0, 1].

location	0.2	0.3	0.4	0.5	0.6	0.7	0.8	0.9
number of voters	2	3	5	7	7	5	3	2

This distribution of voters is best described as:
A) skewed left.   B) skewed right.   C) symmetric.   D) bimodal.
Ans: C

37. Consider the following distribution of 34 voters at eight different positions over the interval [0, 1].

location	0.2	0.3	0.4	0.5	0.6	0.7	0.8	0.9
number of voters	3	6	7	4	3	4	4	3

This distribution of voters is best described as:
A) skewed left.   B) skewed right.   C) symmetric.   D) bimodal.
Ans: A

38. A voter is faced with a dilemma in a three-candidate election. Her favorite candidate does not seem able to win. However, there is a chance that her second choice candidate could win. The election will be determined using approval voting. The voter's most promising strategy would be to:
    A)   vote for both her first and second choices.
    B)   vote for her second choice only.
    C)   vote for her first choice only.
    D)   not vote.
    Ans: A

39. How many votes are available in the electoral college?
    A) 51   B) 100   C) 538   D) 561
    Ans: C

40. How many electoral votes are needed to win an election?
    A) 359   B) 270   C) 136   D) 26
    Ans: B

41. Assume there are three states with 3, 8, and 14 voters, and they are all toss-up states. If both the Democratic and Republican candidates choose strategies that maximize their expected popular vote (the proportional rule), and they have the same total resources (D = R = 100), what resources should be allocated for each state?
    A) 5, 22, and 52   B) 6, 28, and 65   C) 12, 32, and 56   D) 15, 28, and 57
    Ans: C

42. Assume there are three states with 3, 8, and 14 voters, and they are all toss-up states. If both the Democratic and Republican candidates choose strategies that maximize their expected electoral vote (the 3/2's rule), and they have the same total resources (D = R = 100), what resources should be allocated for each state?
    A) 5, 22, and 52   B) 6, 28, and 65   C) 12, 32, and 56   D) 15, 28, and 57
    Ans: B

43. Assume there are three states with 7, 8, and 21 voters, and they are all toss-up states. If both the Democratic and Republican candidates choose strategies that maximize their expected popular vote (the proportional rule), and they have the same total resources (D = R = 100), what resources should be allocated for each state?
    A) 13, 16, and 70   B) 19, 22, and 58   C) 20, 24, and 56   D) 21, 24, and 63
    Ans: B

44. Assume there are three states with 7, 8, and 21 voters, and they are all toss-up states. If both the Democratic and Republican candidates choose strategies that maximize their expected electoral vote (the 3/2's rule), and they have the same total resources (D = R = 100), what resources should be allocated for each state?
    A) 13, 16, and 70   B) 19, 22, and 58   C) 20, 24, and 56   D) 21, 24, and 63
    Ans: A

45. Voting in such a way that an acceptable candidate can be elected if a first choice is not viable is called:
    A) sincere voting.   B) strategic voting.   C) plurality voting.   D) approval voting.
    Ans: B

46. When voters may vote for as many candidates as they like, the selection method is called:
    A) sincere voting.   B) strategic voting.   C) plurality voting.   D) approval voting.
    Ans: D

Use the following to answer questions 47-49:

Use the following information to answer the question(s) below.

Suppose 36 voters are distributed at nine different positions over the interval [0, 1], as suggested by this incomplete table.

location	0.1	0.2	0.3	0.4	0.5	0.6	0.7	0.8	0.9
number of voters	?	?	?	?	?	?	?	?	?

47. Which situation below would result in a bimodal distribution?
    A)   18 voters at 0.3 and 18 voters at 0.7
    B)   3 voters at each of the nine positions
    C)   All 36 voters at 0.1
    D)   9 voters at each of these four positions: 0.2, 0.4, 0.6, 0.8
    Ans: A

48. Which situation below would result in a skewed distribution?
    A)   18 voters at 0.3 and 18 voters at 0.7
    B)   3 voters at each of the nine positions
    C)   All 36 voters at 0.1
    D)   9 voters at each of these four positions: 0.2, 0.4, 0.6, 0.8
    Ans: C

49. Which situation below would result in a symmetric distribution?
    A)   12 voters at each of 0.3 and 0.7, 6 voters at each of 0.4 and 0.6
    B)   6 voters at each of the first 6 positions
    C)   All 36 voters at 0.1
    D)   9 voters at each of these four positions: 0.2, 0.4, 0.8, 0.9
    Ans: A

50. Suppose 16 voters are distributed at different positions over the interval [0, 1], as shown below.

location	0.1	0.2	0.3	0.4	0.5	0.6	0.7	0.8	0.9
number of voters	4	0	0	1	4	7	0	0	0

What can you say about the distribution?
A) It is bimodal.   B) It is unimodal.   C) It is symmetric.   D) It is sincere.
Ans: B

51. Suppose 16 voters are distributed at different positions over the interval [0, 1], as shown below.

location	0.1	0.2	0.3	0.4	0.5	0.6	0.7	0.8	0.9
number of voters	2	0	4	5	4	1	0	0	0

What can you say about the distribution?
A)   It is symmetric.   C)   It is skewed to the right.
B)   It is skewed to the left.   D)   It reflects strategic voting.
Ans: B

52. Suppose 16 voters are distributed at different positions over the interval [0, 1], as shown below.

location	0.1	0.2	0.3	0.4	0.5	0.6	0.7	0.8	0.9
number of voters	2	0	4	5	0	5	0	0	0

What is the mean position of the voters?
A) 0.3   B) 0.4   C) 0.6   D) None of these
Ans: B

53. Suppose 16 voters are distributed at different positions over the interval [0, 1], as shown below.

location	0.1	0.2	0.3	0.4	0.5	0.6	0.7	0.8	0.9
number of voters	2	0	4	5	0	5	0	0	0

What is the median position of the voters?
A) 0.3   B) 0.4   C) 0.6   D) None of these
Ans: B

54. Suppose 20 voters are distributed at different positions over the interval [0, 1], as shown below.

location	0.1	0.2	0.3	0.4	0.5	0.6	0.7	0.8	0.9
number of voters	2	0	4	3	0	7	2	0	2

What is the mean position of the voters?
A) 0.4   B) 0.5   C) 0.6   D) None of these
Ans: B

55. Suppose 20 voters are distributed at different positions over the interval [0, 1], as shown below.

location	0.1	0.2	0.3	0.4	0.5	0.6	0.7	0.8	0.9
number of voters	2	0	4	3	0	7	2	0	2

What is the median position of the voters?
A) 0.4   B) 0.5   C) 0.6   D) None of these
Ans: B

56. Suppose 20 voters are distributed at nine different positions over the interval [0, 1], as suggested by this incomplete table.

location	0.1	0.2	0.3	0.4	0.5	0.6	0.7	0.8	0.9
number of voters	?	?	?	?	?	?	?	?	?

If the distribution is symmetric, which of the following conditions would be true?
A)   The mean and the median are equal.   C)   The mean is greater than the median.
B)   The mean is less than the median.
Ans: A

57. Suppose 20 voters are distributed at nine different positions over the interval [0, 1], as suggested by this incomplete table.

location	0.1	0.2	0.3	0.4	0.5	0.6	0.7	0.8	0.9
number of voters	?	?	?	?	?	?	?	?	?

If the distribution is skewed to the left, which of the following conditions would be true?
A)   The mean and the median are equal.   C)   The mean is greater than the median.
B)   The mean is less than the median.
Ans: B

58. If state A has three times the population of state B then:
    A) A will have about three times the electoral college members as B.
    B) A will have about two times the electoral college members as B.
    C) A will have the same number of electoral college members as B.
    Ans: B

59. A toss-up state is:
    A) a state where the outcome is close.
    B) a state where the outcome is easily determined.
    C) a state whose electoral college votes does not make a difference in the result.
    D) a state whose electoral college members are free to vote their individual choice.
    Ans: A

60. The electoral college is designed to enable the most popular candidate to win election.
    A) True   B) False
    Ans: B

Chapter 12: Free-Response

Use the following to answer questions 1-3:

Use the following information to answer the question(s) below.

Consider the following distribution of 33 voters at 8 different positions over the interval [0,1].

Position	0.1	0.3	0.4	0.5	0.6	0.7	0.8	0.9
Number of voters	3	4	7	2	3	6	4	4

1. What is the equilibrium position?
   Ans: 0.5

2. What is the mean?
   Ans: 0.55

3. What is the median?
   Ans: 0.5

4. Suppose there are three classes of voters that rank four candidates as shown below.

Class I. Seven voters.	They prefer B and D, between whom they are indifferent, to A and C, between whom they are indifferent.
Class II. Six voters.	They prefer A and D, between whom they are indifferent, to B and C, between whom they are indifferent.
Class III. Five voters.	They prefer B and C, between whom they are indifferent, to A and D, between whom they are indifferent.

Assuming that each class of voters chooses its dominant strategy, who wins?
Ans: D

5. Suppose there are four classes of voters that rank four candidates as shown below.

Class I. Four voters.	They prefer A and C, between whom they are indifferent, to B and D, between whom they are indifferent.
Class II. Three voters.	They prefer A and B and D, among whom they are indifferent, to C.
Class III. Seven voters.	They prefer B to A and C and D, among whom they are indifferent.
Class IV. Five voters.	They prefer C to A and B and D, among whom they are indifferent.

Assuming that each class of voters chooses its dominant strategy, who wins?
Ans: B

6. Give an example of a voter distribution over the interval [0,1] that is skewed to the left.
Ans: Answers will vary. One example is shown below.

Position	0.1	0.3	0.4	0.5	0.6	0.7	0.8	0.9
Number of voters	3	4	5	2	1	6	6	1

7. Explain the justification for the Electoral College.
   Ans: The Electoral College was designed to place the selection of a president in the hands of a body that, while its members would be chosen by the people, would be sufficiently removed from them that it could make more deliberative choices.

8. Describe the composition of the Electoral College.
   Ans: Each state gets one electoral vote for each of its two senators and for each of its representatives in the House of Representatives. The District of Columbia is given three electoral votes.

9. Assume there are three states with 6, 8, and 23 electoral voters, and they are all toss-up states. If both the Democratic and Republican candidates choose strategies that maximize their expected electoral vote (the 3/2 rule), and they have the same total resources (D=R=100), what resources should be allocated for each state?
   Ans: 10, 15, and 75

10. Assume there are three states with 6000, 8000, and 23000 voters, and they are all toss-up states. If both the Democratic and Republican candidates choose strategies that maximize their expected popular vote (the proportional rule), and they have the same total resources (D=R=100), what resources should be allocated for each state?
    Ans: 16, 22, and 62

11. Assume there are three classes of voters that rank three candidates as follows.

Class I. Three voters:	A, B, C
Class II. Twelve voters:	C, A, B
Class III. Ten voters:	B, A, C

Which candidate is the Condorcet winner? According to the poll assumption, who will win the election? How does this compare to the desires of the Class I and III voters who, together, are a majority?

Ans: The Condorcet winner is A. But A is not one of the top two candidates, so the plurality winner C will win the election. However, the Class I and III voters together chose C as their least favorite candidate.

12. Assume there are three classes of voters that rank three candidates as follows.

Class I. Three voters:	A, B, C
Class II. Seven voters:	C, A, B
Class III. Five voters:	B, A, C

Which candidate is the Condorcet winner? According to the poll assumption, who will win the election? How does this compare to the desires of the Class I and III voters who, together, are a majority?

Ans: There is no Condorcet winner, so C will win the election. However, the Class I and III voters prefer B over C.

Use the following to answer questions 13-15:

Use the following information to answer the question(s) below.

Assume there are four classes of voters that rank four candidates as follows.

Class I. Five voters:	C, B, A, D
Class II. Three voters:	B, C, A, D
Class III. Six voters:	D, C, B, A
Class IV. Two voters:	B, C, D, A

13. Which candidate is the plurality winner?
   Ans: D

14. Which candidate is the Condorcet winner?
   Ans: C

15. Suppose there is a poll that differentiates the top two candidates. Which candidate will win the election after the poll?
    Ans: C

16. Describe the spoiler problem.
    Ans: The spoiler problem is caused by a candidate who cannot win but *spoils* the election for a candidate who otherwise would win.

17. What is the bandwagon effect?
    Ans: Voting for a candidate not on the basis of merit but because of the expectation that he or she will win.

18. What makes a candidate a Condorcet candidate?
    Ans: A Condorcet candidate is the candidate who can defeat each of the other candidates in pairwise contests.

19. Describe the expected popular vote (EPV).
    Ans: In toss-up states, it is the number of voters in each toss-up state, multiplied by the probability that the voter votes for the Democratic (or Republican) candidate, summed across all toss-up states.

20. Describe the expected electoral vote (EEV).
    Ans: In toss-up states, it is the number of electoral votes of each toss-up state, multiplied by the probability that the Democratic (or Republican) candidate wins more than 50% of the popular votes in that state, summed across all toss-up states.

21. Define an equilibrium position.
    Ans: A position is in equilibrium if no candidate has an incentive to depart from it unilaterally.

22. What is approval voting?
    Ans: Approval voting allows voters to vote for as many candidates as they like or find acceptable. Each candidate approved of receives one vote, and the candidate with the most approval votes wins.

23. Describe the 2/3 separation opportunity.
    Ans: If candidates A and B choose distinct positions that are equidistant from the median of a symmetric unimodal distribution and at least 2/3 of the voters lie between A and B, C can defeat both A and B by taking a position exactly between them.

24. Describe the 1/3 separation obstacle.
    Ans: If candidates A and B choose distinct positions that are equidistant from the median of a symmetric unimodal distribution and no more than 1/3 of the voters lie between A and B, C can take no position that will displace both A and B and enable C to win.

25. Explain the median-voter theorem.
    Ans: In a two-candidate election, the median is the unique equilibrium position.

26. Explain the poll assumption.
    Ans: Voters adjust, if necessary, their sincere voting strategies to differentiate between the top two candidates (as revealed in the poll) by voting for the one they prefer.

27. How is strategic voting different from sincere voting?
    Ans: Strategic voting might not be sincere, but instead aims to elect an acceptable candidate if the first choice is not viable.

28. Give an example of a set of five data that is bimodal.
    Ans: Answers will vary. For example, { 4, 4, 5, 5, 7}

29. Give an example of five data that is unimodal.
    Ans: Answers will vary. For example, { 4, 4, 5, 7, 8}

30. Suppose voters are distributed so that they are only located at certain positions along the left-right continuum. What is this type of distribution called?
    Ans: A discrete distribution of voters.

Chapter 13: Multiple-Choice

1. In a fair-division procedure, the goal is for all participants to receive identical amounts.
   A) True   B) False
   Ans: B

2. In a fair-division procedure, participants may receive different amounts.
   A) True   B) False
   Ans: A

3. Which of the following fair-division procedures is not envy-free?
   A)   Adjusted winner procedure   C)   Last-diminisher method
   B)   Knaster inheritance procedure   D)   Divide-and-choose
   Ans: C

Use the following to answer questions 4-6:

Use the following information to answer the question(s) below.

Tom and Sandy must make a fair division of three objects left by their great aunt Sally. They have assigned points to the objects as shown below.

Object	Tom's points	Sandy's points
Painting	40	30
Jewelry	10	50
Car	50	20

4. Using the adjusted winner procedure, who gets the car?
   A) Tom   B) Sandy
   Ans: A

5. Using the adjusted winner procedure, what does Tom end up with?
   A)   Car and painting   C)   Painting and 1/5 car
   B)   Car only   D)   Car and 3/7 painting
   Ans: D

6. Using the adjusted winner procedure, how many points of value does Tom feel he ends with?
   A) 67.14   B) 90   C) 50   D) 50.43
   Ans: A

7. Chris and Terry must make a fair division of a stereo, television, and microwave. They place point values on the objects as shown below. Using the adjusted winner procedure, what does Terry receive?

Object	Chris's points	Terry's points
Stereo	25	45
Television	60	35
Microwave	15	20

A) Stereo and 1/4 of microwave
B) Microwave and 6/7 of television

C) Stereo and 6/7 of microwave
D) Stereo and microwave

Ans: C

8. Chris and Terry must make a fair division of a stereo, television, and microwave. They place point values on the objects as shown below. Using the adjusted winner procedure, what point value does Chris feel he receives in the end?

Object	Chris's points	Terry's points
Stereo	25	45
Television	60	35
Microwave	15	20

A) 60   B) 62.14   C) 50   D) 37.86
Ans: B

9. Andi and Toni must make fair division of a car, a house, and a boat. The point values they place on the objects are given below. Using the adjusted winner procedure, what does Andi end with?

Object	Andi's points	Toni's points
Car	35	45
House	40	30
Boat	25	25

A) House and boat
B) House and 2/5 of boat

C) House and 2/7 of car
D) House and 3/5 of boat

Ans: D

10. Andi and Toni must make fair division of a car, a house, and a boat. The point values they place on the objects are given below. Using the adjusted winner procedure, what point value does Andi end with?

Object	Andi's points	Toni's points
Car	35	45
House	40	30
Boat	25	25

A) 65   B) 55   C) 50   D) 60
Ans: B

Use the following to answer questions 11-13:

Use the following information to answer the question(s) below.

At the end of the lease on their apartment, Toni and Terry decide to rent separate places and so must make a fair division of the property they purchased together. The items to be divided and the point values each person places on them are given below.

Item	Toni	Terry
CD player	15	20
Sofa	30	25
Microwave	20	25
TV	35	30

11. If Toni and Terry use the adjusted winner procedure to divide the property, who gets the microwave?
A) Toni   B) Terry
Ans: B

12. If Toni and Terry use the adjusted winner procedure to divide the property, what will Terry end with?
A)   CD, microwave, and TV
B)   CD, microwave, and 1/6 TV
C)   CD and microwave only
D)   CD, microwave, and 4/13 TV
Ans: D

13. If Toni and Terry use the adjusted winner procedure to divide the property, how many points of value will each person think they end up with?
A) 45   B) 50   C) 54.23   D) 56.5
Ans: C

Use the following to answer questions 14-16:

Use the following information to answer the question(s) below.

Jack and Jill went up the hill and found an antique water pail. Jack and Jill must now make a fair division of the pail using the Knaster inheritance procedure. Jack bids $80 for the value of the pail and Jill bids $65.

14. What is the outcome of the fair division?
    A)   Jack gets the pail and pays Jill $36.25.
    B)   Jack gets the pail and pays Jill $40.
    C)   Jack gets the pail and pays Jill $32.50.
    D)   Jack gets the pail and Jill gets $65.
    Ans: A

15. How much value does Jill think she ends with?
    A) $36.25   B) $32.50   C) $40   D) $43.75
    Ans: A

16. How much value does Jack believe he ends with?
    A) $36.25   B) $32.50   C) $40   D) $43.75
    Ans: D

17. Andi, Chris, and Kim must make a fair division of a car left to them by their father. Using the Knaster inheritance procedure, the values they bid on the car are given below. Find the results of the fair division.

	Andi	Chris	Kim
Car	$2400	$3000	$2700

    A)   Chris gets the car and pays $1900; Andi gets $900, and Kim gets $1000.
    B)   Chris gets the car, Andi gets $800; Kim gets $900.
    C)   Chris gets the car and pays $1500; Andi gets $1200, and Kim gets $1350.
    D)   Chris gets the car and pays $2550; Andi gets $1200, and Kim gets $1350.
    Ans: A

18. Andi, Chris, and Kim must make a fair division of a car left to them by their father. Using the Knaster inheritance procedure, the values they bid on the car are given below.

	Andi	Chris	Kim
Car	$2400	$3000	$2700

    How much value does Chris think he ends up with?
    A) $3000   B) $1300   C) $1100   D) $1000
    Ans: C

Use the following to answer questions 19-21:

Use the following information to answer the question(s) below.

Three children must make fair division of a painting and sculpture left them by their mother. Using the Knaster inheritance procedure, the value each child places on the objects is shown below.

Object	A	B	C
Painting	$4000	$6300	$6000
Sculpture	$2300	$1800	$2400

19. Who gets the sculpture?
    A) A   B) B   C) C
    Ans: C

20. What does A get after the fair division?
    A) $2466.67   B) $2100   C) Sculpture and $166.67   D) $3150
    Ans: A

21. What does B get after the fair division?
    A)   Painting and $366.67   C)   Painting and pays $3600
    B)   Painting and pays $3233.34   D)   Painting and pays $2250
    Ans: B

Use the following to answer questions 22-24:

Use the following information to answer the question(s) below.

Ashley, Brook, Chris, and Dana must make a fair division of the estate of their uncle Bob. The estate consists of a farm house, a car, and a horse. Using the Knaster inheritance procedure, the value each person places on each item is shown below.

Item	Ashley	Brook	Chris	Dana
House	$35,000	$50,000	$48,000	$42,000
Car	$3000	$2500	$2750	$2800
Horse	$6000	$5800	$6250	$5200

22. Who gets the horse?
    A) Ashley   B) Brook   C) Chris   D) Dana
    Ans: C

23. What does Ashley end the fair division with?
    A) Car and $18,000
    C) Car and $22,000
    B) Car and $8000
    D) Car and $9731.25
    Ans: D

24. What value does Chris end the fair division with?
    A) $9731 B) $14,250 C) $15,981.25 D) $1731.25
    Ans: C

Use the following to answer questions 25-28:

Use the following information to answer the question(s) below.

Suppose that Andi and Terry view a cake as shown below. They agree to divide the cake using the divide-and-choose procedure.

25. If Andi divides the cake, where will the cut be made?
    A) 3 columns from the left
    C) 2 columns from the left
    B) 2 1/2 columns from the left
    D) 1 1/2 columns from the left
    Ans: C

26. If Andi divides the cake, which side will Terry choose?
    A) The right side B) The left side
    Ans: A

27. If Andi divides the cake and Terry chooses, how many units will Andi believe he gets?
    A) 3 B) 3 1/2 C) 4 D) 5
    Ans: C

28. If Andi divides the cake and Terry chooses, how many units of cake will Terry believe she gets?
    A) 3 1/2 B) 4 C) 5 D) 6
    Ans: C

Use the following to answer questions 29-32:

Use the following information to answer the question(s) below.

Suppose Chris and Toni each view a cake as shown below. They agree to use the divide-and-choose procedure.

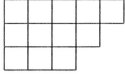 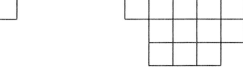

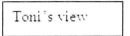

29. If Chris divides, where will the cut be made?
    A)   2 columns from the left   C)   2 2/3 columns from the left
    B)   2 1/3 columns from the left   D)   3 columns from the left.
    Ans: A

30. If Chris divides, which side will Toni choose?
    A) Right   B) Left
    Ans: A

31. If Chris divides and Toni chooses, how many units will Toni believe he gets?
    A) 6   B) 7   C) 7 1/2   D) 8
    Ans: D

32. If Chris divides and Toni chooses, how much will Chris feel is left?
    A) 6   B) 7   C) 7 1/2   D) 8
    Ans: A

Use the following to answer questions 33-36:

Use the following information to answer the question(s) below.

Alex, Betty, and Chris each view a cake as shown below. They will share the cake using the last-diminisher method with the order Alex, Betty, and Chris cutting and passing off the right side of the cake.

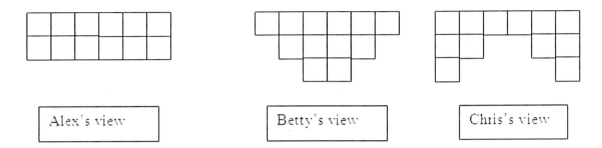

Alex's view   Betty's view   Chris's view

33. After Alex cuts the cake, he will hand the portion on the right to Betty. Where will Alex make his cut?
    A)   1 1/2 columns from the right   C)   2 1/2 columns from the right
    B)   2 columns from the right   D)   2 2/3 columns from the right
    Ans: B

34. After Alex cuts the cake, he will hand the portion on the right to Betty. Will Betty trim the piece before handing it to Chris?
    A) Yes   B) No
    Ans: B

35. After Alex cuts the cake, he will hand the portion on the right to Betty, who decides whether or not to trim the piece and then hands it off to Chris. Will Chris trim the piece he receives from Betty?
    A) Yes   B) No
    Ans: A

36. Who will make the last cut and thus keep the first piece of cake?
    A) Alex   B) Betty   C) Chris
    Ans: C

Use the following to answer questions 37-41:

Use the following information to answer the question(s) below.

Dana, Kim, and Lu each view a cake as shown below. They will share the cake using the last-diminisher method with the order Dana, Kim, and Lu cutting and passing off the right side of the cake.

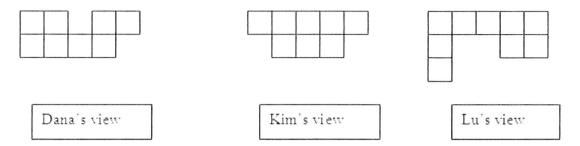

Dana's view   Kim's view   Lu's view

37. Dana first cuts a piece off the right side of the cake and hands it to Kim. Where will Dana cut the cake?
    A)   1 1/3 columns from the right   C)   1 2/3 columns from the right
    B)   1 1/2 column from the right   D)   2 columns from the right
    Ans: B

38. Dana first cuts a piece she believes is worth 3 units off the right side of the cake and hands it to Kim. How many units will Kim think this slice is worth?
    A) 1 1/2   B) 2   C) 2 1/2   D) 3
    Ans: B

39. Dana first cuts a piece she believes is worth 3 units off the right side of the cake and hands it to Kim. Will Kim trim the slice?
    A) Yes   B) No
    Ans: B

40. Who will be the last to trim and thus keep the first piece of cake?
    A) Dana   B) Kim   C) Lu
    Ans: C

41. How many units will Lu believe the piece handed him by Kim is worth?
    A) 2   B) 2 1/2   C) 3 1/2   D) 4
    Ans: C

42. Though they don't realize it, Dana, Chris, Kelly, and Terry each view a cake the same way. They will share the cake using the last-diminisher method. When the first person cuts and passes a piece of the cake, what happens?
A)   No one else trims the cake.
B)   Every person trims the cake.
C)   Only the second person trims the cake.
D)   Only the fourth person trims the cake.
Ans: A

43. Though they don't realize it, Dana, Chris, Kelly, and Terry each view a cake the same way. They will share the cake using the last-diminisher method, in the order given above. When the first person cuts and passes a piece of the cake, who eventually retains this piece?
A) Dana   B) Chris   C) Kelly   D) Terry
Ans: D

44. Four heirs need to make a fair division of the property left in an estate. The objects and the point values assigned to them are given below. If the heirs want to use the trimming procedure, with the order Chris, Kelly, Dana, and Kim, would the house need to be sold?

Object	Chris's points	Kelly's points	Dana's points	Kim's points
House	20	15	18	20
Car	10	12	10	5
Painting	10	8	12	15
Furniture	5	10	10	5
Money	55	55	50	55

A) Yes   B) No
Ans: B

45. Four heirs need to make a fair division of the property left in an estate. The objects and the point values assigned to them are given below. If the heirs want to use the trimming procedure, with the order Chris, Kelly, Dana, and Kim, would the house need to be sold?

Object	Chris's points	Kelly's points	Dana's points	Kim's points
House	20	25	18	25
Car	10	12	10	5
Painting	10	8	12	15
Furniture	5	10	10	5
Money	55	45	50	50

A) Yes   B) No
Ans: A

46. Four heirs need to make a fair division of the property left in an estate. The objects and the point values assigned to them are given below. The heirs want to use the trimming procedure, with the order Chris, Kelly, Dana, and Kim. Chris divides the estate into the following parts: (1) house, (2) car and 10 points from money, (3) painting and 10 points from money, (4) furniture and 15 points from money, and (5) remaining 20 points from money. Which parts will Kelly trim?

Object	Chris's points	Kelly's points	Dana's points	Kim's points
House	20	15	18	25
Car	10	12	10	5
Painting	10	8	12	15
Furniture	5	10	10	5
Money	55	55	50	50

A) Part #4 only   B) Parts #2, #3, and #4   C) Parts #2 and #4   D) None
Ans: C

Use the following to answer questions 47-49:

Use the following information to answer the question(s) below.

Tom and Huck need to paint a fence and agree to use a modification of the divide-and-choose procedure to make a fair division of the chore. The boys' views of the fence are shown below.

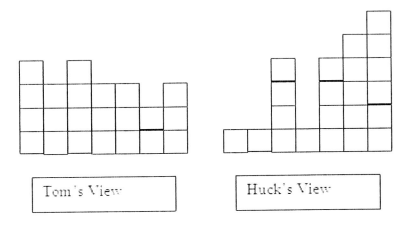

47. If Tom divides, will Huck choose the piece he believes is larger or smaller in modifying the procedure?
   A)   Huck chooses the part he feels is smaller.
   B)   Huck chooses the part he feels is larger.
   Ans: A

48. If Tom divides and Huck chooses, how many units of fence will Tom think each boy is painting?
   A)   Tom paints 11 and Huck paints 11.   C)   Tom paints 16 and Huck paints 6.
   B)   Tom paints 6 and Huck paints 16.   D)   Tom paints 12 and Huck paints 10.
   Ans: A

49. If Tom divides and Huck chooses, how many units of fence will Huck think each boy is painting?
   A)   Tom paints 11 and Huck paints 11.   C)   Tom paints 16 and Huck paints 6.
   B)   Tom paints 6 and Huck paints 16.   D)   Tom paints 12 and Huck paints 10.
   Ans: C

50. Andi and Terry need to make a fair division of a sofa they bought when sharing an apartment. They agree that Andi is entitled to 2/3 of the sofa and Terry is entitled to 1/3 of the sofa. They agree to use a modification of the Knaster inheritance procedure to divide the sofa. Andi believes the sofa is worth $360 and Terry believes the sofa is worth $315. Using the Knaster inheritance procedure, how much will Andi pay Terry for the sofa?
   A) $105   B) $110   C) $120   D) $315
   Ans: B

Use the following to answer questions 51-60:

Use the following information to answer the question(s) below.

Suppose Kim and Chris want to take turns, using the bottom-up strategy, to allocate several textbooks currently held jointly. Their ranked preferences are listed below:

	1st	2nd	3rd	4th	5th	6th
Chris	Botany	Sociology	Physiology	Biology	Ecology	Chemistry
Kim	Biology	Chemistry	Botany	Sociology	Ecology	Physiology

51. If Kim chooses first, what is Kim's first choice?
   A) Biology   B) Chemistry   C) Botany   D) Sociology
   Ans: C

52. If Chris chooses first, what is Chris's first choice?
   A) Botany   B) Sociology   C) Physiology   D) Biology
   Ans: A

53. If Kim chooses first, what is Chris's first choice?
   A) Botany   B) Sociology   C) Physiology   D) Biology
   Ans: B

54. If Chris chooses first, what is Kim's first choice?
    A) Biology   B) Chemistry   C) Botany   D) Sociology
    Ans: A

55. If Chris chooses first, when is the Ecology book chosen?
    A)   It is Chris's second choice   C)   It is Kim's second choice
    B)   It is Chris's third choice   D)   It is Kim's third choice
    Ans: C

56. If Kim chooses first, when is the Ecology book chosen?
    A)   It is Chris's second choice   C)   It is Kim's second choice
    B)   It is Chris's third choice   D)   It is Kim's third choice
    Ans: A

57. If Chris chooses first, when is the Chemistry book chosen?
    A)   It is Chris's second choice.   C)   It is Kim's second choice.
    B)   It is Chris's third choice.   D)   It is Kim's third choice.
    Ans: D

58. If Kim chooses first, when is the Physiology book chosen?
    A)   It is Chris's second choice.   C)   It is Kim's second choice.
    B)   It is Chris's third choice.   D)   It is Kim's third choice.
    Ans: B

59. If Chris chooses first, when is the Sociology book chosen?
    A)   It is Chris's first choice.   C)   It is Kim's second choice.
    B)   It is Chris's second choice.   D)   It is Kim's third choice.
    Ans: B

60. If Kim chooses first, when is the Sociology book chosen?
    A)   It is Chris's first choice.   C)   It is Kim's second choice.
    B)   It is Chris's second choice.   D)   It is Kim's third choice.
    Ans: A

61. David and Max purchased raffle tickets together and, to their surprise, won three prizes. Now they must make a fair division of their winnings. Using the adjusted winner procedure, what does David end up with?

Object	David's points	Max's points
Fly rod	50	45
Fly fishing lessons	10	35
100 hand-tied flies	40	20

A) Fly rod only
B) Flies, fly rod
C) Flies, 11/19 of fly rod
D) Flies, 8/19 of fly rod
Ans: D

62. Jen and Lynn must make a fair division of four objects inherited from their great aunt. Using the adjusted winner procedure, what does Lynn end up with?

Object	Jen's points	Lynn's points
Dinnerware	30	35
Silver	15	45
Jewelry	35	10
Photographs	20	10

A) Dinnerware, silver
B) Silver, 8/13 of dinnerware
C) Silver, 5/13 of dinnerware
D) Jewelry, photos
Ans: B

63. David and Max purchased raffle tickets together and, to their surprise, won three prizes. Now they must make a fair division of their winnings. If David and Max use the adjusted winner procedure, how many points of value will each person think they end up with?

Object	David's points	Max's points
Fly rod	50	45
Fly fishing lessons	10	35
100 hand-tied flies	40	20

A) 50   B) 61   C) 73   D) 100
Ans: B

64. Kim and Tori must make a fair division of three objects. Using the adjusted winner procedure, what does Kim end up with?

Object	Kim's points	Tori's points
Ring	20	35
Necklace	70	45
Bracelet	10	20

A) 20/23 of the necklace
B) 3/23 of the necklace
C) The necklace and 1/2 of the ring
D) The ring and the bracelet

Ans: A

65. Charles and Monte must make a fair division of a cabin. They use the Knaster inheritance procedure. Charles bids $65,000 for the value of the cabin and Monte bids $57,000. What is the outcome of the fair division?
A) Charles gets the cabin and pays Monte $30,500.
B) Charles gets the cabin and pays Monte $4000.
C) Charles gets the cabin and pays Monte $57,000.
D) Charles gets the cabin and pays Monte $34,500.

Ans: A

66. Charles and Monte must make a fair division of a cabin. They use the Knaster inheritance procedure. Charles bids $65,000 for the value of the cabin and Monte bids $57,000. How much value does Monte believe he ends up with?
A) $30,500   B) $4000   C) $57,000   D) $34,500

Ans: D

67. Four people must make a fair division of two classic cars. They use the Knaster inheritance procedure. Their bids are shown below:

	A	B	C	D
T-Bird	60,000	90,000	50,000	50,000
Mustang	70,000	45,000	100,000	80,000

Who gets the Mustang?
A) A   B) B   C) C   D) D

Ans: C

Use the following to answer questions 68-70:

Use the following information to answer the question(s) below.

Suppose Jack and Joe want to take turns, using the bottom-up strategy, to allocate a selection of cookies. Their ranked preferences are listed below:

	1st	2nd	3rd	4th	5th	6t
Jack	Chocolate	Peanut butter	Macadamia	Macaroon	Sugar	Oatn
Joe	Peanut butter	Oatmeal	Macaroon	Macadamia	Chocolate	Su\

68. If Jack chooses first, what is his first choice?
    A) Chocolate   B) Peanut butter   C) Macadamia   D) Macaroon
    Ans: B

69. If Joe chooses first, what is his first choice?
    A) Chocolate   B) Peanut butter   C) Macadamia   D) Macaroon
    Ans: B

70. If Jack chooses first, when is the chocolate cookie chosen?
    A)   It is Jack's second choice.   C)   It is Jack's third choice.
    B)   It is Joe's second choice.   D)   It is Joe's third choice.
    Ans: A

Chapter 13: Free-Response

1. After having been roommates for four years at college, Alex and Bob are moving on. Several items they have accumulated belong jointly to the pair, but now must be divided between the two. They assign points to the items as follows:

Object	Alex's points	Bob's points
Bicycle	10	12
Textbooks	20	16
Barbells	5	2
Rowing machine	7	10
Music collection	8	11
Computer	15	17
Novels	20	22
Desk	15	10

Use the adjusted winner procedure to determine a fair division of the property.

Ans: Alex gets the textbooks, the barbells, the desk, and 16/21 of the novels. Bob gets the rest.

2. In recent labor-management negotiations, several issues were identified, and points assigned to them indicating relative importance to each side, as follows:

Issue	Management's points	Labor's points
Base pay	20	23
Incentive pay	10	5
Health care benefits	6	12
Worker safety	8	15
Opportunity for promotion	20	13
Retirement package	20	20
Employee accountability	16	12

Use the adjusted winner procedure to determine a fair resolution between labor and management.

Ans: Management gets its way with regard to incentive pay, opportunity for promotion, and employee accountability, and 60% of its way on the issue of the retirement package. Labor gets its way on the rest of the issues.

3. A husband and wife are getting divorced. The property to be divided, and the relative value of the items to each, are as follows:

Object	Husband's points	Wife's points
House	30	15
Car	25	25
Cabin	20	40
Boat	16	15
Television	5	3
Stereo	4	2

Use the adjusted winner procedure to determine a fair division of the property.
Ans: The husband gets the house, the boat, the television, the stereo, and 20% use of the car. The wife gets the cabin and 80% use of the car.

4. The administration and the student body at a local college are at odds over several issues. The relative importance of each issue to each group is as follows:

Issue	Administration's points	Student's points
Mandatory meal plan	40	15
Mandatory campus living	5	30
Cars on campus	5	20
Campus curfew	10	15
Weekday fraternity parties	40	20

Use the adjusted winner procedure to determine a fair resolution.
Ans: The administration gets its way on the mandatory meal plan, and 11/12 of its way with regard to weekday fraternity parties. The student body gets its way on the rest of the issues.

5. Henry and Lisa inherit a house. If their monetary bids on the house are $135,000 and $114,000, respectively, what is the fair division arrived at by the Knaster inheritance procedure?
Ans: Henry receives the house and gives Lisa $62,250.

6. Two people inherit a painting. If their monetary bids on the painting are $12,560 and $9750, what is the fair distribution arrived at by the Knaster inheritance procedure?
Ans: The first person receives the painting and gives the second person $5,577.50.

7. John, Ken, and Linda inherit a painting. If their monetary bids on the painting are $25,200, $21,600, and $18,000, respectively, what is the fair distribution arrived at by the Knaster inheritance procedure?
Ans: John receives the painting and pays $15,600. Ken receives $8,400 and Linda receives $7,200.

8. John, Ken, and Linda inherit a painting. Their monetary bids on the painting are $25,200, $21,600, and $18,000, respectively. If Linda had known of John and Ken's evaluations in advance, should she have changed her own evaluation?
   Ans: Yes. Her bid should be just slightly lower than John's and higher than Ken's. Her new bid is $25,194.

9. A parent leaves a house, a farm, and a piece of property to be divided equally among four children who submit dollar bids on these objects as follows:

	Children			
Objects	First	Second	Third	Fourth
House	120,000	125,000	100,000	90,000
Farm	80,000	60,000	70,000	75,000
Property	40,000	30,000	25,000	45,000

   What is the fair division arrived at by the Knaster inheritance procedure?
   Ans: The first child receives the farm and pays $11,250. The second child receives the house and pays $62,500. The third child receives $57,500 and the fourth child receives the piece of property and $16,250.

10. Three indivisible objects A, B, and C are to be shared equally among four people. Assume that the objects have monetary values to the four people as follows:

	People			
Object	First	Second	Third	Fourth
A	8600	3500	2300	4800
B	5500	4200	4400	2700
C	3600	5100	3400	2300

   What is the fair distribution arrived at by the Knaster inheritance procedure?
   Ans: The first person receives objects A and B and pays $8,025. The second person receives object C and pays $250. The third person receives $4,175 and the fourth person receives $4,100.

11. Suppose that Bob and Carol view a cake as shown below:

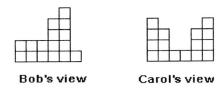

Bob's view   **Carol's view**

Assume that Bob and Carol use divide-and-choose to divide the cake between them, and that all cuts are made corresponding to vertical lines. If Bob is the divider, how many units of value will Bob and Carol think he or she is receiving?

Ans: Bob makes a vertical cut in the middle of the fourth column. Carol chooses the piece on the left. Bob thinks he gets 8 square units of value. Carol thinks she gets 8.5 square units of value.

12. Suppose that Bob and Carol view a cake as shown below:

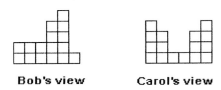

Bob's view   **Carol's view**

Bob and Carol will use divide-and-choose to divide the cake between them, and all cuts made correspond to vertical lines. Will Bob like the results better if he is the divider or the chooser? Explain your answer.

Ans: Bob will like the results better if he is the chooser. If he is the divider, he will divide the cake into two pieces he thinks are both worth 8 units and so the piece he is left with is worth 8 units in his mind. If Carol divides, Bob can choose a piece Carol thinks is worth 8 units but Bob believes is worth 10 units.

13. Suppose that Bob and Carol view a cake as shown below:

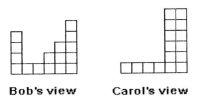

Bob's view   **Carol's view**

Assume that Bob and Carol use divide-and-choose to divide the cake between them and that all cuts are vertical. If Bob is the divider, how many units of value will Bob and Carol think he or she is receiving? Is this different if Carol is the divider? Explain.

Ans: If Bob cuts, he makes a vertical cut between the fourth and fifth column. Carol chooses the piece on the right. Bob thinks he gets 8 square units of value. Carol thinks she gets 12 square units of value. If Carol cuts, she makes a vertical cut two-thirds of the way across the fifth column. Bob chooses the piece on the left. Carol thinks she gets 8 square units of value. Bob thinks he gets 10 square units of value.

14. Suppose that Bob and Carol view a cake as shown below:

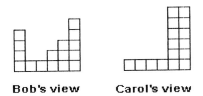

Bob's view   **Carol's view**

Assume that Bob and Carol know how each other values the cake (and that neither is spiteful). Suppose they are to divide the cake using the rules of divide-and-choose but not necessarily the strategies. If Bob is the divider, where will he cut the cake and how many units of value will Bob and Carol think he or she is receiving?

Ans: Bob makes a vertical cut almost two-thirds of the way across the fifth column. Carol chooses the piece on the right. Bob thinks he gets almost 10 square units of value. Carol thinks she gets slightly more than 8 square units of value.

15. Suppose that Bob, Carol, and Ted view a cake as shown below:

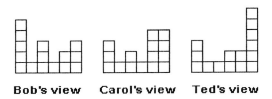

Bob's view   **Carol's view**   **Ted's view**

Assume that each player regards a piece as acceptable if and only if it is at least five square units of value. Assume all cuts are vertical. Provide a total of three drawings to show how each player views a division of the cake, by Bob, into three pieces he or she considers to be the same size or value.

Ans:

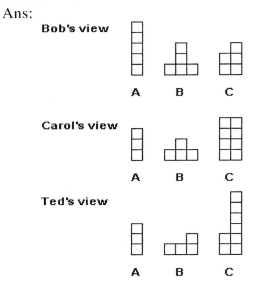

16. Suppose that Bob, Carol, and Ted view a cake as shown below:

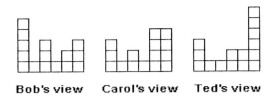

Bob's view   **Carol's view**   **Ted's view**

Assume that each player regards a piece as acceptable if and only if it is at least five square units of value. Assume all cuts are vertical. Provide a total of three drawings to show how each player views a division of the cake by Bob into three pieces he considers to be the same size or value. Now use the Steinhaus lone-divider method to get a proportional allocation, indicating who approves of which piece and how large a piece each player thinks he or she is receiving.

Ans:

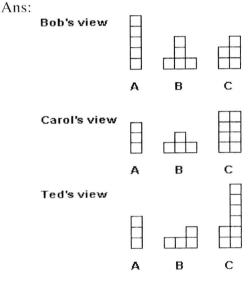

Carol approves of only piece C, and Ted approves of only piece C. Thus, Bob is the only one to approve of piece A. Bob is given piece A. Carol and Ted use divide-and-choose on pieces B and C recombined. If Carol is the divider, she makes a vertical cut in the middle of the fifth column. Ted chooses the piece on the right. Bob thinks he gets 5 square units of value. Carol thinks she gets 6 square units of value. Ted thinks he gets 7 square units of value.

17. Assume that Bob, Carol, Ted, and Alice view a cake as shown below:

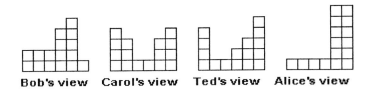

Bob's view   Carol's view   Ted's view   Alice's view

Notice that each player views the cake as having 16 units of value. Assume that the four players use the last-diminisher method to divide the cake among themselves. Give a step-by-step description of the cuts made and the pieces with which each player exits assuming that the order in which they proceed is Bob, then Carol, then Ted, and then Alice.

Ans: Bob makes a vertical cut between the second and third columns. The piece made up of the first and second columns is, in Bob's eyes, 4 out of the 16 units of value, and thus one-fourth of the cake.

Carol sees this piece as 7 out of 16 square units of value, so she trims it by making a vertical cut between the first and second columns. The piece made up of column one is, in Carol's eyes, one-fourth of the cake.

Ted passes, as does Alice, because they both think column one represents no more than one-fourth of the cake.

Carol takes this piece (column one) and exits the game.

Bob now makes a vertical cut between columns three and four. The piece made up of columns two and three is, in Bob's eyes, 4 square units of value.

Ted passes, as does Alice, because both think the piece represents no more than one-fourth of the cake.

Bob takes this piece, columns two and three, and exits the game.

Ted and Alice now use divide-and-choose on the rest of the cake (the fourth, fifth, and sixth columns).

Ted, as divider, makes a vertical cut between the fifth and sixth columns.

Alice chooses the piece made up of columns four and five (she thinks there are seven square units of value).

Ted receives the piece made up of column six (he thinks there are 5 square units of value).

18. Assume that Bob, Carol, Ted, and Alice view a cake as shown below:

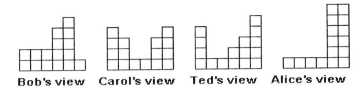

Bob's view   Carol's view   Ted's view   Alice's view

Notice that each player views the cake as having 16 units of value. Assume that the four players use the last diminisher method to divide the cake among themselves. Give a step-by-step description of the cuts made and the pieces with which each player exits assuming that the order in which they proceed is Alice, then Ted, then Carol, and then Bob.

Ans: Alice makes a vertical cut between the fourth and fifth columns. The piece made up of the first four columns is, in Alice's eyes, 4 out of 16 square units of value, and thus is one-fourth of the cake.

Ted sees this piece as 8 out of 16 units of value, so he trims it by making a vertical cut between the first and second columns. The piece made up of column one is, in Ted's eyes, one-fourth of the cake.

Carol passes, as does Bob, because they both think column one represents no more than one-fourth of the cake.

Ted takes this piece (column one) and exits the game.

Alice now makes a vertical cut one-sixth of the way across column five. The piece made up of columns two, three, four, and one-sixth of column five is, in Alice's eyes, 4 square units of value.

Carol sees this piece as 5.5 out of 16 square units of value, so she trims it by making a vertical cut between the third and fourth columns. The piece made up of columns two and three is, in Carol's eyes, one-fourth of the cake.

Bob passes because he thinks this piece represents no more than one-fourth of the cake.

Carol takes this piece (columns two and three) and exits the game.

Alice and Bob now use divide-and-choose on the rest of the cake (the fourth, fifth, and sixth columns).

Alice, as divider, makes a vertical cut 11/12 of the way across the fifth column.

Bob chooses the piece on the right (1/12 of column five plus column six).

Alice receives the piece on the left (column four plus 11/12 of column five).

19. Suppose players 1, 2, and 3 view a cake as shown below, and that all cuts are vertical.

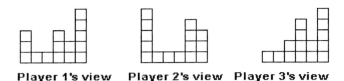

Player 1's view   Player 2's view   Player 3's view

Describe the steps in using the last-diminisher method to divide the cake. Assume players will use the order of player 1, then player 2, and then player 3 and that all pieces will be cut from the left side of the cake. Use drawings to clarify your description.

Ans: Player 1 cuts between the third and fourth columns, viewing the piece made of columns one, two, and three as worth 5 square units of value and so one-third of the cake.

Player 2 views the piece made of the first three columns as worth 7 square units of value and so trims between the first and second columns. The piece made up of the first column is, in player 2's eyes, worth one-third of the cake.

Player 3 views this as worth no more than one-third of the cake and so passes.

Player 2 receives the piece made up of column one and exits the game.

Player 1 and player 3 now use divide-and-choose on the remainder of the cake (columns two through six).

Player 1 cuts the cake halfway through the fifth column. Player 3 chooses the part made of columns two, three, four, and half of five, for a total (in player 3's eyes) of 8 square units of value. Player 1 is left with the portion made of half of column 5 and column six for a total, in player 1's eyes, of 6 square units of value.

20. Suppose players 1, 2, and 3 view a cake as shown below and that all cuts are vertical.

Player 1's view   **Player 2's view**   **Player 3's view**

Illustrate the envy-free procedure for $n = 3$ (yielding an allocation of part of the cake) by following steps a-c below:

a) Provide a total of three drawings to show how each player views a division of the cake by player 1 into three pieces he or she considers to be the same size or value. Label the pieces A, B, and C.

b) Redraw the picture from player 2's view and illustrate the trimmings of piece B that he or she would do. Label the trimmed piece B' and the actual trimmings T.

c) Indicate which piece each player would choose (and what he or she thinks its size is) if the players choose in the following order: player 3, player 2, player 1, according to the rules of the procedure.

Ans: a)

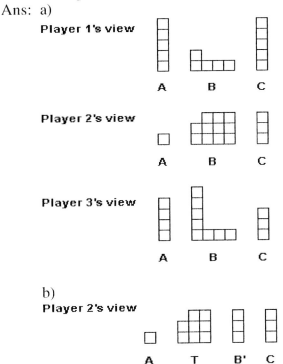

b)

c) Player 3 will choose A (which he thinks is worth 4 square units).
Player 2 will choose B (which he thinks is worth 3 square units).
Player 1 will receive C (which he thinks is worth 5 square units).

21. Apply the remainder of the Selfridge-Conway procedure to what was obtained in question 20 by completing steps a-c below:

a) Draw a picture of T from each player's view.

b) The procedure calls for the player (other than player 1) who did not receive the trimmed piece to divide T into three pieces he or she considers to be the same size. Illustrate this division, and label the pieces X, Y, and Z.

c) Indicate which parts of T (and the sizes or values) the players will choose when they go in the order: player 2, player 1, player 3.

Ans: a)

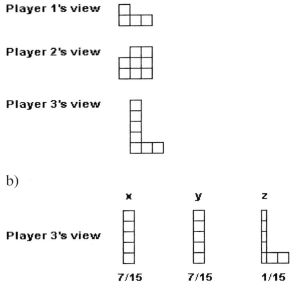

b)

c) Player 2 chooses first and will take Z. Player 1 chooses next and takes either X or Y (he considers them equal). Player 3 receives the remaining piece.

22. Suppose Chris and Terry need to make a fair division of a stereo they jointly purchased. Suppose also that both agree Chris is entitled to 2/3 of the stereo and Terry to 1/3. Chris and Terry place monetary bids on the value of the stereo of $500 and $450, respectively. Modify the Knaster inheritance procedure to make a fair division of the stereo.

Ans: Chris gets the stereo and pays Terry $158.33.

23. Aunt Sally dies and leaves her estate to be shared among Ariel, Binky, and Chris. The estate consists of a painting and a sculpture by a modern artist. Aunt Sally had decreed that Ariel was to receive half her estate and that Binky and Chris were to share equally the remaining half. The values that each heir placed on the painting and sculpture are given below. Modify the Knaster inheritance procedure to make a fair division of the estate.

Object	Ariel	Binky	Chris
Painting	4000	6300	6000
Sculpture	2300	1800	2400

Ans: Ariel gets $3862.50.
Binky gets the painting and pays $3918.75.
Chris gets the sculpture and $56.25.

24. Explain why the divide-and-choose method of cake division is considered an envy-free procedure for dividing a cake between two participants.
Ans: Divide-and-choose is envy-free because the divider believes both pieces are of equal worth and the chooser gets to pick a piece he believes is worth at least half.

25. Tom and Jerry must rake all the leaves in a yard. They each view the yard as shown below and agree to divide the chore by the divide-and-choose method. Tom will divide the yard in two parts and Jerry will choose the side he has to rake. Describe the results of this fair division.

Tom's view   Jerry's view

Ans: Tom divides the yard in the middle of the third column. Jerry chooses the left side to rake.

26. Suppose Kelly and Jan want to take turns, using the bottom-up strategy, to allocate several textbooks currently held jointly. Their ranked preferences are listed below:

	1st	2nd	3rd	4th	5th	6th
Kelly	Painting	Music	Architecture	Sculpture	Design	Textiles
Jan	Design	Architecture	Painting	Sculpture	Music	Textiles

If Kelly chooses first, how are books allocated?
Ans: Kelly selects Painting, Sculpture, Music. Jan selects Architecture, Design, Textiles.

27. Suppose Kelly and Jan want to take turns, using the bottom-up strategy, to allocate several textbooks currently held jointly. Their ranked preferences are listed below:

	1st	2nd	3rd	4th	5th	6th
Kelly	Painting	Music	Architecture	Sculpture	Design	Textiles
Jan	Design	Architecture	Painting	Sculpture	Music	Textiles

If Jan chooses first, how are books allocated?
Ans: Jan selects Architecture, Sculpture, Design. Kelly selects Painting, Music, Textiles.

28. Suppose Tony and Jess want to take turns, using the bottom-up strategy, to allocate several items. If Tony and Jess rank the same item as first on their preference lists, who gets this item?
Ans: Whoever goes first.

29. Suppose Tony and Jess want to take turns, using the bottom-up strategy, to allocate several items. If Tony and Jess have the same last choice on their preference lists, who gets this item?
Ans: Whoever goes second.

30. If Jack and Jill want to take turns, using the bottom-up strategy, to allocate ten items, under what situation could it be possible that each person would get their top five choices?
Ans: If Jack's top five choices are Jill's bottom five choices.

31. Abby and Annie must make a fair division of four objects inherited from their grandmother. If Abby and Annie use the adjusted winner procedure, what is the division of the objects?

Object	Abby's points	Annie's points
Brass bed	30	45
Cedar chest	50	10
Hand-sewn quilt	15	25
Photo albums	5	20

Ans: Annie gets the quilt, the photo albums, and 7/15 of the bed. Abby gets the rest.

32. Paul and Henry must make a fair division of three objects. If Paul and Henry use the adjusted winner procedure, what is the division of the objects?

Object	Paul's points	Henry's points
Wooden toy collection	60	20
Antique desk	25	45
China	15	35

Ans: Paul gets the toys and 2/7 of the desk. Henry gets the rest.

33. Four people must make a fair division of two classic cars. They use the Knaster inheritance procedure. Their bids are shown below:

	A	B	C	D
T-Bird	60,000	90,000	50,000	50,000
Mustang	70,000	45,000	100,000	80,000

What is the division of the objects?
Ans: A gets $45,937.50.
   B gets the T-Bird and pays $42,812.50.
   C gets the Mustang and pays $49,062.50.
   D gets $45,937.50.

34. Three people must make a fair division of four objects. Using the Knaster inheritance procedure, the value each person places on the objects is shown below.

	A	B	C
Object 1	160	320	360
Object 2	280	370	30
Object 3	430	260	160
Object 4	420	270	130

What is the division of the objects?
Ans: A gets Object 3 and Object 4, and pays $140.
   B gets Object 2 plus $156.68.
   C gets Object 1 and pays $16.68.

35. Suppose Dave and Merrie want to take turns, using the bottom-up strategy, to allocate the contents of a box of computer software they received as a gift. Their ranked preferences are listed below:

	1st	2nd	3rd	4th	5th	6th
Dave	Flight simulator	Action game	Role-playing game	Strategy game	Solitaire suite	Word-processing
Merrie	Solitaire suite	Strategy game	Action game	Role-playing game	Word-processing suite	Flight simulator

If Merrie chooses first, what is the division of the objects?

Ans: Merrie gets the solitaire game, the action game, and the role-playing game. Dave gets the rest.

Chapter 14: Multiple-Choice

1. The Hamilton method of apportionment can display the population paradox.
   A) True B) False
   Ans: A

2. The Jefferson method of apportionment can display the population paradox.
   A) True B) False
   Ans: B

3. The Webster method of apportionment can display the population paradox.
   A) True B) False
   Ans: B

4. The Jefferson method of apportionment can display the Alabama paradox
   A) True B) False
   Ans: B

5. An apportionment method exists that satisfies the quota condition and is free from both the population paradox and the Alabama paradox.
   A) True B) False
   Ans: B

6. Which method of apportionment always satisfies the quota condition?
   A) Hamilton B) Hill-Huntington C) Jefferson D) Webster
   Ans: A

7. For a given set of populations and house sizes, different methods of apportionment may lead to different apportionments.
   A) True B) False
   Ans: A

8. For a given set of populations and house sizes, different methods of apportionment may lead to the same apportionment.
   A) True B) False
   Ans: A

9. Which of the following is a true statement?
   A)   Jefferson's method of apportionment is not biased with respect to a state's population.
   B)   Jefferson's method of apportionment is biased toward states with smaller populations.
   C)   Jefferson's method of apportionment is biased toward states with larger populations.
   Ans: C

10. A county is divided into three districts with the populations shown below. There are 10 seats on the county council that need to be apportioned. Find the quota for the Applewood district.

District	Population
Applewood	8280
Boxwood	4600
Central	5220

A) 4.57   B) 4   C) 5   D) 8.28
Ans: A

11. We are scheduling seven course sections for a total of 217 students. Enrollments are: 109 in Calculus I, 79 in Calculus II, and 29 in Advanced Calculus. Find the quota of sections for Calculus II.
A) 2   B) 2.55   C) 3.64   D) 3
Ans: B

12. A small county has populations in three districts as shown below. They are to apportion 10 seats on the county council. Find the quota for Riverdale.

District	Population
Parkview	43,000
Hillside	32,800
Riverdale	24,200

A) 4.13   B) 2   C) 4   D) 2.42
Ans: D

13. A county is divided into three districts with the populations shown below. There are 10 seats on the county council that need to be apportioned, using the Hamilton method. Find the apportionment for the Applewood district.

District	Population
Applewood	8280
Boxwood	4600
Central	5220

A) 4   B) 3   C) 5   D) 2
Ans: C

14. We are scheduling seven course sections for a total of 217 students. Enrollments are: 109 in Calculus I, 79 in Calculus II, 29 in Advanced Calculus. Find the apportionment for Advanced Calculus using the Hamilton method.
A) 0   B) 1   C) 2   D) 3
Ans: B

15. A county is divided into three districts with the populations shown below. There are 10 seats on the county council that need to be apportioned, using the Hamilton method. Find the apportionment for the Boxwood district.

District	Population
Applewood	8280
Boxwood	4600
Central	5220

A) 2   B) 3   C) 1   D) 4
Ans: A

16. A county is divided into three districts with the populations shown below. There are 10 seats on the county council that need to be apportioned. If the county uses the Jefferson method, what would be the first critical divisor for the Applewood district?

District	Population
Applewood	8280
Boxwood	4600
Central	5220

A) 1656   B) 1810   C) 1840   D) 2070
Ans: A

17. A county has three districts with the populations shown below. The 11 seats on the county council are to be apportioned using the Jefferson method. Find the apportionment for each district.

District	Population
A	43,000
B	32,800
C	24,200

A) 5, 3, 3   B) 5, 4, 2   C) 6, 3, 2   D) 4, 4, 3
Ans: B

18. A state has four districts with the populations shown below. The House of Representatives has 20 seats that are to be apportioned using the Jefferson method. Find the first critical divisor for district A.

District	Population
A	87,000
B	56,000
C	72,000
D	35,000

A) 4350   B) 10,875   C) 12,500   D) 12,429
Ans: D

19. A county is divided into three districts with the populations shown below. There are 10 seats on the county council that need to be apportioned. What would be the standard divisor?

District	Population
Applewood	8280
Boxwood	4600
Central	5220

A) 1533   B) 1656   C) 1740   D) 1810
Ans: D

20. A county has three districts with the populations shown below. The 11 seats on the county council are to be apportioned using the Jefferson method. Find the initial multiplier that would be used.

District	Population
A	43,000
B	32,800
C	24,200

A) 1.226   B) 1.127   C) 1.109   D) 1.057
Ans: D

21. A county has three districts with the populations shown below. The 11 seats on the county council are to be apportioned using the Webster method. Find the tentative apportionment for district A.

District	Population
A	43,000
B	32,800
C	24,200

A) 4   B) 4.5   C) 4.73   D) 5
Ans: D

22. A county has three districts with the populations shown below. The 11 seats on the county council are to be apportioned using the Webster method. Find the apportionment for each district.

District	Population
A	43,000
B	32,800
C	24,200

A) 5, 4, 2   B) 5, 3, 3   C) 4, 4, 3   D) 6, 3, 2
Ans: B

23. A state has four districts with the populations shown below. The House of Representatives has 20 seats that are to be apportioned using the Jefferson method. Find the apportionment for each district.

District	Population
A	87,000
B	56,000
C	72,000
D	35,000

    A) 6, 5, 6, 3   B) 7, 4, 5, 4   C) 6, 4, 6, 4   D) 7, 4, 6, 3
    Ans: D

24. A country has four states with the populations shown below. The House of Representatives is to have 15 members. Use the Webster method of apportionment to find the number of seats for each state.

State	Population
A	52,600
B	39,900
C	34,000
D	23,500

    A) 6, 4, 3, 2   B) 5, 4, 4, 2   C) 6, 3, 3, 3   D) 5, 4, 3, 3
    Ans: B

25. A small county has populations in three districts as shown below. They are to apportion 15 seats on the county council using the Webster method. Find the apportionment for each district.

District	Population
Parkview	43,000
Hillside	32,800
Riverdale	24,200

    A) 7, 5, 3   B) 6, 6, 3   C) 6, 5, 4   D) 7, 4, 4
    Ans: C

26. A small county has populations in three districts as shown below. They are to apportion 15 seats on the county council using the Hill-Huntington method. Find the apportionment for each district.

District	Population
Parkview	43,000
Hillside	32,800
Riverdale	24,200

    A) 7, 5, 3   B) 6, 6, 3   C) 6, 5, 4   D) 7, 4, 4
    Ans: C

27. A country has four states with the populations shown below. The House of
    Representatives is to have 15 members, apportioned by the Hill-Huntington method.
    Find the tentative apportionment for district C.

State	Population
A	52,600
B	39,900
C	34,000
D	23,500

    A) 3   B) 3.4   C) 3.46   D) 4
    Ans: A

28. A country has four states with the populations shown below. The House of
    Representatives is to have 15 members. Use the Hill-Huntington method of
    apportionment to find the number of seats for each state.

State	Population
A	52,600
B	39,900
C	34,000
D	23,500

    A) 5, 4, 4, 2   B) 6, 4, 3, 2   C) 5, 4, 3, 3   D) 6, 3, 3, 3
    Ans: A

29. A county has four districts with the populations shown below. They are to use the Hill-
    Huntington method of apportionment to distribute 20 seats on a county council. Find the
    tentative apportionment for district B.

District	Population
A	87,000
B	56,000
C	72,000
D	35,000

    A) 3   B) 4   C) 5   D) 6
    Ans: C

30. Given three states with the populations shown below, and a national senate with 10 seats,
    use the Hill-Huntington method of apportionment to distribute the seats to the states.

State	Population
Apathy	69,000
Bliss	43,500
Confusion	37,500

    A) 4, 3, 3   B) 4, 4, 2   C) 5, 4, 1   D) 5, 3, 2
    Ans: D

31. Find the geometric mean of 5 and 6.
    A) 5.5   B) 5.48   C) 4.69   D) 3.32
    Ans: B

32. Find the geometric mean of 8 and 9.
    A) 5.83   B) 8.5   C) 8.74   D) 8.49
    Ans: D

33. Find the geometric mean of 3 and 7.
    A) 4.38   B) 5.00   C) 4.58   D) 3.16
    Ans: C

34. We are scheduling seven course sections for a total of 217 students. Enrollments are: 109 in Calculus I, 79 in Calculus II, and 29 in Advanced Calculus. Find the apportionment for each course using the Jefferson method.
    A) 4, 2, 1   B) 3, 3, 1   C) 4, 3, 0   D) 3, 2, 2
    Ans: A

35. We are scheduling seven course sections for a total of 217 students. Enrollments are: 109 in Calculus I, 79 in Calculus II, and 29 in Advanced Calculus. Find the apportionment for each course using the Hill-Huntington method.
    A) 4, 2, 1   B) 4, 3, 0   C) 3, 3, 1   D) 3, 2, 2
    Ans: C

36. Suppose a country has four states with the populations shown below and a parliament with 30 seats. Use the Jefferson method of apportionment to apportion the seats between the states.

State	Population
A	182,575
B	243,170
C	322,115
D	252,140

    A) 5, 7, 10, 8   B) 6, 7, 9, 8   C) 5, 7, 11, 7   D) 6, 8, 8, 8
    Ans: A

37. A state has a population of 24,000 and holds 3 of 28 seats in a parliament. What is the district population of the state?
    A) 857   B) 2571   C) 4320   D) 8000
    Ans: D

38. A county council has 15 seats on its county council which are apportioned among four regions. The population of the West region is 3560 and the West region holds four seats on the council. What is the district population for the West region?
A) 949   B) 890   C) 237   D) 59
Ans: B

39. A county council has 15 seats that are apportioned among four regions. The population of the West region is 3560 and the West region holds four seats on the council. What is the representative share for the West region?
A) 0.004213   B) 0.001124   C) 0.2667   D) 0.01685
Ans: B

40. A small country has four states and a parliament with 23 seats. One state has a population of 4277 and holds five seats in the parliament. Find the representative share for the state.
A) 0.001169   B) 0.2174   C) 0.005378   D) 0.02689
Ans: A

41. A country has three states and a national senate with 10 seats. The state populations and the apportionment of the senate seats are shown below. Find the difference in representative shares of states A and B.

State	Population	Seats
A	69,000	5
B	43,500	3
C	37,500	2

A) 0.2   B) 0.0000035   C) 0.00000125   D) 0.0000725
Ans: B

42. A country has three states and a national senate with 10 seats. The state populations and the apportionment of the senate seats are shown below. Find the difference in district population of states A and B.

State	Population	Seats
A	69,000	5
B	43,500	3
C	37,500	2

A) 25,500   B) 20,000   C) 1400   D) 700
Ans: D

43. A small county has populations in three districts as shown below. They have apportioned 15 seats on the county council and obtained the apportionment for each district shown. Find the difference in representative share between the Parkview and Hillside districts.

District	Population	Apportionment
Parkview	43,000	6
Hillside	32,800	5
Riverdale	24,200	4

A) 0.06667   B) 0.00004237   C) 0.0000129   D) 0.0000008522
Ans: C

44. A small county has populations in three regions as shown below. They have apportioned 15 seats on the county council and obtained the apportionment for each region shown. Find the difference in district population between the Parkview and Hillside regions.

District	Population	Apportionment
Parkview	43,000	6
Hillside	32,800	5
Riverdale	24,200	4

A) 10,200   B) 607   C) 6267   D) 2867
Ans: B

45. Find the relative difference of 7 and 9.
A) 28.57%   B) 2%   C) 22.22%   D) 43.75%
Ans: A

46. Find the relative difference of 12 and 17.
A) 41.67%   B) 70.58%   C) 29.41%   D) 17.24%
Ans: A

47. A country has three states and a national senate with 10 seats. The state populations and the apportionment of the senate seats are shown below. Find the relative difference in representative shares of states A and B.

State	Population	Seats
A	69,000	5
B	43,500	3
C	37,500	2

A) 66.7%   B) 4.83%   C) 5.07%   D) 6.70%
Ans: C

48. A country has three states and a national senate with 10 seats. The state populations and the apportionment of the senate seats are shown below. Find the relative difference in district population of states A and B.

State	Population	Seats
A	69,000	5
B	43,500	3
C	37,500	2

A) 4.83% B) 1.61% C) 1.01% D) 5.07%
Ans: D

49. A small county has populations in three regions as shown below. They have apportioned 15 seats on the county council and obtained the apportionment for each region shown below. Find the relative difference in district population between the Parkview and Hillside regions.

Region	Population	Apportionment
Parkview	43,000	6
Hillside	32,800	5
Riverdale	24,200	4

A) 9.25% B) 8.47% C) 1.85% D) 1.41%
Ans: A

50. A small county has populations in three regions as shown below. They have apportioned 15 seats on the county council and obtained the apportionment for each region shown below. Find the relative difference in representative shares between the Parkview and Hillside regions.

Region	Population	Apportionment
Parkview	43,000	6
Hillside	32,800	5
Riverdale	24,200	4

A) 9.2% B) 8.5% C) 16.7% D) 20.0%
Ans: A

51. Use the method of Hamilton to round each of the numbers in the sum
$0.85 + 0.8 + 2.16 + 5.52 + 0.67 = 10$ to a whole number, preserving the total of 10.

A) $1 + 1 + 2 + 6 + 0 = 10$ C) $0 + 1 + 3 + 5 + 1 = 10$
B) $0 + 1 + 2 + 6 + 1 = 10$ D) $1 + 1 + 2 + 5 + 1 = 10$
Ans: D

52. Use the method of Hamilton to round each of the numbers in the sum
    2.50 + 1.65 + 0.54 + 1.63 + 3.68 = 10 to a whole number, preserving the total of 10.
    A)   3 + 2 + 0 + 2 + 3 = 10   C)   2 + 2 + 1 + 2 + 3 = 10
    B)   2 + 2 + 0 + 2 + 4 = 10   D)   3 + 2 + 0 + 1 + 4 = 10
    Ans: B

53. Round the following to whole percentages using the Jefferson method:
    36.3% + 11.7% + 7.9% + 5.6% + 10.4% + 28.1% = 100%
    A)   37 + 12 + 8 + 5 + 10 + 28   C)   37 + 12 + 8 + 6 + 11 + 29
    B)   36 + 12 + 8 + 6 + 10 + 28   D)   37 + 12 + 8 + 6 + 10 + 28
    Ans: A

54. Round the following to whole percentages using the Jefferson method:
    6.5% + 38.1% + 1.2% + 17.0% + 12.5% + 24.7% = 100%
    A)   7 + 38 + 1 + 17 + 13 + 24   C)   6 + 38 + 1 + 17 + 12 + 24
    B)   7 + 38 + 1 + 17 + 13 + 25   D)   6 + 39 + 1 + 17 + 13 + 24
    Ans: D

55. Round the following to whole percentages using the Webster method:
    36.3% + 11.7% + 7.9% + 5.6% + 10.4% + 28.1% = 100%
    A)   36 + 11 + 8 + 6 + 11 + 28   C)   37 + 12 + 8 + 5 + 9 + 28
    B)   36 + 12 + 8 + 6 + 10 + 28   D)   37 + 11 + 8 + 6 + 9 + 28
    Ans: B

56. Round the following to whole percentages using the Webster method:
    6.6% + 38.1% + 1.1% + 17.0% + 12.6% + 24.6% = 100%
    A)   7 + 38 + 1 + 17 + 13 + 25   C)   7 + 38 + 1 + 17 + 13 + 24
    B)   7 + 38 + 1 + 17 + 12 + 25   D)   6 + 38 + 1 + 17 + 13 + 24
    Ans: C

57. The Anysville Transit System (ATS) has four bus routes, as identified below:

Route	Average passengers per day
1	682
2	2383
3	857
4	1425

    The ATS is replacing the entire old bus fleet with 35 new buses. Use the Webster method
    to determine how many buses each route should get.
    A) 4, 14, 8, 9   B) 4, 15, 7, 9   C) 4, 16, 6, 9   D) 4, 16, 5, 10
    Ans: C

58. The Anysville Transit System (ATS) has four bus routes, as identified below:

Route	Average passengers per day
1	682
2	2383
3	857
4	1425

The ATS is replacing the entire old bus fleet with 25 new buses. Use the Hill-Huntington method to determine how many buses each route should get.
A) 4, 14, 8, 9   B) 4, 15, 7, 9   C) 4, 16, 6, 9   D) 4, 16, 5, 10
Ans: C

59. The Collie Creek High School district received a gift of 28 computers. The computers are to be divided among the three schools in the district.

School	Number of students
Central High	384
East High	296
West High	204

Use the Jefferson method to determine how many computers each school should get.
A) 12, 9, 7   B) 12, 10, 6   C) 11, 10, 7   D) 11, 9, 8
Ans: B

60. The Collie Creek High School district received a gift of 28 computers. The computers are to be divided among the three schools in the district.

School	Number of students
Central High	384
East High	296
West High	204

Use the method of Hamilton to determine how many computers each school should get.
A) 12, 9, 7   B) 12, 10, 6   C) 11, 10, 7   D) 11, 9, 8
Ans: A

Chapter 14: Free-Response

1. Explain the Alabama paradox.
   Ans: The Alabama paradox occurs when a state loses a seat as a result of an increase in the House size. It can happen when an increase in House size causes the quota for some states to increase more than others and a state that originally assigned its upper quota then receives only its lower quota.

2. Explain the population paradox.
   Ans: The population paradox occurs when one state's apportionment decreases and another state's apportionment increases even though the first state has gained population and the second state has lost population.

3. The Hamilton method of apportionment always satisfies what is called the "quota condition." What does this mean?
   Ans: The quota in an apportionment problem is the exact share that would be allocated if a whole number were not required. A method is said to satisfy the quota condition if each state's apportionment is equal to its lower quota (the largest whole number no more than the quota) or its upper quota (the smallest whole number no less than the quota).

4. Find the geometric mean of 4 and 9.
   Ans: The geometric mean of 4 and 9 is $\sqrt{36} = 6$.

5. Round the following numbers by the method used in the Hill-Huntington apportionment procedure: 3.67, 9.42, 2.46, and 6.49
   Ans: 3.67 rounds to 4
   9.42 rounds to 9
   2.46 rounds to 3
   6.49 rounds to 7

6. Given the cities and the populations below, use the Hamilton method of apportionment to distribute 25 seats on a regional board.

City	Population
Greenville	34,569
Riverdale	27,943
Oceanside	21,350
Parkview	16,138

   Ans: Greenville 9
   Riverdale 7
   Oceanside 5
   Parkview 4

7. Use the Hamilton method of apportionment to distribute 15 representatives to the three states with the populations shown below.

State	Population
A	253,000
B	182,000
C	85,000

Ans: A 7
     B 5
     C 3

8. Use the Hamilton method of apportionment to distribute 12 seats on a city council to three districts with the populations shown below.

District	Population
North	30,000
Central	10,100
South	34,900

Ans: North 5
     Central 2
     South 5

9. Given the cities and the populations below, use the Jefferson method of apportionment to distribute 25 seats on a regional board.

City	Population
Greenville	34,569
Riverdale	27,943
Oceanside	21,350
Parkview	16,138

Ans: Greenville 9
     Riverdale 7
     Oceanside 5
     Parkview 4

10. Use the Jefferson method of apportionment to distribute 15 representatives to the three states with the populations shown below.

State	Population
A	253,000
B	182,000
C	85,000

Ans: A 8
     B 5
     C 2

11. Use the Jefferson method of apportionment to distribute 12 seats on a city council to three districts with the populations shown below.

District	Population
North	30,000
Central	10,100
South	34,900

Ans: North 5
     Central 1
     South 6

12. Given the cities and the populations below, use the Webster method of apportionment to distribute 25 seats on a regional board.

City	Population
Greenville	34,569
Riverdale	27,943
Oceanside	21,350
Parkview	16,138

Ans: Greenville 9
     Riverdale 7
     Oceanside 5
     Parkview 4

13. Use the Webster method of apportionment to distribute 15 representatives to the three states with the populations shown below.

State	Population
A	253,000
B	182,000
C	85,000

Ans: A 7
     B 5
     C 3

14. Use the Webster method of apportionment to distribute 12 seats on a city council to three districts with the populations shown below.

District	Population
North	30,000
Central	10,100
South	34,900

Ans: North 5
     Central 2
     South 5

15. Given the cities and the populations below, use the Hill-Huntington method of apportionment to distribute 25 seats on a regional board.

City	Population
Greenville	34,569
Riverdale	27,943
Oceanside	21,350
Parkview	16,138

Ans: Greenville 9
   Riverdale 7
   Oceanside 5
   Parkview 4

16. Use the Hill-Huntington method of apportionment to distribute 15 representatives to the three states with the populations shown below.

State	Population
A	253,000
B	182,000
C	85,000

Ans: A 7
   B 5
   C 3

17. Use the Hill-Huntington method of apportionment to distribute 12 seats on a city council to three districts with the populations shown below.

District	Population
North	30,000
Central	10,100
South	34,900

Ans: North 5
   Central 2
   South 5

18. A city is divided into four regions for distributing the 20 representatives on a public utility board. The regions and their populations are shown below. The board uses the Hamilton method of apportionment to distribute seats. Find the district population for each region based on this apportionment.

Region	Population
North	8700
South	5600
East	7200
West	3500

Ans: North 1242.86
     South 1400
     East   1200
     West   1166.67

19. A country has three states with the populations shown below. The House of Representatives for the country is to have 15 members. Find the district population for each state if the country uses the Jefferson method of apportionment.

State	Population
A	245,000
B	320,000
C	155,000

Ans: A 49000
     B 45714.29
     C 51666.67

20. A city is divided into four regions for distributing the 20 representatives on a public utility board. The regions and their populations are shown below. The board uses the Hamilton method of apportionment to distribute seats. Find the representative share for each region based on this apportionment.

Region	Population
North	8700
South	5600
East	7200
West	3500

Ans: North .0008046
     South .0007143
     East   .0008333
     West   .0008571

21. A country has three states with the populations shown below. The House of Representatives for the country is to have 15 members. Find the representative share for each state if the country uses the Jefferson method of apportionment.

State	Population
A	245,000
B	320,000
C	155,000

Ans: A .0000204
   B .0000219
   C .0000194

22. A town board has 10 members, divided among three regions of the town using the Hamilton method of apportionment. The regions and their populations are shown below. Find the difference in district population for the North and South regions.

Region	Population
North	13,400
Central	21,900
South	8700

Ans: 116.67

23. A small country has four states and a House of Representatives with 20 seats. Given the states, populations, and apportionment below, find the relative difference in district population between states A and C.

State	Population	Apportionment
A	234,000	5
B	124,000	3
C	346,500	7
D	268,500	5

Ans: 5.77%

24. A town board has 10 members, divided among three regions of the town using the Hamilton method of apportionment. The regions and their populations are given below. Find the difference in representative share for the North and South regions.

Region	Population
North	13,400
Central	21,900
South	8700

Ans: 6×10^{-6}

25. A small country has four states and a House of Representatives with 20 seats. Given the states, populations, and apportionment below, find the relative difference in representative share between states A and C.

State	Population	Apportionment
A	234,000	5
B	124,000	3
C	346,500	7
D	268,500	5

Ans: 5.79%

26. The manager of a busy restaurant is working on a schedule for the restaurant's 25 food servers. There are three shifts, as identified below:

Shift	Average number of customers
1	235
2	610
3	453

Use the Jefferson method to determine how many food servers should be scheduled for each shift.
Ans: 4, 12, 9

27. The manager of a busy restaurant is working on a schedule for the restaurant's 25 food servers. There are three shifts, as identified below:

Shift	Average number of customers
1	164
2	560
3	328

Use the Webster method to determine how many food servers should be scheduled for each shift.
Ans: 4, 13, 8

28. The manager of a busy restaurant is working on a schedule for the restaurant's 25 food servers. There are three shifts, as identified below:

Shift	Average number of customers
1	124
2	480
3	391

Use the Hill-Huntington method to determine how many food servers should be scheduled for each shift.
Ans: 3, 12, 10

29. The manager of a busy restaurant is working on a schedule for the restaurant's 25 food servers. There are three shifts, as identified below:

Shift	Average number of customers
1	122
2	451
3	674

Use the Hamilton method to determine how many food servers should be scheduled for each shift.
Ans: 2, 9, 14

30. Find the geometric mean of 10 and 6.
Ans: 7.75

Chapter 15: Multiple-Choice

1. In the following two-person zero-sum game, the payoffs represent gains to the row player I and losses to column player II.

$$\begin{bmatrix} 1 & 3 \\ 4 & 2 \end{bmatrix}$$

Which of the following statements is true?
A)   The game has no saddle point.
B)   The game has a saddle point; the value of the game is 3.
C)   The game has a saddle point; the value of the game is 2.
D)   The game has a saddle point; the value of the game is 2.5.
Ans: A

2. In the following two-person zero-sum game, the payoffs represent gains to the row player I and losses to column player II.

$$\begin{bmatrix} 3 & 5 \\ 4 & 2 \end{bmatrix}$$

Which of the following statements is true?
A)   The game has no saddle point.
B)   The game has a saddle point; the value of the game is 3.
C)   The game has a saddle point; the value of the game is 4.
D)   The game has a saddle point; the value of the game is 3.5.
Ans: A

3. In the following two-person zero-sum game, the payoffs represent gains to the row player I and losses to column player II.

$$\begin{bmatrix} 1 & 4 & 3 \\ 8 & 2 & 6 \\ 5 & 9 & 7 \end{bmatrix}$$

Which of the following statements is true?
A)   The game has no saddle point.
B)   The game has a saddle point; the value of the game is 3.
C)   The game has a saddle point; the value of the game is 4.
D)   The game has a saddle point; the value of the game is 5.
Ans: A

4. In the following two-person zero-sum game, the payoffs represent gains to the row player I and losses to column player II.

$$\begin{bmatrix} 4 & 3 & 6 \\ 2 & 8 & 1 \\ 9 & 7 & 5 \end{bmatrix}$$

Which of the following statements is true?
A) The game has no saddle point.
B) The game has a saddle point; the value of the game is 2.
C) The game has a saddle point; the value of the game is 5.
D) The game has a saddle point; the value of the game is 6.
Ans: A

5. In the following two-person zero-sum game, the payoffs represent gains to the row player I and losses to column player II.

$$\begin{bmatrix} 3 & 7 & 2 \\ 1 & 4 & 6 \\ 9 & 5 & 8 \end{bmatrix}$$

Which of the following statements is true?
A) The game has no saddle point.
B) The game has a saddle point; the value of the game is 4.
C) The game has a saddle point; the value of the game is 5.
D) The game has a saddle point; the value of the game is 6.
Ans: A

6. In the following two-person zero-sum game, the payoffs represent gains to the row player I and losses to column player II.

$$\begin{bmatrix} 1 & 5 & 7 & 3 \\ 6 & 2 & 14 & 12 \\ 15 & 9 & 16 & 4 \\ 10 & 11 & 8 & 13 \end{bmatrix}$$

Which of the following statements is true?
A) The game has no saddle point.
B) The game has a saddle point; the value of the game is 8.
C) The game has a saddle point; the value of the game is 9.
D) The game has a saddle point; the value of the game is 11.
Ans: A

7. In the following two-person zero-sum game, the payoffs represent gains to the row player I and losses to column player II.

$$\begin{bmatrix} 6 & 7 & 11 & 8 \\ 2 & 5 & 4 & 12 \\ 1 & 16 & 3 & 15 \\ 9 & 14 & 13 & 10 \end{bmatrix}$$

Which of the following statements is true?
A) The game has no saddle point.
B) The game has a saddle point; the value of the game is 8.
C) The game has a saddle point; the value of the game is 9.
D) The game has a saddle point; the value of the game is 11.
Ans: C

8. In the following two-person zero-sum game, the payoffs represent gains to the row player I and losses to column player II.

$$\begin{bmatrix} 1 & 3 \\ 4 & 2 \end{bmatrix}$$

Which of the following statements is true?
A) The maximin strategy of player I is to always play the first row; the minimax strategy of player II is to always play the first column.
B) The maximin strategy of player I is to always play the second row; the minimax strategy of player II is to always play the first column.
C) The maximin strategy of player I is to always play the first row; the minimax strategy of player II is to always play the second column.
D) The maximin strategy of player I is to always play the second row; the minimax strategy of player II is to always play the second column.
Ans: D

9. In the following two-person zero-sum game, the payoffs represent gains to the row player I and losses to column player II.

$$\begin{bmatrix} 3 & 5 \\ 4 & 2 \end{bmatrix}$$

Which of the following statements is true?
A) The maximin strategy of player I is to always play the first row; the minimax strategy of player II is to always play the first column.
B) The maximin strategy of player I is to always play the second row; the minimax strategy of player II is to always play the first column.
C) The maximin strategy of player I is to always play the first row; the minimax strategy of player II is to always play the second column.
D) The maximin strategy of player I is to always play the second row; the minimax strategy of player II is to always play the second column.
Ans: A

10. In the following two-person zero-sum game, the payoffs represent gains to the row player I and losses to column player II.

$$\begin{bmatrix} 1 & 4 & 3 \\ 8 & 2 & 6 \\ 5 & 9 & 7 \end{bmatrix}$$

The maximin strategy of player I is:
A) to always play the first row.
B) to always play the second row.
C) to always play the third row.
D) to play two or more of the rows.
Ans: C

11. In the following two-person zero-sum game, the payoffs represent gains to the row player I and losses to column player II.

$$\begin{bmatrix} 1 & 4 & 3 \\ 8 & 2 & 6 \\ 5 & 9 & 7 \end{bmatrix}$$

The minimax strategy of player II is:
A) to always play the first column.
B) to always play the second column.
C) to always play the third column.
D) to play two or more of the columns.
Ans: C

12. In the following two-person zero-sum game, the payoffs represent gains to the row player I and losses to column player II.

$$\begin{bmatrix} 4 & 3 & 6 \\ 2 & 8 & 1 \\ 9 & 7 & 5 \end{bmatrix}$$

The maximin strategy of player I is:
A) to always play the first row.
B) to always play the second row.
C) to always play the third row.
D) to play two or more of the rows.
Ans: C

13. In the following two-person zero-sum game, the payoffs represent gains to the row Player I and losses to column Player II.

$$\begin{bmatrix} 4 & 3 & 6 \\ 2 & 8 & 1 \\ 9 & 7 & 5 \end{bmatrix}$$

The minimax strategy of Player II is:
A) to always play the first column.
B) to always play the second column.
C) to always play the third column.
D) to play two or more of the columns.
Ans: C

14. In the following two-person zero-sum game, the payoffs represent gains to the row player I and losses to column player II.

$$\begin{bmatrix} 3 & 7 & 2 \\ 1 & 4 & 6 \\ 9 & 5 & 8 \end{bmatrix}$$

The maximin strategy of Player I is:
A) to always play the first row.
B) to always play the second row.
C) to always play the third row.
D) to play two or more of the rows.
Ans: C

15. In the following two-person zero-sum game, the payoffs represent gains to the row player I and losses to column player II.

$$\begin{bmatrix} 3 & 7 & 2 \\ 1 & 4 & 6 \\ 9 & 5 & 8 \end{bmatrix}$$

The minimax strategy of player II is:
A)   to always play the first column.
B)   to always play the second column.
C)   to always play the third column.
D)   to play two or more of the columns.
Ans: B

16. In the following two-person zero-sum game, the payoffs represent gains to the row player I and losses to column player II.

$$\begin{bmatrix} 1 & 5 & 7 & 3 \\ 6 & 2 & 14 & 12 \\ 15 & 9 & 16 & 4 \\ 10 & 11 & 8 & 13 \end{bmatrix}$$

The maximin strategy of player I is:
A)   to always play the first row.
B)   to always play the second row.
C)   to always play the third row.
D)   to always play the fourth row.
Ans: D

17. In the following two-person zero-sum game, the payoffs represent gains to the row player I and losses to column player II.

$$\begin{bmatrix} 1 & 5 & 7 & 3 \\ 6 & 2 & 14 & 12 \\ 15 & 9 & 16 & 4 \\ 10 & 11 & 8 & 13 \end{bmatrix}$$

The minimax strategy of player II is:
A)   to always play the first column.
B)   to always play the second column.
C)   to always play the third column.
D)   to always play the fourth column.
Ans: B

18. In the following two-person zero-sum game, the payoffs represent gains to the row player I and losses to column player II.

$$\begin{bmatrix} 6 & 7 & 11 & 8 \\ 2 & 5 & 4 & 12 \\ 1 & 16 & 3 & 15 \\ 9 & 14 & 13 & 10 \end{bmatrix}$$

The maximin strategy of player I is:
A)   to always play the first row.
B)   to always play the second row.
C)   to always play the third row.
D)   to always play the fourth row.
Ans: D

19. In the following two-person zero-sum game, the payoffs represent gains to the row player I and losses to column player II.

$$\begin{bmatrix} 6 & 7 & 11 & 8 \\ 2 & 5 & 4 & 12 \\ 1 & 16 & 3 & 15 \\ 9 & 14 & 13 & 10 \end{bmatrix}$$

The minimax strategy of player II is:
A)   to always play the first column.
B)   to always play the second column.
C)   to always play the third column.
D)   to always play the fourth column.
Ans: A

20. In the following game of batter-versus-pitcher in baseball, the batter's batting averages are shown in the game matrix.

	Pitcher Fastball	Curve
Batter Fastball	.300	.100
Curve	.200	.400

Which of the following statements is true?
A)   The game has no saddle point.
B)   The game has a saddle point; the value of the game is .200.
C)   The game has a saddle point; the value of the game is .300.
D)   The game has a saddle point; the value of the game is .400.
Ans: A

21. In the following game of batter-versus-pitcher in baseball, the batter's batting averages are shown in the game matrix.

	Pitcher Fastball	Curve
Batter Fastball	.400	.100
Curve	.200	.300

Which of the following statements is true?
A)   The game has no saddle point.
B)   The game has a saddle point; the value of the game is .200.
C)   The game has a saddle point; the value of the game is .300.
D)   The game has a saddle point; the value of the game is .400.
Ans: A

22. In the following game of batter-versus-pitcher in baseball, the batter's batting averages are shown in the game matrix.

```
                            |
                            | Pitcher
                            | Fastball              Curve
        ---------------------------------------------------------------------
        Batter    Fastball  | .300                  .100
                            |
                  Curve     | .200                  .400
                            |
```

What is the pitcher's optimal strategy?
A) Pitch more fastballs than curves.   C) Pitch fastballs and curves equally.
B) Pitch more curves than fastballs.
Ans: A

23. In the following game of batter-versus-pitcher in baseball, the batter's batting averages are shown in the game matrix.

```
                            |
                            | Pitcher
                            | Fastball              Curve
        ---------------------------------------------------------------------
        Batter    Fastball  | .300                  .100
                            |
                  Curve     | .200                  .400
                            |
```

What is the batter's optimal strategy?
A) Expect more fastballs than curves.
B) Expect more curves than fastballs.
C) Expect equal numbers of curves and fastballs.
Ans: B

24. In the following game of batter-versus-pitcher in baseball, the batter's batting averages are shown in the game matrix.

```
                             |
                             | Pitcher
                             | Fastball              Curve
    -----------------------------------------------------------------------
        Batter    Fastball | .400                  .100
                             |
                   Curve   | .200                  .300
                             |
```

What is the pitcher's optimal strategy?
A)   Pitch more fastballs than curves.   C)   Pitch fastballs and curves equally.
B)   Pitch more curves than fastballs.
Ans: B

25. In the following game of batter-versus-pitcher in baseball, the batter's batting averages are shown in the game matrix.

```
                             |
                             | Pitcher
                             | Fastball              Curve
    -----------------------------------------------------------------------
        Batter    Fastball | .400                  .100
                             |
                   Curve   | .200                  .300
                             |
```

What is the batter's optimal strategy?
A)   Expect more fastballs than curves.
B)   Expect more curves than fastballs.
C)   Expect equal numbers of curves and fastballs.
Ans: B

26. You can choose to buy an extended warranty for your computer for $200. During this period, you will experience either a minor ($100) or major ($500) repair bill. If you buy the warranty, you will not have to pay the repair bill. Assume the company wants to make as much money as possible, and you wish to spend as little as possible.

    Which of the following is a true statement?
    A)   This game has no saddle point.
    B)   This game has a saddle point; the value of the game is $100.
    C)   This game has a saddle point; the value of the game is $200.
    D)   This game has a saddle point; the value of the game is $500.
    Ans: C

27. You can choose to buy an extended warranty for your computer for $200. During this period, you will experience either a minor ($100) or major ($500) repair bill. If you buy the warranty, you pay 50% of any repair bill: that is, you will pay either $50 or $250 for the subsequent repair. Assume the company wants to make as much money as possible, and you wish to spend as little as possible.

    Which of the following is a true statement?
    A)   This game has no saddle point.
    B)   This game has a saddle point; the value of the game is $200.
    C)   This game has a saddle point; the value of the game is $250.
    D)   This game has a saddle point; the value of the game is $450.
    Ans: C

28. As the buyer for your business, you can choose to buy an extended warranty for each new computer for $200 each. During this period, each computer will experience either a minor ($100) or major ($500) repair bill. Repairs for each computer under warranty are reduced by 50% to $50 or $250. Assume the computer company wants to make as much money as possible, and you wish to spend as little as possible.

    What is your optimal strategy?
    A)   Never buy the warranty.
    B)   Always buy the warranty.
    C)   Buy the warranty for less than half of the computers.
    D)   Buy the warranty for more than half of the computers.
    Ans: C

29. As the buyer for your business, you can choose to buy an extended warranty for each new computer for $200 each. During this period, each computer will experience either a minor ($100) or major ($500) repair bill. Repairs for each computer under warranty are reduced by 50% to $50 or $250. Assume the computer company wants to make as much money as possible, and you wish to spend as little as possible.

What is the computer company's optimal strategy?
A)   Always sell the warranty.
B)   Never sell the warranty.
C)   Sell the warranty for less than half of the computers.
D)   Sell the warranty for more than half of the computers.
Ans: C

30. You are considering cheating on your income tax return. If you cheat you will pay $1000 in taxes; if you don't cheat you will pay $2000. If you are audited and you didn't cheat, your auditor will be kind and reduce your taxes from $2000 to $1500. If you are audited and you did cheat, you will be caught and have to pay a total of $2500, including penalties.

Statistically, which is the best option for you to choose?
A)   Definitely cheat.   C)   Probably don't cheat.
B)   Probably cheat.   D)   Definitely don't cheat.
Ans: C

31. If you cheat on your income tax return you will pay $1000 in taxes; if you don't cheat you will pay $2000. If you are audited and you didn't cheat, your auditor will be kind and reduce your taxes from $2000 to $1500. If you are audited and you did cheat, you will be caught and have to pay a total of $2500, including penalties.

Assuming the government wants to receive as much money as possible, statistically, which is the best option for the government to choose?
A) Always audit.   B) Usually audit.   C) Occasionally audit.   D) Never audit.
Ans: C

32. In American football the "third down and short" situation occurs often. The probabilities of obtaining a first down, shown below, are dependent on the choice of the offense and the anticipated choice of the defense.

		Defense Run	Pass
Offense	Run	0.4	0.8
	Pass	0.6	0.2

In such situations, what is the optimal solution for the defense?
A)   Always anticipate a run.
B)   Always anticipate a pass.
C)   Anticipate a run more often than a pass.
D)   Anticipate a pass more often than a run.
Ans: C

33. In American football the "third down and short" situation occurs often. The probabilities of obtaining a first down, shown below, are dependent on the choice of the offense and the anticipated choice of the defense.

		Defense Run	Pass
Offense	Run	0.4	0.8
	Pass	0.6	0.2

In such situations, what is the optimal solution for the offense?
a) Always choose to run.
b) Always choose to pass.
c) Choose to run more often than pass.
d) Choose to pass more often than run.
Ans: C or D

34. Consider the following partial-conflict game played in a non-cooperative manner.

		Player II Choice A	Choice B
Player I	Choice A	(3,3)	(5,1)
	Choice B	(1,5)	(2,2)

What outcomes constitute a Nash equilibrium?
A) Only when both players select choice A
B) Only when both players select choice B
C) Only when one player selects choice A; the other selects choice B
D) Only when both players select choice A or both players select choice B
Ans: A

35. Consider the following partial-conflict game played in a non-cooperative manner.

		Player II Choice A	Choice B
Player I	Choice A	(3,3)	(5,1)
	Choice B	(1,5)	(2,2)

Which of the following statements is true?
A) The dominant strategy for player I is to select choice A.
B) The dominant strategy for player I is to select choice B.
C) Player I has no dominant strategy.
Ans: A

Use the following to answer questions 36-39:

Use the following information to answer the question(s) below.

Consider the following partial-conflict game played in a non-cooperative manner.

```
              |
              | Player II
              | Choice A          Choice B
--------------------------------------------------------------------------
   Player I   Choice A | (4,1)         (3,2)
              |
              Choice B | (2,3)         (1,4)
              |
```

36. Which of the following statements is true?
    A) Both player I and player II have dominant strategies.
    B) Neither player I nor II has a dominant strategy.
    C) Only player I has a dominant strategy.
    D) Only player II has a dominant strategy.
    Ans: A

37. Which of the following is a Nash equilibrium?
    A) Player I selects choice A; player II selects choice A.
    B) Player I selects choice A; player II selects choice B.
    C) Player I selects choice B; player II selects choice A.
    D) Player I selects choice B; player II selects choice B.
    Ans: B

38. Assume that the game is played continually, and players can change their choices at noon each day. If the game begins with both players selecting choice B, what should happen at the first opportunity to change?
    A) Nothing.   C) Player II switches to choice A.
    B) Player I switches to choice A.   D) Both players switch to choice A.
    Ans: B

39. Assume that the game is played continually, and players can change their choices at noon each day. If the game begins with both players selecting choice A, what should happen at the first opportunity to change?
    A) Nothing.   C) Player II switches to choice B.
    B) Player I switches to choice B.   D) Both players switch to choice B.
    Ans: C

40. Suppose on a committee of three people Kim (the chair), Chris, and Terry each have one vote, but Kim breaks any tie. In attempting to elect someone to host the summer picnic, each person has a priority list:

	Kim's Priorities	Chris's Priorities	Terry's Priorities
1st choice	Kim	Chris	Terry
2nd choice	Terry	Kim	Chris
3rd choice	Chris	Terry	Kim

Which of the following are Nash equilibria?

  I: Every person votes for his/her first choice.
  II: Every person votes for his/her second choice.

A) I only   B) II only   C) Both I and II   D) Neither I nor II
Ans: D

41. Suppose on a committee of three people Kim (the chair), Chris, and Terry each have one vote, but Kim breaks any tie. In attempting to elect someone to host the summer picnic, each person has a priority list:

	Kim's Priorities	Chris's Priorities	Terry's Priorities
1st choice	Kim	Chris	Terry
2nd choice	Terry	Kim	Chris
3rd choice	Chris	Terry	Kim

Which of the following are Nash equilibria?

  I: Every person votes for Kim.
  II: Every person votes for Chris.

A) I only   B) II only   C) Both I and II   D) Neither I nor II
Ans: C

42. Suppose on a committee of three people Kim (the chair), Chris, and Terry each have one vote, but Kim breaks any tie. In attempting to elect someone to drive the van, each person has a priority list:

	Kim's Priorities	Chris's Priorities	Terry's Priorities
1st choice	Chris	Kim	Terry
2nd choice	Kim	Chris	Chris
3rd choice	Terry	Terry	Kim

Which of the following are Nash equilibria?

    I: Every person votes for his/her 1st choice.
    II: Kim and Chris vote for Chris; Terry votes for Terry.

A) I only   B) II only   C) Both I and II   D) Neither I nor II
Ans: C

43. Suppose on a committee of three people Kim (the chair), Chris, and Terry each have one vote, but Kim breaks any tie. In attempting to elect someone to drive the van, each person has a priority list:

	Kim's Priorities	Chris's Priorities	Terry's Priorities
1st choice	Chris	Kim	Terry
2nd choice	Kim	Chris	Chris
3rd choice	Terry	Terry	Kim

Which of the following are Nash equilibria?

    I: Every person votes for Chris.
    II: Every person votes for his/her 2nd choice.

A) I only   B) II only   C) Both I and II   D) Neither I nor II
Ans: C

44. The game of Chicken is an example of:

    I: a variable-sum game.
    II: a partial-conflict game.
    A) I only   B) II only   C) Both I and II   D) Neither I nor II
    Ans: C

45. The game of Prisoners' Dilemma is an example of:

    I: a variable-sum game.
    II: a partial-conflict game.
    A) I only   B) II only   C) Both I and II   D) Neither I nor II
    Ans: C

46. The "status-quo paradox":

    I: doesn't really happen.
    II: can allow a favored candidate to lose.
    A) I only   B) II only   C) Both I and II   D) Neither I nor II
    Ans: B

47. In a pure strategy game, each player consistently selects one particular option.
    A) True   B) False
    Ans: A

48. In a symmetrical game, both players will always choose the same particular option.
    A) True   B) False
    Ans: B

49. Every "zero-sum" game is a "fair" game.
    A) True   B) False
    Ans: B

50. Game theory is used by intelligence services to check for security violations.
    A) True   B) False
    Ans: A

51. In a truel where the choices are simultaneous, what is the optimal strategy for each player?
    A) fire at another player   B) fire at himself   C) do not fire
    Ans: A

52. In a truel where the choices are sequential, what is the optimal strategy for the first player?
    A) fire at another player   B) fire at himself   C) do not fire
    Ans: C

53. In a truel where the choices are simultaneous, what is the probability that any particular player will survive?
    A) 0   B) 1/4   C) 1/3   D) 1
    Ans: B

54. For a truel where the choices are sequential, which statement is true?
    A)   The game tree has 3 termination nodes.
    B)   The game tree has 5 termination nodes.
    C)   The game tree has 6 termination nodes.
    D)   The game tree has 9 termination nodes.
    Ans: B

55. For a truel where the choices are sequential, which statement is true?
    A)   The game tree has no cut branches.   C)   The game tree has 4 cut branches.
    B)   The game tree has 2 cut branches.   D)   The game tree has 6 cut branches.
    Ans: C

56. In the following two-person zero-sum game, the payoffs represent gains to the row player I and losses to the column player II.

$$\begin{bmatrix} 5 & 2 \\ 2 & 1 \end{bmatrix}$$

Which of the following statements is true?
    A)   The game has no saddle point.
    B)   The game has a saddle point; the value of the game is 1.
    C)   The game has a saddle point; the value of the game is 2.
    D)   The game has a saddle point; the value of the game is 5.
    Ans: C

57. In the following two-person zero-sum game, the payoffs represent gains to the row player I and losses to the column player II.

$$\begin{bmatrix} 5 & 8 & 6 \\ 4 & 3 & 1 \\ 2 & 6 & 7 \end{bmatrix}$$

Which of the following statements is true?
A)   The game has no saddle point.
B)   The game has a saddle point; the value of the game is 5.
C)   The game has a saddle point; the value of the game is 6.
D)   The game has a saddle point; the value of the game is 8.
Ans: B

58. In the following two-person zero-sum game, the payoffs represent gains to the row player I and losses to the column player II.

$$\begin{bmatrix} 8 & 1 & 5 & 2 \\ 5 & 4 & 7 & 8 \\ 1 & 3 & 4 & 5 \\ 8 & 4 & 3 & 5 \end{bmatrix}$$

Which of the following statements is true?
A)   The game has no saddle point.
B)   The game has a saddle point; the value of the game is 2.
C)   The game has a saddle point; the value of the game is 3.
D)   The game has a saddle point; the value of the game is 4.
Ans: D

59. In the following two-person zero-sum game, the payoffs represent gains to the row player I and losses to the column player II. Which of the following statements is true?

$$\begin{bmatrix} 5 & 2 \\ 2 & 1 \end{bmatrix}$$

A)   The maximin strategy of player I is to always play the first row; the minimax strategy of player II is to always play the first column.
B)   The maximin strategy of player I is to always play the second row; the minimax strategy of player II is to always play the first column.
C)   The maximin strategy of player I is to always play the first row; the minimax strategy of player II is to always play the second column.
D)   The maximin strategy of player I is to always play the second row; the minimax strategy of player II is to always play the second column.
Ans: C

60. In the following two-person zero-sum game, the payoffs represent gains to the row player I and losses to the column player II.

$$\begin{bmatrix} 5 & 8 & 6 \\ 4 & 3 & 1 \\ 2 & 6 & 7 \end{bmatrix}$$

The maximin strategy of player I is:
A)   to always play the first row.
B)   to always play the second row.
C)   to always play the third row.
D)   to play two or more of the rows.
Ans: A

61. In the following two-person zero-sum game, the payoffs represent gains to the row player I and losses to the column player II.

$$\begin{bmatrix} 5 & 8 & 6 \\ 4 & 3 & 1 \\ 2 & 6 & 7 \end{bmatrix}$$

The minimax strategy of player II is:
A)   to always play the first column.
B)   to always play the second column.
C)   to always play the third column.
D)   to play two or more of the columns.
Ans: A

62. In the following two-person zero-sum game, the payoffs represent gains to the row player I and losses to the column player II.

$$\begin{bmatrix} 8 & 1 & 5 & 2 \\ 5 & 4 & 7 & 8 \\ 1 & 3 & 4 & 5 \\ 8 & 4 & 3 & 5 \end{bmatrix}$$

The maximin strategy of player I is:
A)   to always play the first row.
B)   to always play the second row.
C)   to always play the third row.
D)   to play two or more of the rows.
Ans: B

63. In the following two-person zero-sum game, the payoffs represent gains to the row player I and losses to the column player II.

$$\begin{bmatrix} 8 & 1 & 5 & 2 \\ 5 & 4 & 7 & 8 \\ 1 & 3 & 4 & 5 \\ 8 & 4 & 3 & 5 \end{bmatrix}$$

The minimax strategy of player II is:
A)   to always play the first column.
B)   to always play the second column.
C)   to always play the third column.
D)   to play two or more of the columns.
Ans: B

64. Consider the following partial-conflict game played in a non-cooperative manner. The first payoff is to player I; the second is to player II.

	Player II	
Player I	Choice A	Choice B
Choice A	(1, 1)	(2, 6)
Choice B	(6, 2)	(5, 5)

What outcomes constitute a Nash equilibrium?
A)   Only when both players select A
B)   Only when both players select B
C)   Only when one player selects A and the other selects B
D)   Only when both players select A or both players select B
Ans: B

65. Consider the following partial-conflict game played in a non-cooperative manner. The first payoff is to player I; the second is to player II.

	Player II	
Player I	Choice A	Choice B
Choice A	(2, 4)	(3, 6)
Choice B	(6, 3)	(4, 2)

What outcomes constitute a Nash equilibrium?
A)   Only when both players select A
B)   Only when both players select B
C)   Only when one player selects A and the other selects B
D)   Only when both players select A or both players select B
Ans: C

Chapter 15: Free-Response

1. Create a two-by-two matrix that represents a two-person zero-sum game in which each player has two options and the game has a saddle point.
   Ans: For example,

   $$\begin{bmatrix} 0 & 1 \\ -1 & 0 \end{bmatrix}$$

2. Create a two-by-two matrix that represents a two-person zero-sum game in which each player has two options and the game has no saddle point.
   Ans: For example,

   $$\begin{bmatrix} 1 & -1 \\ -1 & 1 \end{bmatrix}$$

3. Create a two-by-two matrix that represents a two-person zero-sum game in which each player has two options and at least one player has a dominated strategy.
   Ans: For example,

   $$\begin{bmatrix} 0 & 1 \\ -1 & 0 \end{bmatrix}$$

4. Create a three-by-three matrix that represents a two-person zero-sum game in which each player has three options and the game has a saddle point.
   Ans: For example,

   $$\begin{bmatrix} 0 & 1 & 1 \\ -1 & 0 & -1 \\ -1 & -1 & 1 \end{bmatrix}$$

5. Create a three-by-three matrix that represents a two-person zero-sum game in which each player has three options and the game has no saddle point.
   Ans: For example,

   $$\begin{bmatrix} 1 & -1 & 0 \\ -1 & 0 & 1 \\ 0 & 1 & -1 \end{bmatrix}$$

6. Create a three-by-three matrix that represents a two-person zero-sum game in which each player has three options and at least one player has a dominated strategy.
   Ans: For example,

$$\begin{bmatrix} 0 & 1 & 1 \\ -1 & 0 & -1 \\ -1 & -1 & 1 \end{bmatrix}$$

7. In the following two-person zero-sum game, the payoffs represent gains to the row player I and losses to column player II.

$$\begin{bmatrix} 4 & 2 \\ 9 & 6 \end{bmatrix}$$

   Does this game have a saddle point? What is each player's minimax or maximin strategy? Justify your response.
   Ans: It has a saddle point at 4. Play the 1st row and the 1st column.

8. In the following two-person zero-sum game, the payoffs represent gains to the row player I and losses to column player II.

$$\begin{bmatrix} 2 & 7 \\ 5 & 9 \end{bmatrix}$$

   Does this game have a saddle point? What is each player's minimax or maximin strategy? Justify your response.
   Ans: It has a saddle point at 5. Play the 2nd row and the 1st column.

9. In the following two-person zero-sum game, the payoffs represent gains to the row player I and losses to column player II.

$$\begin{bmatrix} 2 & 9 & 6 \\ 5 & 7 & 3 \end{bmatrix}$$

   Does this game have a saddle point? What is each player's minimax or maximin strategy? Justify your response.
   Ans: No saddle point. Play the 2nd row and the 1st column.

10. In the following two-person zero-sum game, the payoffs represent gains to the row player I and losses to column player II.

$$\begin{bmatrix} 4 & 7 & 5 \\ 2 & 8 & 6 \end{bmatrix}$$

Does this game have a saddle point? What is each player's minimax or maximin strategy? Justify your response.
Ans: It has a saddle point at 4. Play the 1st row and the 1st column.

11. In the following two-person zero-sum game, the payoffs represent gains to the row player I and losses to column player II.

$$\begin{bmatrix} 2 & 7 & 4 \\ 1 & 9 & 5 \\ 3 & 8 & 6 \end{bmatrix}$$

Does this game have a saddle point? What is each player's minimax or maximin strategy? Justify your response.
Ans: It has a saddle point at 3. Play the 3rd row and the 1st column.

12. In the following two-person zero-sum game, the payoffs represent gains to the row player I and losses to column player II.

$$\begin{bmatrix} 3 & 6 & 7 \\ 1 & 8 & 5 \\ 4 & 2 & 9 \end{bmatrix}$$

Does this game have a saddle point? What is each player's minimax or maximin strategy? Justify your response.
Ans: It has no saddle point. Play the 1st row and the 1st column.

13. In the following game of batter-versus-pitcher in baseball, the batter's batting averages are shown in the game matrix:

		Pitcher Fastball	Knuckleball
Batter	Fastball	.400	.200
	Knuckleball	.100	.300

Solve the game determining the best mix of selections for both batter and pitcher.
Ans: Batter expects 1/2 fastball and 1/2 knuckleball. Pitcher plays 1/4 fastball and 3/4 knuckleball.

14. In the following game of batter-versus-pitcher in baseball, the batter's batting averages are shown in the game matrix:

		Pitcher Fastball	Knuckleball
Batter	Fastball	.500	.400
	Knuckleball	.300	.200

Solve the game determining the best mix of selections for both batter and pitcher.
Ans: Batter always expects fastball. Pitcher always plays knuckleball.

15. In the following game of batter-versus-pitcher in baseball, the batter's batting averages are shown in the game matrix:

		Pitcher Fastball	Knuckleball
Batter	Fastball	.500	.200
	Knuckleball	.200	.300

Solve the game, determining the best mix of selections for both batter and pitcher.
Ans: Batter expects 3/4 knuckleball and 1/4 fastball. Pitcher plays 3/4 knuckleball and ¼ fastball.

16. In the game of matching pennies, player I wins a penny if the coins match and player II wins if the coins do not match. Present this game as a two-by-two matrix, where each player has two outcomes from which to select.
Ans:

$$\begin{bmatrix} 1 & -1 \\ -1 & 1 \end{bmatrix}$$

17. In the game of matching pennies, player I wins a penny if the coins match and player II wins if the coins do not match. Is this a zero-sum game? Is this a fair game?
Ans: Yes; yes

18. In a game, each player chooses one of three coins: penny, nickel, or dime. If both players choose the same coin, both players loose their coin. Otherwise, the player with the more valuable coin wins the less valuable coin from the other player. Represent this game as a three-by-three matrix of ordered pairs.
Ans:

$$\begin{bmatrix} (-1,-1) & (1,-1) & (-1,1) \\ (1,-1) & (-5,-5) & (-5,5) \\ (1,-1) & (5,-5) & (-10,-10) \end{bmatrix}$$

19. In a game, each player chooses one of three coins: penny, nickel, or dime. If both players choose the same coin, both players loose their coin. Otherwise, the player with the more valuable coin wins the less valuable coin from the other player. Is this a symmetric game? Is there a dominated strategy?
Ans: Yes; no

20. You want to carry insurance for your small business. The annual policy costs $1000 this year. If you are sued and you have no insurance, you will pay $5000. If you have insurance and are sued you pay nothing, and your partner gives you $500 for your wise foresight, so that the policy costs you only $500. Represent this game as a two-by-two matrix.
    Ans:

	Insurance	No Insurance
Sue	$500	$5000
Don't Sue	$1000	$0

21. If you cheat on your income tax return you will pay $1000 in taxes; if you don't cheat you will pay $2000. If you are audited and you didn't cheat, your auditor will be kind and reduce your taxes from $2000 to $1500. If you are audited and you did cheat, you will be caught and have to pay a total of $2500, including penalties. Statistically, how often should you cheat?
    Ans: 1/4

22. If you cheat on your income tax return you will pay $1000 in taxes; if you don't cheat you will pay $2000. If you are audited and you didn't cheat, your auditor will be kind and reduce your taxes from $2000 to $1500. If you are audited and you did cheat, you will be caught and have to pay a total of $2500, including penalties. Statistically, how often should the government audit you?
    Ans: 1/2

23. Consider the following partial-conflict game played in a non-cooperative manner. The first payoff is to player I; the second to player II.

	Player II Choice A	Choice B
Player I Choice A	(4,1)	(3,2)
Choice B	(2,3)	(1,4)

    Discuss the players' possible strategies when this game is played.
    Ans: Dominating strategies: player 1 chooses A, player 2 chooses B.

24. Consider the following partial-conflict game played in a non-cooperative manner. The first payoff is to player I; the second is to player II.

<table>
<tr><td></td><td colspan="2" align="center">Player II</td></tr>
<tr><td>Player I</td><td>Choice A</td><td>Choice B</td></tr>
<tr><td>Choice A</td><td>(6, 1)</td><td>(3, 3)</td></tr>
<tr><td>Choice B</td><td>(5, 5)</td><td>(1, 6)</td></tr>
</table>

Discuss the players' possible strategies when this game is played.
Ans: Player I chooses A; player II chooses B.

25. Consider the following partial-conflict game played in a non-cooperative manner. The first payoff is to player I; the second is to player II.

<table>
<tr><td></td><td colspan="2" align="center">Player II</td></tr>
<tr><td>Player I</td><td>Choice A</td><td>Choice B</td></tr>
<tr><td>Choice A</td><td>(1, 9)</td><td>(3, 3)</td></tr>
<tr><td>Choice B</td><td>(5, 5)</td><td>(9, 1)</td></tr>
</table>

Discuss the players' possible strategies when this game is played.
Ans: Player I chooses B; player II chooses A.

26. Construct the game tree for a truel played sequentially, for which the outcomes have the following payoffs. What are the optimal strategies for this game?

Sole survivor	2 point
One of two survivors	4 points
One of three survivors	3 points
Non-survivor	1 point

Ans: First player shoots one of the other players.

27. Construct the game tree for a truel played sequentially, for which the outcomes have the following payoffs. What are the optimal strategies for this game?

Sole survivor	4 point
One of two survivors	3 points
One of three survivors	2 points
Non-survivor	1 point

Ans: No one shoots.

28. Construct the game tree for a truel played sequentially, for which the outcomes have the following payoffs. What are the optimal strategies for this game?

Sole survivor	1 point
One of two survivors	4 points
One of three survivors	3 points
Non-survivor	2 point

Ans: First player shoots one of the other players.

29. In the following two-person zero-sum game, the payoffs represent gains to the row player I and losses to the column player II. Does this game have a saddle point? What is each player's minimax or maximin strategy?

$$\begin{bmatrix} 5 & 7 \\ 4 & 3 \end{bmatrix}$$

Ans: This game has a saddle point at 5. The maximin strategy of player I is to play the 2nd row; the minimax strategy of player II is to play the 2nd column.

30. In the following two-person zero-sum game, the payoffs represent gains to the row player I and losses to the column player II. Does this game have a saddle point? What is each player's minimax or maximin strategy?

$$\begin{bmatrix} 2 & 8 & 6 \\ 7 & 5 & 1 \\ 6 & 8 & 9 \end{bmatrix}$$

Ans: There is no saddle point. The maximin strategy of player I is to play the 3rd row; the minimax strategy of player II is to play the 1st column.

31. In the following two-person zero-sum game, the payoffs represent gains to the row player I and losses to the column player II. Does this game have a saddle point? What is each player's minimax or maximin strategy?

$$\begin{bmatrix} 7 & 3 & 5 & 1 \\ 3 & 4 & 6 & 4 \\ 2 & 8 & 2 & 5 \\ 9 & 7 & 7 & 7 \end{bmatrix}$$

Ans: This game has a saddle point at 6. The maximin strategy of player I is to play the 4th row; the minimax strategy of player II is to play the 4th column.

Chapter 16: Multiple-Choice

1. Determine the check digit that should be appended to the U.S. Postal Service money order identification number 2384943094.
   A) 1   B) 4   C) 6   D) 8
   Ans: A

2. Determine the check digit that should be appended to the U.S. Postal Service money order identification number 5849202911.
   A) 1   B) 4   C) 5   D) 8
   Ans: C

3. Determine the check digit that should be appended to the U.S. Postal Service money order identification number 5428792351.
   A) 1   B) 4   C) 6   D) 8
   Ans: A

4. Suppose a U.S. Postal Service money order is numbered x3843291010, where the first digit is obscured. What is the missing digit?
   A) 4   B) 5   C) 9   D) The missing digit can't be determined.
   Ans: B

5. Suppose a U.S. Postal Service money order is numbered x4839203210, where the first digit is obscured. What is the missing digit?
   A) 4   B) 5   C) 8   D) The missing digit can't be determined.
   Ans: A

6. Determine the check digit that should be appended to the American Express Traveler's Cheque identification number 483920381.
   A) 2   B) 6   C) 7   D) 8
   Ans: C

7. Determine the check digit that should be appended to the American Express Traveler's Cheque identification number 783920381.
   A) 6   B) 5   C) 4   D) 1
   Ans: C

8. Determine the check digit that should be appended to the American Express Traveler's Cheque identification number 293021243.
   A) 1   B) 4   C) 6   D) 8
   Ans: A

9. Suppose an American Express Travelers Cheque is numbered x483920594, where the first digit is obscured. What is the missing digit?
   A) 1   B) 6   C) 8   D) The missing digit can't be determined.
   Ans: A

10. Suppose an American Express Travelers Cheque is numbered x392063210, where the first digit is obscured. What is the missing digit?
    A) 1   B) 4   C) 8   D) The missing digit can't be determined.
    Ans: A

11. Determine the check digit that should be appended to the Avis rental car identification number 483901.
    A) 2   B) 5   C) 7   D) 8
    Ans: B

12. Determine the check digit that should be appended to the Avis rental car identification number 821922.
    A) 3   B) 4   C) 7   D) 8
    Ans: A

13. Is the number 4839212 a legitimate Avis rental car number?
    A) Yes   B) No
    Ans: B

14. Is the number 3910291 a legitimate Avis rental car number?
    A) Yes   B) No
    Ans: B

15. Determine the check digit that should be appended to the UPS identification number 102839414.
    A) 1   B) 3   C) 4   D) 6
    Ans: D

16. Determine the check digit that should be appended to the UPS identification number 112843215.
    A) 1   B) 2   C) 5   D) 6
    Ans: B

17. Is the number 1028343293 a legitimate UPS package number?
    A) Yes   B) No
    Ans: A

18. Is the number 1023894326 a legitimate UPS package number?
    A) Yes   B) No
    Ans: B

19. Determine the check digit that should be appended to the airline ticket identification number 28143298311.
    A) 2   B) 3   C) 4   D) 5
    Ans: A

20. Determine the check digit that should be appended to the airline ticket identification number 85493049210.
    A) 2   B) 3   C) 4   D) 5
    Ans: A

21. Is the number 102432854931 a legitimate airline ticket number?
    A) Yes   B) No
    Ans: B

22. Is the number 103932091202 a legitimate airline ticket number?
    A) Yes   B) No
    Ans: B

23. Determine the check digit that should be appended to the UPC identification number 0 12500 29301.
    A) 0   B) 1   C) 3   D) 9
    Ans: B

24. Determine the check digit that should be appended to the UPC identification number 0 13500 47501.
    A) 0   B) 2   C) 3   D) 8
    Ans: D

25. Determine the check digit that should be appended to the UPC identification number 0 15700 37501.
    A) 0   B) 1   C) 3   D) 7
    Ans: C

26. Is the number 0 11300 84392 4 a legitimate UPC number?
    A) Yes   B) No
    Ans: B

27. Is the number 0 11300 29432 5 a legitimate UPC number?
    A) Yes   B) No
    Ans: B

28. If the UPC number 0 11500 22810 8 is incorrectly entered as 0 11500 28810 8, will the error be detected by the check digit?
    A) Yes   B) No
    Ans: A

29. If the UPC number 0 89901 24334 1 is incorrectly entered as 0 84401 24334 1, will the error be detected by the check digit?
   A) Yes   B) No
   Ans: B

30. Suppose the sixth digit of the UPC number 0 5443x 30250 0 is obscured. What is the missing digit?
   A) 0   B) 3   C) 5   D) The missing digit can't be determined.
   Ans: A

31. Determine the check digit that should be appended to the bank identification number 01200021.
   A) 2   B) 4   C) 7   D) 8
   Ans: D

32. Determine the check digit that should be appended to the bank identification number 05200035.
   A) 1   B) 3   C) 8   D) 9
   Ans: D

33. Determine the check digit that should be appended to the bank identification number 04200052.
   A) 1   B) 3   C) 7   D) 9
   Ans: A

34. Is the number 075000325 a legitimate bank identification number?
   A) Yes   B) No
   Ans: B

35. Is the number 096000361 a legitimate bank identification number?
   A) Yes   B) No
   Ans: B

36. Determine the check digit, as described in the text, that should be appended to the blood bank identification number 312680013325001.
   A) 7   B) 6   C) 5   D) 3
   Ans: C

37. Determine the check digit (as described in the text) that should be appended to the photofinishing identification number 312545006987005.
   A) 4   B) 3   C) 7   D) 6
   Ans: A

38. Determine the check digit (as described in the text) that should be appended to the blood bank identification number 312540016220550.
    A) 1   B) 0   C) 8   D) 2
    Ans: B

39. Is the number 3125700143750015 a legitimate photofinishing identification number, as described in the text?
    A) Yes   B) No
    Ans: A

40. Is the number 3125850025490085 a legitimate blood bank identification number, as described in the text?
    A) Yes   B) No
    Ans: B

41. Determine the check digit that should be appended to the ISBN 0-7167-6531.
    A) 4   B) 5   C) 6   D) 7
    Ans: A

42. Determine the check digit that should be appended to the ISBN 0-7167-9811.
    A) 2   B) 5   C) 6   D) 8
    Ans: B

43. Suppose the fourth digit of the ISBN 0-71x7-1011-0 is obscured. What is the missing digit?
    A) 2   B) 3   C) 6   D) The missing digit can't be determined.
    Ans: C

44. Is the number 0-7167-2431-X a legitimate ISBN?
    A) Yes   B) No
    Ans: B

45. Is the number 0-7167-1532-0 a legitimate ISBN?
    A) Yes   B) No
    Ans: B

46. Suppose the seventh digit of the ISBN 0-7137-1x11-0 is obscured. What is the missing digit?
    A) 2   B) 5   C) 8   D) X
    Ans: C

47. Suppose the first digit of the ISBN x-7127-1011-0 is obscured. What is the missing digit?
    A) 5   B) 6   C) 9   D) 0
    Ans: A

48. Determine the check digit that should be appended to the Postnet code for ZIP+4 code 10010-4525.
A) 2 B) 4 C) 7 D) 8
Ans: A

49. Determine the check digit that should be appended to the Postnet code for ZIP+4 code 47301-5600.
A) 3 B) 4 C) 6 D) 7
Ans: B

50. Suppose the third digit of the Postnet code 282x4-2486-3 is obscured. What is the missing digit?
A) 1 B) 3 C) 7 D) The missing digit can't be determined.
Ans: A

51. Determine the check digit for a money order with identification number 7886482952.
A) 2 B) 3 C) 5 D) 8
Ans: C

52. Determine the check digit for a money order with identification number 9508978667.
A) 2 B) 3 C) 5 D) 8
Ans: A

53. Determine the missing fifth digit for a money order with identification number 3323_336342.
A) 2 B) 3 C) 5 D) 8
Ans: D

54. Determine the check digit for the United Parcel Service (UPS) identification number 946641681.
A) 2 B) 5 C) 6 D) 9
Ans: C

55. Determine the check digit for an airline ticket with number 17511695535.
A) 2 B) 5 C) 6 D) 9
Ans: B

56. Determine the check digit for the ISBN 0-7167-0792.
A) 2 B) 5 C) 6 D) 9
Ans: C

57. Determine the missing ninth digit for the ISBN 0-7167-108_-2.
A) 2 B) 5 C) 6 D) 9
Ans: C

58. Determine the check digit for the UPC number 0 01339 19780.
    A) 2   B) 5   C) 6   D) 9
    Ans: B

59. Determine the missing second digit for the UPC number 4 _6470 32350 8.
    A) 2   B) 5   C) 6   D) 9
    Ans: A

60. The last digit of Master Card number 5123 4567 8901 234 is:
    A) 2   B) 5   C) 6   D) 9
    Ans: B

Chapter 16: Free-Response

1. If the third digit of the U.S. Postal Service money order number 64389235311 is mistyped, can the check digit detect the error? Explain.
   Ans: Yes. All single errors except exchange of 0 and 9 are detected.

2. If the third digit of the American Express Traveler's Cheque number 390124323 is mistyped, can the check digit detect the error? Explain.
   Ans: Not always. If it is replaced by 9, the error is undetected.

3. If the third and fourth digits of the Avis rental car number 3960040 are transposed, can the check digit detect the error? Explain.
   Ans: Yes. The check digit will detect the error.

4. If the last digit of the Avis rental car number 3960040 is mistyped, can the check digit detect the error? Explain.
   Ans: Yes. It is the check digit and will be wrong.

5. A UPC code is reported to read 0-48000-03254-5, but the second digit is read in error. Can the correct second digit be determined?
   Ans: It should be 8.

6. If the last two digits of the UPC code 5-12500-65590-6 are exchanged, can the check digit detect the error? Explain.
   Ans: Yes. The sum will not be correct.

7. A bank identification number is reported to be 017000250, but your source reports that the final digit is difficult to read and may be wrong. Is this a viable bank identification number? If not, can the correct final digit be determined?
   Ans: No. It is 5.

8. If the third and fourth digits of the bank identification number 250150205 are transposed, can the check digit detect the error? Explain.
   Ans: Yes. The sum will be incorrect.

9. If the third and fourth digits of the blood bank identification number 4128001234567896 are exchanged, can the check digit, as described in the text, detect the error? Explain.
   Ans: Yes. The change affects the sum.

10. The last digit of the photofinishing identification number 4128001243890110 (as described in the text) may be wrong. If not, can the correct final digit be determined?
    Ans: No. The final digit should be 6.

11. Is 0-1370-2990-X a viable ISBN number? If not, can the second digit be changed to produce a viable ISBN number?
    Ans: Yes.

12. If the first and second digits of the ISBN number 0-7167-2378-6 are transposed, can the check digit detect the error? Explain.
    Ans: Yes. The sum will no longer be a multiple of 11.

13. If the third and fourth digits of the ISBN number 0-7167-4782-0 are transposed, can the check digit detect the error? Explain.
    Ans: Yes. The sum will no longer be a multiple of 11.

14. If the first two digits of the Postnet code 1001025001 are transposed, can the check digit detect the error? Explain.
    Ans: No. Exchanges are not detected.

15. If the first digit of the Postnet code 1001025001 is mistyped, can the check digit detect the error? Explain.
    Ans: Yes. The sum will be incorrect.

16. The ISBN code system detects all single-digit errors and single transpositions. Even so, it has a major drawback. What is it?
    Ans: It requires the use of "X."

17. Why are there different methods of creating check digits?
    Ans: There are different requirements and different costs for error in various codes.

18. How are bar codes used by the U.S. Postal Service to encode ZIP codes?
    Ans: They are used on letters to automate address routing.

19. What are guard bars?
    Ans: They are end marks to frame the Postnet code.

20. Where is the check digit of a VIN located?
    Ans: In the center, at the ninth position.

21. If the first and third digits of a UPC code are transposed, can the check digit detect the error? Explain.
    Ans: No. The sum will be unchanged.

22. If the first and third digits of a bank identification number are transposed, can the check digit detect the error? Explain.
    Ans: Yes. Digits have different weights.

23. If the first and third digits of a food bank identification number, as described in the text, are transposed, can the check digit detect the error? Explain.
    Ans: Yes. Digits have different weights.

24. Is the number 0-499290-3 a viable UPC Version E number? If not, change the final digit to produce a viable UPC Version E number.
    Ans: Yes.

25. Is the number 0-413882-5 a viable UPC Version E number? If not, change the final digit to produce a viable UPC Version E number.
    Ans: No. Change to 0.

26. Determine if the Master Card number 5211 2846 5342 1386 is valid.
    Ans: This card number is not valid.

27. Is 20-7039-362-3 a valid ISBN? If not, change the check digit to correct the error.
    Ans: This ISBN is valid.

28. Is 1023798 a valid Avis rental car identification number? If not, change the check digit to correct the error.
    Ans: This number is not valid. The check digit should be 4, so the correct number is 1023794.

29. Determine the check digit for a money order with identification number 5600517526.
    Ans: 1

30. Determine the check digit for an airline ticket with number 76288305230.
    Ans: 4

Chapter 17: Multiple-Choice

1. Use the Venn diagram method to determine the code word of the message 1010.
   A) 1010110   B) 1010111   C) 1010001   D) 1010011
   Ans: C

2. Use the Venn diagram method to determine the code word of the message 1001.
   A) 1001111   B) 1001101   C) 1001001   D) 1001010
   Ans: B

3. Use the nearest-neighbor Venn diagram method to decode the received word 1101101.
   A) 1001   B) 0100   C) 1101   D) 1011
   Ans: A

4. Use the nearest-neighbor Venn diagram method to decode the received word 1011001.
   A) 1011   B) 1010   C) 1001   D) 0010
   Ans: B

5. Suppose the Venn diagram message 1110 is received as 1110001. Will the original message be recovered?
   A) Yes   B) No
   Ans: B

6. Suppose the Venn diagram coded message 1110 is received as 1110110. Will the original message be recovered?
   A) Yes   B) No
   Ans: A

7. What is the distance between received words 1100101 and 1101010?
   A) 1   B) 2   C) 3   D) 4
   Ans: D

8. What is the distance between received words 1001010 and 1010010?
   A) 1   B) 2   C) 3   D) 4
   Ans: B

9. Add the binary sequences 1001010 and 1010010. How many 1s digits are in the sum?
   A) 2   B) 3   C) 4   D) Another answer
   Ans: A

10. Add the binary sequences 0100110 and 1101010. How many 1s digits are in the sum?
    A) 1   B) 3   C) 5   D) Another answer
    Ans: B

11. If two binary sequences that each have an even number of 1s are added, the sum:
    A)   will always have an even number of 1s.
    B)   will sometimes have an even number of 1s.
    C)   will always have an odd number of 1s.
    Ans: A

12. Let C be the code { 1100, 1010, 1001, 0110, 0101, 0011}. Which of the following is a true statement?
    A)   The code can detect and correct any single-digit error.
    B)   The code can detect any single-digit error and correct some but not all single-digit errors.
    C)   The code can detect any single-digit error, but cannot correct any single-digit error.
    D)   The code can detect some but not all single-digit errors.
    Ans: C

13. Let C be the code { 110, 101, 011, 000}. Which of the following is a true statement?
    A)   The code can detect and correct any single-digit error.
    B)   The code can detect any single-digit error and can correct some but not all single-digit errors.
    C)   The code can detect any single-digit error, but cannot correct any single-digit error.
    D)   The code can detect some but not all single-digit errors.
    Ans: C

14. You propose a code in which each digit of the message word is repeated to form the code word. For example, 101 is coded as 110011. Which of the following is a true statement?
    A)   The code can detect and correct any single-digit error and any double error.
    B)   The code can detect and correct any single-digit error and detect any double error, but cannot correct every double error.
    C)   The code can detect and correct any single-digit error, but cannot detect every double error.
    D)   The code can detect any single-digit error, but cannot correct every single-digit error.
    Ans: D

15. You propose a code in which each three-digit binary message word a_1 a_2 a_3 has appended a parity-check digit $c_1 = a_1 + a_2 + a_3$. Which of the following is a true statement?
    A)   The code can detect and correct any single-digit error.
    B)   The code can detect any single-digit error and correct some but not all single-digit errors.
    C)   The code can detect any single-digit error, but cannot correct any single-digit error.
    D)   The code can detect some but not all single-digit errors.
    Ans: C

16. You propose a code in which each two-digit binary message word a_1 a_2 has appended a parity-check digit $c_1 = a_1 + a_2$. Which of the following is a true statement?
    A)   The code can detect and correct any single-digit error.
    B)   The code can detect any single-digit error and correct some but not all single-digit errors.
    C)   The code can detect any single-digit error, but cannot correct any single-digit error.
    D)   The code can detect some but not all single-digit errors.
    Ans: C

17. You propose a code in which each three-digit binary message word a_1 a_2 a_3 has appended two parity-check digits $c_1 = a_1 + a_2$ and $c_2 = a_2 + a_3$. Which of the following is a true statement?
    A)   The code can detect and correct any single-digit error.
    B)   The code can detect any single-digit error and correct some but not all single-digit errors.
    C)   The code can detect any single-digit error, but cannot correct any single-digit error.
    D)   The code can detect some but not all single-digit errors.
    Ans: C

18. For the code C = { 00000,11111}, how many errors would have to occur during transmission for a received word to be encoded incorrectly?
    A) 2   B) 3   C) 4   D) 5
    Ans: B

19. For the code C = { 000000,111111}, how many errors would have to occur during transmission for a received word to be encoded incorrectly?
    A) 2   B) 3   C) 4   D) 5
    Ans: B

20. For the code C = { 000000, 000111, 111000, 111111}, how many errors would have to occur during transmission for a received word to be encoded incorrectly?
    A) 1   B) 2   C) 3   D) 6
    Ans: B

21. Let C be the code { 1010, 0101, 1111, 0000}. What is the weight of this code?
    A) 0   B) 1   C) 2   D) 4
    Ans: C

22. Let C be the code { 101010, 010101, 111111, 000000}. What is the weight of this code?
    A) 0   B) 1   C) 3   D) 6
    Ans: C

23. Use the encoding scheme A $\rightarrow$ 0, B $\rightarrow$ 10, C $\rightarrow$ 11 to encode the sequence ABACAB.
    A) 010011010   B) 01011010   C) 01001101   D) Another sequence
    Ans: A

24. Use the encoding scheme A → 0, B → 10, C → 11 to decode the sequence 0101101011.
    A) ABCABC B) ABACABAC C) ABCBCB D) Another sequence
    Ans: A

25. Use the Caesar cipher to encrypt the message ROME BURNS.
    A) URPH EXUQV   C) HORU VQUXE
    B) OLJB YROKP   D) Another sequence
    Ans: A

26. Use the Caesar cipher to decrypt the message ZHVW.
    A) WEST B) EAST C) REST D) Another message
    Ans: A

27. Using modular arithmetic, $(13 \cdot 21)$ mod 10 is equal to:
    A) 2. B) 3. C) 7. D) Another number.
    Ans: B

28. Using modular arithmetic, $(13 \cdot 21)$ mod 12 is equal to:
    A) 3. B) 9. C) 10. D) Another number.
    Ans: B

29. Using modular arithmetic, 4^3 mod 10 is equal to:
    A) 2. B) 4. C) 6. D) Another number.
    Ans: B

30. Using modular arithmetic, 5^3 mod 11 is equal to:
    A) 0. B) 4. C) 7. D) Another number.
    Ans: B

31. Using modular arithmetic, 15^3 mod 41 is equal to:
    A) 0. B) 13. C) 31. D) Another number.
    Ans: B

32. Using modular arithmetic, 13^3 mod 34 is equal to:
    A) 13. B) 21. C) 30. D) Another number.
    Ans: B

33. For the RSA scheme with p = 5, q = 11, and r = 7, compute the value of m.
    A) 10 B) 20 C) 40 D) 55
    Ans: B

34. For the RSA scheme with p = 5, q = 19, and r = 7, compute the value of m.
    A) 18 B) 36 C) 72 D) 95
    Ans: B

35. For the RSA scheme with p = 17 and q = 23, which of the following could be chosen as a value for r?
A) 6   B) 4   C) 9   D) 16
Ans: C

36. For the RSA scheme with m = 8 and r = 5, what is the value of s?
A) 1   B) 2   C) 3   D) 5
Ans: D

37. For the RSA scheme with m = 9 and r = 5, what is the value of s?
A) 1   B) 2   C) 4   D) 5
Ans: B

38. Use the RSA scheme with n = 85 and r = 7 to determine the message sent for the string "14."
A) 11   B) 13   C) 59   D) 74
Ans: D

39. Use the RSA scheme with n = 85 and r = 7 to determine the message sent for the string "22."
A) 13   B) 30   C) 69   D) 78
Ans: D

40. Use the RSA scheme with n = 133 and r = 11 to determine the message sent for the string "8."
A) 8   B) 31   C) 50   D) 88
Ans: C

41. Use the RSA scheme with n = 133 and r = 11 to determine the message sent for the string "10."
A) 11   B) 33   C) 110   D) 121
Ans: B

42. Use the RSA scheme with n = 85 and s = 3 to decode the message "7."
A) 3   B) 21   C) 62   D) 63
Ans: A

43. Use the RSA scheme with n = 85 and s = 3 to decode the message "13."
A) 39   B) 46   C) 63   D) 72
Ans: D

44. Use the RSA scheme with n = 133 and s = 5 to decode the message "32."
A) 21   B) 27   C) 53   D) 128
Ans: D

45. Use the RSA scheme with n = 133 and s = 5 to decode the message "29."
    A) 12   B) 15   C) 17   D) 22
    Ans: D

46. When using the Venn diagram for determining length seven binary code words for length
    four messages, which of the following are true statements?

    I: Every code word has an even number of 1s.
    II: Every possible string of seven binary digits is a code word.
    III: Every possible string of seven binary digits can be read as a code word or a code
    word
    with a single-digit error.
    A) I only   B) I and III only   C) II only   D) III only
    Ans: D

47. When using the Venn diagram for determining length seven binary code words for length
    four messages, what is the minimum distance between two code words?
    A) 7   B) 3   C) 2   D) 1
    Ans: B

48. When using the Venn diagram for determining length seven binary code words for length
    four messages, what is the weight of the code?
    A) 7   B) 3   C) 2   D) 1
    Ans: B

49. If a code is used to detect and correct single-digit errors, which of the following are true
    statements?

    I: Its weight should be at least 2.
    II: The distance between any two code words should be at least 2.
    A) I only   B) II only   C) Both I and II   D) Neither I nor II
    Ans: C

50. Which of the following are true statements?

    I: Morse code is a variable-length code.
    II: Morse code is an example of a data compression code.
    A) I only   B) II only   C) Both I and II   D) Neither I nor II
    Ans: C

51. Use the Caesar cipher to encrypt the message PICNIC.
    A) TMGRMG   B) SLFQLF   C) IBVGBV   D) RKEPKE
    Ans: B

52. Use the Vigenere cipher with the key word HANK to encrypt the message HOME RUN.
    A) OOZO YUA   B) OOZL RHU   C) HZMR RFN   D) PPAP ZVB
    Ans: A

53. Use the Vigenere cipher with the key word DRUID to encrypt the message INCOMING GIANT.
    A)   MFXXQMFB PMEFO   C)   LEWWPLEA OLDEN
    B)   ZHKRPZHO JLRHB   D)   HNTRLIEJ FIRQS
    Ans: C

54. Given that BEST was used as the key word to encrypt with the Vigenere cipher, decrypt the message BTJBDSL.
    A) PATRIOT   B) POPCORN   C) AIRPORT   D) APRICOT
    Ans: D

55. Given that PLEASE was used as the key word to encrypt QCMNY JDZH with the Vigenere cipher, decrypt the message.
    A) BRING CASH   B) BRING FOOD   C) BRING FISH   D) BRING MORE
    Ans: B

56. What is the distance between received words 0111011 and 0101001?
    A) 1   B) 2   C) 3   D) 4
    Ans: B

57. What is the distance between received words 1101000 and 1100110?
    A) 1   B) 2   C) 3   D) 4
    Ans: C

58. Use the nearest-neighbor Venn diagram method to decode the received word 0100110.
    A) 0110   B) 0010   C) 0100   D) 0101
    Ans: D

59. Use the Venn diagram method to determine the code word of the message 0111.
    A) 0111011   B) 0111001   C) 0111010   D) 0111110
    Ans: B

60. Use the Venn diagram method to determine the code word of the message 1101.
    A) 1101011   B) 1101001   C) 1101000   D) 1101110
    Ans: C

61. The expression $\neg (P \wedge Q)$ is logically equivalent to:
    A) $P \vee Q$ B) $\neg P \vee \neg Q$ C) $\neg P \wedge \neg Q$ D) $\neg P \vee Q$
    Ans: B

62. The expression P ∧ Q is called the _____ of P and Q.
    A) negation   B) correlation   C) conjunction   D) disjunction
    Ans: C

63. The expression P ∨ Q is called the _____ of P and Q.
    A) negation   B) correlation   C) conjunction   D) disjunction
    Ans: D

Chapter 17: Free-Response

1. Suppose you create a binary code by appending to each message word a_1 a_2 a_3 a_4 three parity-check digits $c_1 = a_1 + a_2 + a_4$, $c_2 = a_2 + a_3 + a_4$, and $c_3 = a_2 + a_3 + a_4$. Will the resulting code detect and/or correct all single-digit errors?
   Ans: It detects all singles, but doesn't correct all.

2. Suppose you create a binary code by appending to each message word a_1 a_2 a_3 two parity-check digits $c_1 = a_1 + a_2$ and $c_2 = a_2 + a_3$. Will the resulting code detect and/or correct all single-digit errors?
   Ans: It detects all singles, but doesn't correct all.

3. Suppose you create a binary code by appending to each message word a_1 a_2 a_3 three parity-check digits $c_1 = a_1 + a_2$, $c_2 = a_2 + a_3$, and $c_3 = a_1 + a_3$. Will the resulting code detect and/or correct all single-digit errors?
   Ans: Yes. The weight is 3.

4. Append a fourth check digit to each seven-digit code created by the Venn diagram method $c_4 = a_1 + a_2 + a_3 + a_4$. With this additional check digit, can double errors be detected and/or corrected?
   Ans: Yes. The weight is 4.

5. For the message word a_1 a_2 a_3 a_4, append four check digits $c_1 = a_1$, $c_2 = a_2$, $c_3 = a_3$ and $c_4 = a_4$. Will the resulting code detect and/or correct all single-digit errors? Can double errors be detected and/or corrected?
   Ans: It detects all single errors, but doesn't correct all. It does not detect all double-digit errors.

6. Construct a code for five-digit binary message words that has four parity-check digits. Can it detect and/or correct single-digit errors?
   Ans: For example, $c_1 = a_1 + a_2$; $c_2 = a_2 + a_3$; $c_3 = a_3 + a_4$; $c_4 = a_4 + a_5$. It detects all singles, but doesn't correct all.

7. Construct a code for five-digit binary message words that has three parity-check digits. Can it detect and/or correct single-digit errors?
   Ans: For example, $c_1 = a_1 + a_2 + a_3$; $c_2 = a_2 + a_3 + a_4$; $c_3 = a_3 + a_4 + a_5$. It detects all singles, but doesn't correct all.

8. Create a binary linear code with eight possible code words that can detect and correct any single-digit error.
   Ans: For example, { 111000000, 000111000, 000000111, 111000111, 111111000, 000111111, 111111111, 000000000}.

9. Create a binary linear code with four possible code words that can detect and correct any single-digit or double-digit error.
   Ans: For example, { 11111111, 11110000, 00001111, 00000000}.

10. Give an example of a circumstance where the code C = { 00000, 11111} could be of use.
    Ans: It detects and corrects all single and double errors.

11. Use the Caesar cipher to encrypt the message ABANDON HOPE.
    Ans: DEDQGRQ KRSH

12. Use the Caesar cipher to decrypt the message DOO LV ZHOO.
    Ans: ALL IS WELL

13. How does the weight of a code compare to the number of errors that can be detected?
    Ans: If a code has weight t, then t-1 errors can be detected.

14. How does the weight of a code compare to the number of errors that can be corrected?
    Ans: If a code has weight t, then if t is even, (t-2)/2 errors can be corrected; if t is odd, (t-1)/2 errors can be corrected.

15. Using modular arithmetic, determine $(42 \cdot 17)$ mod 23.
    Ans: 1

16. Using modular arithmetic, determine $(16 \cdot 31)$ mod 41.
    Ans: 4

17. Using modular arithmetic, determine 12^7 mod 53.
    Ans: 45

18. Using modular arithmetic, determine 17^7 mod 41.
    Ans: 13

19. Determine the value of s so that 9s = 1 mod 17.
    Ans: 2

20. Determine the value of s so that 11s = 1 mod 13.
    Ans: 6

21. For the RSA scheme with p = 5, q = 11, choose a value for r. Then encode the message sent for the string "23."
    Ans: For example, choose r = 3. Then 23^3 mod 55 is 12.

22. For the RSA scheme selected above, decode the message "7," if possible.
    Ans: As above, if r = 3 and m = 20, s = 7. So 7^7 mod 55 is 28.

23. For the RSA scheme with p = 17, q = 23, choose a value for r. Then encode the message sent for the string "13."
    Ans: For example, if r = 7, then 13^7 mod 391 is 55.

24. For the RSA scheme selected above, decode the message "7," if possible.
    Ans: If r = 7 and m = 176, then s = 25. So 7^{25} mod 391 is 44.

25. Why is RSA considered a superior encryption scheme?
    Ans: It is a public key scheme that is effectively impossible to break.

26. Add the pair of binary sequences 1101001 and 1010011.
    Ans: 0111010

27. Add the pair of binary sequences 1001010 and 1010010.
    Ans: 0001000

28. Use the Vigenere cipher with the key word SPRING to encrypt the message APRIL SHOWERS.
    Ans: SEIQY YZDNMEY

29. Given that TROUT was used as the key word to encrypt ZFBY YBJVCGZ with the Vigenere cipher, decrypt the message.
    Ans: GONE FISHING

30. Use the nearest-neighbor Venn diagram method to decode the received word 1011000.
    Ans: 1111

31. Construct the truth table for ¬ (P ∧ Q).
    Ans:

P	Q	¬(P ∧ Q)
T	T	F
T	F	T
F	T	T
F	F	T

32. Construct the truth table for ¬(P ⊕ Q).
    Ans:

P	Q	¬(P ⊕ Q)
T	T	T
T	F	F
F	T	F
F	F	T

33. Construct the truth table for ¬P ⊕ ¬Q.
    Ans:

P	Q	¬P ⊕ ¬Q
T	T	F
T	F	T
F	T	T
F	F	F

Chapter 18: Multiple-Choice

1. You own a painting whose dimensions are 24 inches by 30 inches. If you create a slide of this work so that the longest side of the image is 1 inch, what is the scaling factor for the slide?
   A) 1/24   B) 1/30   C) 1/720   D) 4/5
   Ans: B

2. You own a painting whose dimensions are 24 inches by 30 inches. If you create a slide of this work so that the longest side of the image is 1 inch, what is the length of the smaller side of the slide image?
   A) 1 inch   B) 4/5 inch   C) 16/25 inch   D) 1/5 inch
   Ans: B

3. You own a painting whose dimensions are 24 inches by 30 inches. If you create a slide of this work so that the longest side of the image is 1 inch, what is the area of the slide image?
   A)   1 square inch   C)   16/25 square inch
   B)   4/5 square inch   D)   5/4 square inches
   Ans: B

4. You own a painting whose dimensions are 24 inches by 30 inches. If you create a full-size copy of this painting as a poster, what is the scaling factor for the poster?
   A) 1   B) 4/5   C) 1/24   D) 1/30
   Ans: A

5. You own a painting whose dimensions are 24 inches by 30 inches. If you create a postcard-sized reproduction of the painting whose area is 20 square inches, what is the scaling factor for the reproduction?
   A) 1/4   B) 1/6   C) 1/36   D) 2/3
   Ans: B

6. The cost of photographic paper is nearly proportional to the area of the paper. You own a painting whose dimensions are 24 inches by 30 inches. You create a small photographic reproduction whose smaller side is 5 inches. What is the scaling factor for this reproduction?
   A) 0.2083   B) 0.1667   C) 0.0434   D) 0.0278
   Ans: A

7. The cost of photographic paper is nearly proportional to the area of the paper. You own a painting whose dimensions are 24 inches by 30 inches. You create a large photographic reproduction whose smaller side is 8 inches. How does its area compare with that of the original painting?
   A) 0.3333   B) 0.2667   C) 0.1111   D) 0.0711
   Ans: A

8. The cost of photographic paper is nearly proportional to the area of the paper. You own a painting whose dimensions are 24 inches by 30 inches. You create a small photographic reproduction whose smaller side is 5 inches, and a large photographic reproduction whose smaller side is 8 inches. If the paper required for the small reproduction costs $1.50, how much will the paper required for the large reproduction cost?
A) $1.90   B) $2.40   C) $3.84   D) $4.50
Ans: C

9. A scale model of a truck is 1.5 inches high. If the actual truck is 9 feet high, what is the scaling factor of the model?
A) 1 to 6   B) 1 to 18   C) 1 to 36   D) 1 to 72
Ans: D

10. A scale model of a truck is 5 inches long. If the model is built to a scale of 1 to 54, what is the length of the actual truck?
A) 270 feet   B) 101 feet   C) 36.7 feet   D) 22.5 feet
Ans: D

11. A model of a truck is built to a scale of 1 to 54. If the model will hold 7 cubic inches, how much will the actual truck hold?
A) 378 cubic feet   B) 638 cubic feet   C) 1544 cubic feet   D) 4536 cubic feet
Ans: B

12. A model of a truck is built to a scale of 1 to 54. If the model casts a shadow of 8 square inches, how large a shadow will the actual truck cast?
A) 36 square feet   B) 162 square feet   C) 288 square feet   D) 729 square feet
Ans: B

13. Last summer you grew a giant squash that was 6 feet long and proportionally similar to your other squash. These squash tend to be about 1.5 feet long and weigh about a pound. About how much do you think the giant squash weighs?
A)   Less than 10 pounds   C)   Between 20 and 50 pounds
B)   Between 10 and 20 pounds   D)   More than 50 pounds
Ans: D

14. Last summer you grew a giant squash that was 4.5 feet long and proportionally similar to your other squash. These squash tend to be about 1.5 feet long and weigh about a pound. About how much do you think the giant squash weighs?
A)   Less than 10 pounds   C)   Between 20 and 50 pounds
B)   Between 10 and 20 pounds   D)   More than 50 pounds
Ans: C

15. Artificial Christmas trees tend to be proportional in shape. If a 4-foot tree needs approximately 60 ornaments to cover the outer limbs of the tree, how many ornaments will a 6-foot tree need?
    A) Approximately 90 ornaments
    C) Approximately 135 ornaments
    B) Approximately 120 ornaments
    D) Approximately 150 ornaments
    Ans: C

16. Artificial Christmas trees tend to be proportional in shape. If a 4-foot tree needs about two strings of lights, what size tree would need five strings of lights?
    A) A tree shorter than 6 feet
    C) A tree between 8 and 9 feet tall
    B) A tree between 6 and 8 feet tall
    D) A tree taller than 9 feet
    Ans: B

17. Christmas trees tend to be proportional in shape. You have a tree skirt that is circular and with diameter 3 feet, which you bought for a 7-foot tree. If you have a 5-foot tree this year, what size tree skirt will you need? (Round to the nearest size.)
    A) A skirt whose diameter is 2.5 feet
    C) A skirt whose diameter is 1.5 feet
    B) A skirt whose diameter is 2 feet
    D) A skirt whose diameter is 1 foot
    Ans: B

18. In 1965 powdered gelatine cost 10 cents per box at the grocery store. If the 1965 CPI is 31.5 and the 1999 CPI is 166.2, compute this cost in 1999 dollars.
    A) 13 cents   B) 19 cents   C) 48 cents   D) 53 cents
    Ans: D

19. In 1976 a roast beef sandwich cost 89 cents at a local fast food shop. If the 1976 CPI is 56.9 and the 1999 CPI is 166.2, compute this cost in 1999 dollars.
    A) 31 cents   B) $1.43   C) $1.93   D) $2.60
    Ans: D

20. In 1999 a compact car can cost approximately $14,000. What is this cost in 1990 dollars, the year that you bought your last car? (Assume the 1999 CPI is 166.2 and the 1990 CPI is 130.7.)
    A) Approximately $9300
    C) Approximately $11,010
    B) Approximately $13,940
    D) Approximately $17,803
    Ans: C

21. You bought a house for $130,000 in 1999. The previous owner paid $50,000 for the house in 1980. Comparing the converted cost, who paid more for the house? (Assume the 1999 CPI is 166.2 and the 1980 CPI is 82.4.)
    A) You paid much more.
    B) The previous owner paid much more.
    C) You both paid approximately the same amount.
    Ans: A

22. The minimum wage in 1999 is \$5.15. What is the equivalent amount in 1942 dollars? (Assume the 1999 CPI is 166.2 and the 1942 CPI is 16.3.)
    A) About 47 cents   B) About 49 cents   C) About 51 cents   D) About 53 cents
    Ans: C

23. You bought a house in 1999 for \$140,000. The previous owner paid \$55,000 for the same house in 1976. Comparing the converted costs, who paid more for the house? (Assume the 1999 CPI is 166.2 and the 1976 CPI is 56.9.)
    A)   You paid more.   C)   You both paid about the same.
    B)   The previous owner paid more.
    Ans: B

24. Apples cost about \$1.75 Canadian dollars per kilogram in Canada. If a Canadian dollar exchanges for 75 U.S. cents and a kilogram is about 2.2 pounds, what is the equivalent cost in U.S. dollars?
    A)   \$0.60 U.S. per pound   C)   \$2.89 U.S. per pound
    B)   \$1.06 U.S. per pound   D)   \$5.13 U.S. per pound
    Ans: A

25. Ground steak costs about \$2.50 per pound in the United States. If an Australian dollar exchanges for 80 U.S. cents and a kilogram is about 2.2 pounds, what is the equivalent cost in Australian dollars?
    A)   \$0.91 per kilogram   C)   \$4.40 per kilogram
    B)   \$1.42 per kilogram   D)   \$6.88 per kilogram
    Ans: D

26. Trout costs about \$6.50 per pound in the United States. If a Canadian dollar exchanges for 75 U.S. cents and a kilogram is about 2.2 pounds, what is the equivalent cost in Canadian dollars?
    A)   \$2.22 per kilogram   C)   \$10.73 per kilogram
    B)   \$3.94 per kilogram   D)   \$19.07 per kilogram
    Ans: D

27. The weight of a block of granite 1 ft × 2 ft × 4 ft is 1320 lbs. If it stands on a small face (1 ft × 2 ft), what is the pressure on the bottom face?
    A) 1.15 lb/in^2 B) 2.29 lb/in^2 C) 4.58 lb/in^2 D) 9.17 lb/in^2
    Ans: C

28. The weight of a block of granite 1 ft × 2 ft × 4 ft is 1320 lbs. If it stands on a large face (4 ft × 2 ft), what is the pressure on the bottom face?
    A) 1.15 lb/in^2 B) 2.29 lb/in^2 C) 4.58 lb/in^2 D) 9.17 lb/in^2
    Ans: A

29. The weight of a block of granite 1 ft × 2 ft × 4 ft is 1320 lbs. If twelve blocks are used to build a wall 8 ft high, 12 ft long, and 1 ft wide, what is the pressure on the bottom faces?
A) 4.58 lb/in^2 B) 9.17 lb/in^2 C) 18.3 lb/in^2 D) 36.7 lb/in^2
Ans: B

30. A granite sculpture weighs approximately 4500 lbs. If a smaller version 2/3 the height of the original is created from granite, how much will it weigh?
A)   Approximately 3675 lbs.   C)   Approximately 2000 lbs.
B)   Approximately 3000 lbs.   D)   Approximately 1300 lbs.
Ans: D

31. A granite sculpture weighs approximately 4500 lbs. If a smaller version 3/4 the height of the original is created from granite, how much will it weigh?
A)   Approximately 3900 lbs.   C)   Approximately 2500 lbs.
B)   Approximately 3475 lbs.   D)   Approximately 1900 lbs.
Ans: D

32. A wooden carving of an eagle stands 2 inches high and weighs approximately 3 ounces. If a larger carving made from the same material stands 5 feet high, how much will it weigh?
A)   Approximately 50 lbs.   C)   Approximately 170 lbs.
B)   Approximately 70 lbs.   D)   Approximately 5000 lbs.
Ans: D

33. A small steel spoon is 6 inches long and weighs approximately 4 ounces. If it is used as a model for a large steel spoon 4 feet long to be installed at the local cafe, how much would it weigh?
A)   Approximately 16 lbs.   C)   Approximately 128 lbs.
B)   Approximately 32 lbs.   D)   Approximately 2048 lbs.
Ans: C

34. A small steel spoon is 6 inches long and weighs approximately 4 ounces. If it is used as a model for a large steel spoon to be constructed from melting approximately 200 lbs. of steel spoons, how long will the large spoon be?
A)   Approximately 4.6 ft   C)   Approximately 10 ft
B)   Approximately 7.4 ft   D)   Approximately 14 ft
Ans: A

35. An artist wishes to melt 2000 copper pennies to create a large penny proportional to an ordinary penny. The diameter of a penny is approximately 3/4 in. What will be the diameter of the large penny?
A)   Approximately 0.78 ft   C)   Approximately 5 ft
B)   Approximately 2.2 ft   D)   Approximately 9.4 ft
Ans: A

36. An artist wishes to melt copper pennies to create a large penny proportional to an ordinary penny and with diameter 5 inches. An ordinary penny has diameter 3/4 in. How many pennies will be needed?
   A)   Approximately 10
   B)   Approximately 50
   C)   Approximately 150
   D)   Approximately 300
   Ans: D

37. A sparrow has a minimum speed of about 20 miles per hour. If a robin is twice as long as a sparrow and proportional in shape, what is the minimum speed of a robin?
   A)   40 miles per hour
   B)   28 miles per hour
   C)   14 miles per hour
   D)   10 miles per hour
   Ans: B

38. A sparrow has a minimum speed of about 20 miles per hour. If a blue jay is five times as long as a sparrow and proportional in shape, what is the minimum speed of a blue jay?
   A)   100 miles per hour
   B)   45 miles per hour
   C)   9 miles per hour
   D)   4 miles per hour
   Ans: B

39. A spherical balloon has a circumference of 10 inches. If it expands to twice the volume, what happens to its surface area?
   A)   Its surface area more than doubles.
   B)   Its surface area doubles.
   C)   Its surface area increases but does not double.
   Ans: C

40. A spherical balloon has a circumference of 10 inches. If it expands so that its surface area is doubled, what happens to its volume?
   A)   Its volume more than doubles.
   B)   Its volume doubles.
   C)   Its volume increases but does not double.
   Ans: A

41. A spherical balloon has a circumference of 10 inches. If it expands to twice the volume, what happens to its circumference?
   A)   Its circumference more than doubles.
   B)   Its circumference doubles.
   C)   Its circumference increases but does not double.
   Ans: C

42. Assuming that the sail of the *Dimetrodon* developed to dissipate heat when an individual doubled in weight, how much did the sail grow?
    A) It more than doubled in surface area.
    B) It doubled in surface area.
    C) It grew, but did not double in surface area.
    Ans: B

43. When a bird doubles its weight, how much do its wings grow?
    A) They more than double in surface area.
    B) They double in surface area.
    C) They grow, but do not double in surface area.
    Ans: A

44. A baby's head is about 1/3 its length; an adult's head is about 1/7 its length. This type of growth is called:
    A) allometric growth.   C) geometric growth.
    B) proportional growth.   D) isometric growth.
    Ans: A

45. What is the value of the following fraction?
$$\frac{\log 24 - \log 15}{\log 43 - \log 24}$$

    A) 0.806   B) 0.558   C) 0.474   D) 0.325
    Ans: A

46. What is the value of the following fraction?
$$\frac{\log 73 - \log 15}{\log 15 - \log 6}$$

    A) 4.827   B) 1.947   C) 1.727   D) 0.809
    Ans: C

47. If points (1,23) and (3,38) lie on the graph of $y = bx^a$, solve for a.
    A) $a = 0.200$ B) $a = 0.457$ C) $a = 0.810$ D) $a = 1.235$
    Ans: B

48. If points (1,32) and (3,75) lie on the graph of $\log y = bx^a$, solve for a.
    A) $a = 0.775$ B) $a = 0.929$ C) $a = 1.077$ D) $a = 1.156$
    Ans: A

49. If points (0.4, 26) and (1.2, 41) lie on the graph of
$$\log y = B + a \log x$$
solve for a.
    A) $a = 0.415$ B) $a = 0.664$ C) $a = 0.846$ D) $a = 1.273$
    Ans: A

50. If points (0.4, 25) and (1.2, 53) lie on the graph of
$$\log y = B + a \log x$$
solve for a.
    A) $a = 0.684$ B) $a = 0.916$ C) $a = 1.182$ D) $a = 1.544$
    Ans: A

51. A dog food company sells food in cans of two sizes. A "petite" can is 4 inches tall and a "super" can is 1 foot tall. The two types of cans are geometrically similar in shape. What is the linear scaling factor that scales a petite can to the size of a super can?
    A) 1/4   B) 1/3   C) 3   D) 4
    Ans: C

52. A dog food company sells food in cans of two sizes. A "petite" can is 4 inches tall and a "super" can is 1 foot tall. The two types of cans are geometrically similar in shape. The petite can contains 4 cents worth of metal. What is the value of the metal in the super can?
    A) 48 cents   B) 36 cents   C) 16 cents   D) 12 cents
    Ans: B

53. A dog food company sells food in cans of two sizes. A "petite" can is 4 inches tall and a "super" can is 1 foot tall. The two types of cans are geometrically similar in shape. It costs the company 55 cents to produce the dog food in the super can. How much does it cost to produce the dog food in the petite can?
    A) 2 cents   B) 6 cents   C) 14 cents   D) 18 cents
    Ans: A

54. Suppose the radius of a sphere is halved. How does the sphere's new volume compare with its former volume?
    A)   The sphere's new volume is one-half of the former volume.
    B)   The sphere's new volume is one-fourth of the former volume.
    C)   The sphere's new volume is one-eighth of the former volume.
    D)   The sphere's new volume is the same as the former volume.
    Ans: C

55. Kay buys a paperback book that is marked $6.99 U.S. and $9.99 Canadian. She uses this information to estimate that the exchange rate is $1 U.S. =
    A) $2.33 Canadian.   C) $0.70 Canadian.
    B) $1.43 Canadian.   D) $0.43 Canadian.
    Ans: B

56. While vacationing, Mike buys a hat for 71 pesos in a shop in Mexico City. The exchange rate at the time of his visit is $1 U.S. = 9.48 pesos. What was the cost of the hat in U.S. dollars?
    A) $13.35   B) $7.49   C) $6.73   D) $2.48
    Ans: B

57. Karen's car gets 27 miles per gallon. What is this in kilometers per liter?
    A) 4.43 km/liter   B) 11.5 km/liter   C) 43.2 km/liter   D) 63.5 km/liter
    Ans: B

58. An advertisement claims that a bottle of Brand Z mouthwash is the same price as a bottle of Brand X but contains four times more liquid than a bottle of Brand X. A bottle of Brand X mouthwash contains 12 ounces. According to the ad, how much mouthwash must a bottle of Brand Z contain?
    A) 3 ounces   B) 15 ounces   C) 48 ounces   D) 69 ounces
    Ans: D

59. ChocoLot Ice Cream claims to be 20% less expensive than the leading brand. If a gallon of ChocoLot is $1.50, how much is the leading brand?
    A) $1.70   B) $1.80   C) $2.30   D) $3.00
    Ans: B

60. How many square meters are in 2.1 square kilometers?
    A)   2,100 square meters   C)   21,000,000 square meters
    B)   2,100,000 square meters   D)   2,100,000,000 square meters
    Ans: B

Chapter 18: Free-Response

1. You want to copy a poster whose dimensions are 24 inches by 30 inches onto a piece of paper 8.5 inches by 11 inches. You want the image to be as large as possible, but maintain the proportions of the original poster. What scaling factor will you use?
   Ans: 8.5/24, approximately 0.3542

2. You want to copy a poster whose dimensions are 24 inches by 30 inches onto a piece of paper 8.5 inches by 11 inches. You want the image to be as large as possible, but maintain the proportions of the original poster. What are the dimensions of the image?
   Ans: 8.5 inches × 10.625 inches

3. You want to copy a poster whose dimensions are 24 inches by 30 inches onto a piece of paper 11 inches by 17 inches. You want the image to be as large as possible, but maintain the proportions of the original poster. What scaling factor will you use?
   Ans: 11/24, approximately 0.4583

4. You want to copy a poster whose dimensions are 24 inches by 30 inches onto a piece of paper 11 inches by 17 inches. You want the image to be as large as possible, but maintain the proportions of the original poster. What are the dimensions of the image?
   Ans: 11 inches × 13.75 inches

5. When comparing prices for pizzas, you discover that the large pizza has twice as much surface area of a medium pizza and costs less than two medium pizzas. However, your group decides to order two medium pizzas anyway. What additional factors could be omitted in the mathematical model?
   Ans: For example, amount of crust or toppings

6. When comparing the relative dimensions of model trains you discover that their wheels are larger than they should be. Why might they be scaled incorrectly?
   Ans: For example, ease in construction or operation

7. The cost of photographic paper is nearly proportional to the area of the paper. But some shops charge extra for "nonstandard" sizes. Why would they feel the need to do this?
   Ans: For example, unusable scrap material

8. Each year, the area's largest tomatoes and pumpkins are showcased at the county fair. If there is a maximum size for such produce, how can larger and larger specimens be grown each year?
   Ans: For example, new hybrids are developed

9. Other than the crushing strength considerations, what other factors limit the size of trees?
   Ans: For example, root system

10. How does a whale's size impact the depth to which it can descend into the water?
    Ans: For example, larger whales can hold more air.

11. Are all rectangles similar? Why or why not?
    Ans: No. For example, square and non-square rectangles are not similar.

12. Are all circles similar? Why or why not?
    Ans: Yes. All circles have the same shape.

13. Are all pentagons similar? Why or why not?
    Ans: No. For example, regular and non-regular pentagons are not similar.

14. One of the famous problems of Greek antiquity was the *duplication of the cube*, that is, creating a cube similar to but double the volume of an existing cube. What if you instead wish to *triplicate the cube*, building a cube with three times the volume of an existing cube? What would be the scaling factor? Assuming the original cube was 1 cubic unit, what would be the dimensions of the larger cube?
    Ans: $3\sqrt{(1/3)}$; $\sqrt{(1/3)}$ inch $\times$ $3\sqrt{(1/3)}$ inch $\times$ $3\sqrt{(1/3)}$ inch

15. Create an example of an advertisement which misuses proportional change through its use of percent growth.
    Ans: For example, "Half-price rings now another 25% off" implies a 75% discount.

16. Create an example of an advertisement that misuses proportional change through its use of graphics.
    Ans: For example, a bank building scaled by 3 representing triple assets is actually 27 times as large.

17. Use the Consumer Price Index table to estimate when a loaf of bread, 50 cents in 1970, doubled in price.
    Ans: Approximately 1980

18. In 1997 a bottle of soda costs about 75 cents. Use the CPI table to estimate when this soda would have cost 5 cents.
    Ans: Approximately 1916

19. In the Consumer Price Index table, the index numbers tend to grow, but the numbers for the 1930s are less than those for the 1920s. Can you explain this?
    Ans: The Great Depression

20. A miniature model for a sculpture weighs about 10 ounces and stands 8 inches high. The actual model is to be 3 feet high and weigh about 25 pounds. Can it be made from the same material as the model? If not, how should its weight per cubic inch compare to that of the model material?
    Ans: No. The actual material should be about 1/5 the weight of the model.

21. Why do spike heels cause more damage to hardwood floors than loafers?
    Ans: The weight is supported by a small surface area.

22. Large trucks often have multiple wheels on an axle. How would multiple wheels allow trucks to carry heavier loads?
    Ans: The weight is supported by a larger surface area.

23. Why is allometric growth an appropriate model when the National Center for Missing and Exploited Children create sketches of missing people?
    Ans: Children's features grow by different proportions.

24. Find the values of a and b so that the points (0.5, 21) and (1.4, 56) lie on the curve $y = bx^a$.
    Ans: Approximately $a = 0.9526$, $b = 40.6429$.

25. Find the values of a and b so that the points (1.1, 14) and (1.4, 38) lie on the curve $y = bx^a$.
    Ans: Approximately $a = 4.1405$, $b = 9.4350$.

26. A casino plans to redecorate its courtyard, and the plans include a large marble sculpture of a six-sided die. The sculpture will be 3 meters tall. The density of marble is 2700 kg/m^3 and the crushing strength of marble is 7734 kg/m^2. Find the pressure on the bottom face of the sculpture. What problem does your answer pose in regards to the feasibility of the sculpture?
    Ans: The pressure on the bottom face of the sculpture is 8100 kg/m^2. This is more than the crushing strength of marble, so the sculpture would not be able to support itself.

27. On a recent visit to the gym, Clark ran 3 kilometers and Bruce ran 3 miles. Who ran the farthest? How much farther (in kilometers) did he run?
    Ans: Bruce ran farther, by 1.83 km.

28. A scale model of a new building is being built for display. A scale of 1 cm to 3 m is being used. It took 27,000 square centimeters of cardboard to construct the exposed surfaces of the model. How much wood (in square meters) will be required to construct the surfaces of the building?
    Ans: 243,000 square meters

29. Hisashi has a radio-controlled plane that is a scale model of a Boeing 727. The model has a 2-foot wingspan, and the wingspan of a Boeing 727 is 108 feet. If the minimum flight speed for a Boeing 727 is about 165 miles per hour, what is the minimum flight speed for the model plane?
    Ans: About 22 miles per hour

30. How many cubic centimeters are in 3 cubic meters?
    Ans: 3,000,000 cubic centimeters

Chapter 19: Multiple-Choice

1. The numbers 8 and 13 are consecutive Fibonacci numbers. What is the next Fibonacci number in the sequence?
   A) 16   B) 18   C) 21   D) 26
   Ans: C

2. The numbers 21 and 34 are consecutive Fibonacci numbers. What is the next Fibonacci number in the sequence?
   A) 42   B) 47   C) 55   D) 68
   Ans: C

3. Suppose a sequence begins with 1, 3, and continues by adding the previous two numbers to get the next number in the sequence. In this sequence, 7 and 11 are consecutive numbers. What is the next number in this sequence?
   A) 18   B) 17   C) 15   D) 14
   Ans: A

4. Suppose a sequence begins with 1, 3, and continues by adding the previous two numbers to get the next number in the sequence. In this sequence, 18 and 29 are consecutive numbers. What is the next number in this sequence?
   A) 47   B) 41   C) 40   D) 32
   Ans: A

5. The value of the golden ratio is:
   A)   less than 1.
   B)   between 1 and 1.5.
   C)   between 1.5 and 2.
   D)   greater than 2.
   Ans: C

6. What is the value of the product of the golden ratio ϕ and $(1 - \phi)$?
   A) 1   B) –1   C) ϕ D) Another answer
   Ans: B

7. What is the geometric mean of 4 and 16?
   A) 8   B) 10   C) 12   D) Another answer
   Ans: A

8. What is the geometric mean of 9 and 81?
   A) 27   B) 36   C) 45   D) Another answer
   Ans: A

9. The geometric mean of 10 and 16 is:
   A) 13.   B) less than 13.   C) more than 13.
   Ans: B

10. The geometric mean of 25 and 45 is:
    A) 35.   B) more than 35.   C) less than 35.
    Ans: C

11. Which of these letters, S A E, has a shape that is preserved by a reflection isometry?
    A) S only   B) A only   C) E only   D) A and E only
    Ans: D

12. Which of these letters, S A E, has a shape that is preserved by a rotation isometry?
    A) S only   B) A only   C) E only   D) A and E only
    Ans: A

13. Assume the following patterns continue in both directions. Which of these patterns has a translation isometry?
    AAAAAAAAA   ZZZZZZZZZ

    A)   AAAAAAAAA only
    B)   ZZZZZZZZZ only
    C)   Both AAAAAAAAA and ZZZZZZZZZ
    D)   Neither pattern
    Ans: C

14. Assume the following patterns continue in both directions. Which of these patterns has a rotation isometry?
    AAAAAAAAA   ZZZZZZZZZ

    A)   AAAAAAAAA only
    B)   ZZZZZZZZZ only
    C)   Both AAAAAAAAA and ZZZZZZZZZ
    D)   Neither pattern
    Ans: B

15. Assume the following patterns continue in both directions. Which of these patterns has a reflection isometry?
    AAAAAAAAA   ZZZZZZZZZ

    A)   AAAAAAAAA only
    B)   ZZZZZZZZZ only
    C)   Both AAAAAAAAA and ZZZZZZZZZ
    D)   Neither pattern
    Ans: A

16. Assume the following patterns continue in both directions. Which of these patterns has a rotation isometry?

 I **P Ь P Ь P Ь P Ь**   **II** **Ǝ Ɛ Ǝ Ɛ Ǝ Ɛ Ǝ Ɛ**

A) I only   B) II only   C) Both I and II   D) Neither pattern

Ans: B

17. Assume the following patterns continue in both directions. Which of these patterns has a translation isometry?

 I **P Ь P Ь P Ь P Ь**   **II** **Ǝ Ɛ Ǝ Ɛ Ǝ Ɛ Ǝ Ɛ**

A) I only   B) II only   C) Both I and II   D) Neither pattern

Ans: C

18. Assume the following patterns continue in both directions. Which of these patterns has a reflection isometry?

 I **P Ь P Ь P Ь P Ь**   **II** **Ǝ Ɛ Ǝ Ɛ Ǝ Ɛ Ǝ Ɛ**

A) I only   B) II only   C) Both I and II   D) Neither pattern

Ans: B

19. Assume the following patterns continue in both directions. Which of these patterns has a glide reflection isometry?

 I **P Ь P Ь P Ь P Ь**   **II** **AAAAAAAA**

A) I only   B) II only   C) Both I and II   D) Neither pattern

Ans: A

20. Assume the following pattern continues in both directions. What isometries preserve the pattern?

A)   Translation and rotation only
B)   Translation and horizontal reflection only
C)   Translation, rotation, and vertical reflection only
D)   Translation, rotation, glide reflection, and vertical reflection only

Ans: D

21. Assume the following pattern continues in both directions. What isometries preserve the pattern?

    A)   Translation and rotation only
    B)   Translation and vertical reflection only
    C)   Translation, rotation, and vertical reflection only
    D)   Translation, rotation, glide reflection, and vertical reflection only
    Ans: B

22. Assume the following pattern continues in both directions. What isometries preserve the pattern?

    A)   Translation only
    B)   Translation and horizontal reflection only
    C)   Translation and glide reflection only
    D)   Translation, glide reflection, and vertical reflection only
    Ans: C

23. Assume the following pattern continues in both directions. What isometries preserve the pattern?

    A)   Translation and rotation only
    B)   Translation and horizontal reflection only
    C)   Translation and glide reflection only
    D)   Translation, horizontal reflection, and vertical reflection only
    Ans: B

24. Assume the following pattern continues in both directions. What isometries preserve the pattern?

    A)   Translation only
    B)   Translation and glide reflection only
    C)   Translation and rotation only
    D)   Translation, glide reflection, and rotation only
    Ans: C

25. Consider the following statement: "If three points are collinear, their images after an isometry are also collinear." This statement is:
    A) always true.   B) sometimes true, depending on the isometry.   C) never true.
    Ans: A

26. Consider the following statement: "If three numbered points are placed in a circle so that they increase from smallest to largest in clockwise order, their images after an isometry will also lie on a circle and increase from smallest to largest in clockwise order." This statement is:
    A) always true.   B) sometimes true, depending on the isometry.   C) never true.
    Ans: B

27. Consider the following statement: "If four points form the corners of a square, their images after an isometry will also form a square." This statement is:
    A) always true.   B) sometimes true, depending on the isometry.   C) never true.
    Ans: A

28. Consider the following statement: "The image of a right-side print after an isometry is a left-side print." This statement is:
    A) always true.   B) sometimes true, depending on the isometry.   C) never true.
    Ans: B

29. How many symmetry lines can a square have?
    A) 2   B) 4   C) 8   D) Infinitely many
    Ans: B

30. How many symmetry lines can a perfect five-point have?
    A) 5   B) 10   C) 20   D) Infinitely many
    Ans: A

31. How many symmetry lines can a non-square rectangle have?
    A) None   B) Infinitely many   C) 2   D) 4
    Ans: C

32. How many different strip patterns exist?
    A) 4   B) 7   C) 17   D) 24
    Ans: B

33. How many different wallpaper patterns exist?
    A) 7   B) 14   C) 17   D) 24
    Ans: C

34. How many elements are in the symmetry group of a square?
    A) 2   B) 3   C) 4   D) 8
    Ans: D

35. How many elements are in the symmetry group of an equilateral triangle?
    A) 3   B) 4   C) 6   D) 7
    Ans: C

36. How many elements are in the symmetry group of a rectangle?
    A) 2   B) 3   C) 4   D) 8
    Ans: C

37. How many elements are in the symmetry group of a non-rectangle parallelogram?
    A) 1   B) 2   C) 4   D) None
    Ans: B

38. Assume the pattern continues in all directions. What are the isometries of the pattern?

    A)   Translations only   C)   Translations and rotations only
    B)   Translations and reflections only   D)   Translations, reflections, and rotations
    Ans: B

39. Assume the pattern continues in all directions. What are the isometries of the pattern?

    A)   Translations only   C)   Translations and rotations only
    B)   Translations and reflections only   D)   Translations, reflections, and rotations
    Ans: D

40. Assume the pattern continues in all directions. What are the isometries of the pattern?

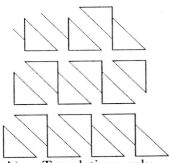

A)   Translations only   C)   Translations and rotations only
B)   Translations and reflections only   D)   Translations, reflections, and rotations
Ans: C

41. Assume the pattern continues in all directions. What are the isometries of the pattern?

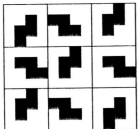

A)   Translations only   C)   Translations and rotations only
B)   Translations and reflections only   D)   Translations, reflections, and rotations
Ans: C

42. Assume the pattern continues in all directions. What are the isometries of the pattern?

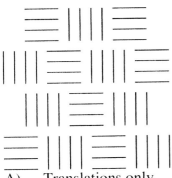

A)   Translations only   C)   Translations and rotations only
B)   Translations and reflections only   D)   Translations, reflections, and rotations
Ans: C

43. Suppose a wallpaper pattern has no rotations and no reflections, but has a glide reflection. Use the flowchart in the textbook to find the standard notation for the pattern.
    A) pg   B) cm   C) pm   D) pgg
    Ans: A

44. Suppose a wallpaper whose smallest rotation is 90° has reflection lines that intersect at 90° angles. Use the flowchart in the textbook to find the standard notation for the pattern.
    A) p4m   B) p4g   C) p4   D) pmm
    Ans: C

45. Suppose a wallpaper pattern with only a 180° rotation has reflection lines that always intersect at a rotational center. Use the flowchart in the textbook to find the standard notation for the pattern.
    A) pmm   B) cmm   C) pmg   D) p2
    Ans: A

46. Is it possible for a wallpaper pattern to have a translation and glide reflection isometries but no reflection isometry?
    A) Yes   B) No
    Ans: A

47. Is it possible for a wallpaper pattern to have translation, rotation, and glide reflection isometries, but no reflection isometry?
    A) Yes   B) No
    Ans: A

48. The symmetry group of a pattern always has:
    I: the identity element.
    II: an even number of elements.
    A) I only   B) II only   C) I and II   D) Neither I nor II
    Ans: A

49. If a figure has two reflection symmetries across perpendicular lines, it:
    A)   always has a rotation symmetry.   C)   never has a rotation symmetry.
    B)   sometimes has a rotation symmetry.
    Ans: A

50. If a figure has translation symmetry and reflection symmetry across the translation line, it:
    A)   always has a glide reflection.   C)   never has a glide reflection.
    B)   sometimes has a glide reflection.
    Ans: B

51. Which of the following rectangles is an approximate golden rectangle?
    A) 12 by 26   B) 50 by 81   C) 80 by 100   D) None of these
    Ans: B

52. Which of the following rectangles is an approximate golden rectangle?
    A) 11 by 27   B) 22 by 31   C) 33 by 54   D) None of these
    Ans: C

53. In the International Crystallographic Union notation, a letter p indicates that a strip pattern:
    A)   has a vertical line of reflection.
    B)   repeats in the horizontal direction.
    C)   has no glide reflection and no horizontal reflection.
    D)   has rotational symmetry.
    Ans: B

54. In the International Crystallographic Union notation, a letter m indicates that a strip pattern:
    A)   has a vertical line of reflection.
    B)   repeats in the horizontal direction.
    C)   has a glide reflection but no horizontal reflection.
    D)   has no glide reflection and no horizontal reflection.
    Ans: A

55. For the shape below, determine how many lines of symmetry exist.

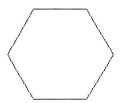

    A) 2   B) 3   C) 6   D) 12
    Ans: C

56. For the shape below, determine how many lines of symmetry exist.

    A) 4   B) 8   C) 16   D) 32
    Ans: B

57. For the shape below, determine how many lines of symmetry exist.

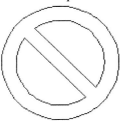

A) None   B) 1   C) 2   D) Infinitely many
Ans: C

58. The square below is transformed by an isometry. Which of the following statements is NOT necessarily true?

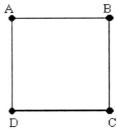

A)   The distance between vertex A and vertex B remain the same after transformation.
B)   Vertices A, B, C, and D still form a square after transformation.
C)   Vertex A is still above vertex D after transformation.
D)   Vertex A is still adjacent to vertex D after transformation.
Ans: C

59. Suppose a sequence begins with 1, 7 and continues by adding the previous two numbers to get the next number in the sequence. What number comes after 38 in this sequence?
A) 60   B) 61   C) 62   D) 63
Ans: B

60. Suppose a sequence begins with 3, 5 and continues by adding the previous two numbers to get the next number in the sequence. What number comes after 34 in this sequence?
A) 55   B) 56   C) 57   D) 58
Ans: A

Chapter 19: Free-Response

1. Starting with 1,1, determine the next five Fibonacci numbers.
   Ans: 1, 1, 2, 3, 5, 8, 13

2. Suppose a sequence begins 1, 4, and continues by adding the previous two numbers to determine the next number. Determine the next five numbers in this sequence.
   Ans: 1, 4, 5, 9, 14, 23, 37

3. Suppose a sequence begins 2, 1, and continues by adding the previous two numbers to determine the next number. Determine the next five numbers in this sequence.
   Ans: 2, 1, 3, 4, 7, 11, 18

4. Suppose a sequence begins 1, 4, and continues by adding the previous two numbers to determine the next number. What do the quotients of consecutive numbers drift toward?
   Ans: The numbers drift toward the golden mean.

5. Suppose a sequence begins 2, 1, and continues by adding the previous two numbers to determine the next number. What do the quotients of consecutive numbers drift toward?
   Ans: The numbers drift toward the golden mean.

6. Show that the difference between the golden mean ϕ and its reciprocal is 1.
   Ans: Approximately $1.618 - (1/1.618) = 1.618 - 6.18 = 1$

7. How does the geometric mean of two numbers compare to their arithmetic mean?
   Ans: The geometric mean is less than or equal to arithmetic mean.

8. Construct a rectangle with area 1 whose ratio of dimensions is the golden mean.
   Ans: Length = $1/[\sqrt{(\text{golden mean})}]$ Width = $\sqrt{(\text{golden mean})}$

9. Draw a figure that has rotational symmetry but no reflectional symmetry.
   Ans: E.g.,

10. Draw a figure that has reflectional symmetry but no rotational symmetry.
    Ans: E.g.,

11. Draw a figure that has both reflectional and rotational symmetry.
    Ans: E.g.,

12. Draw a strip pattern that has only translation and rotation symmetries.
    Ans: E.g.,

    ⌐⌐⌐⌐⌐⌐

13. Draw a strip pattern that has only translation and glide reflection symmetries.
    Ans: E.g.,

    ⌐L⌐L⌐L

14. Draw a strip pattern that has all possible symmetries.
    Ans: E.g.,

    ☐☐☐☐☐

15. Draw a wallpaper pattern that has only translation symmetries.
    Ans: E.g.,
    QQQ
    QQQ
    QQQ

16. Draw a wallpaper pattern that has only translation and rotation symmetries.
    Ans: E.g.,
    SSS
    SSS
    SSS

17. Draw a wallpaper pattern that has only translation and reflection symmetries.
    Ans: E.g.,

    ⌐⌐⌐⌐⌐⌐
    ⌐⌐⌐⌐⌐⌐

18. Draw a wallpaper pattern that has only translation and glide reflection symmetries.
    Ans: E.g.,

    ⌐L⌐L⌐L
    ⌐L⌐L⌐L

19. Draw a wallpaper pattern that has translation, rotation, and reflection symmetries.
    Ans: E.g.,
    XXX
    XXX
    XXX

20. Identify the elements of the symmetry group of a square.
   Ans: The identity, 1/4 turn, 1/2 turn, 3/4 turn, horizontal reflection, vertical reflection, left diagonal reflection, right diagonal reflection.

21. Identify the elements of the symmetry group of a non-equilateral isosceles triangle.
   Ans: The identity and vertical reflection

22. Why do imperfect patterns sometimes pose a challenge to the classification scheme?
   Ans: It's hard to decide if the imperfections are intentional.

23. How do pattern classification schemes aid anthropologists?
   Ans: They describe patterns in a formal scheme.

24. What are some of the isometries of a cube?
   Ans: There are rotations and reflections around lines through the center.

25. What are the isometries of a circle?
   Ans: Rotation and reflection through a plane through the center.

26. Draw a shape that has rotational symmetry but no reflection symmetry.
   Ans: Answers may vary. One example is shown below.

27. Draw a shape that has reflection symmetry but no rotational symmetry.
   Ans: Answers may vary. One example is shown below.

28. Draw a shape that has exactly five lines of reflection symmetry.
   Ans: Answers may vary. One example is shown below.

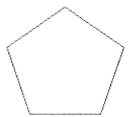

29. Draw a shape that has both reflection symmetry and rotational symmetry.
    Ans: Answers may vary. One example is shown below.

30. How many elements are in the symmetry group of the regular pentagon shown below?

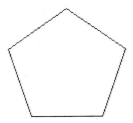

    Ans: 10

31. How does a fern leaf demonstrate a fractal structure?
    Ans: The fern leaf exhibits similarity at ever-finer scales.

32. How does the Sierpinski triangle illustrate an iterated function system?
    Ans: Its construction is a sequence of elements defined recursively by applying a single rule over and over.

Chapter 20: Multiple-Choice

1. Which of the following polygons can tile the plane?
   I: Regular pentagon
   II: Regular hexagon
   A) I only   B) II only   C) Both I and II   D) Neither
   Ans: B

2. Which of the following polygons can tile the plane?
   I: Regular octagon
   II: Non-rectangle parallelogram
   A) I only   B) II only   C) Both I and II   D) Neither
   Ans: B

3. Which of the following polygons can tile the plane?
   I: Non-square rhombus
   II: Non-equilateral isosceles triangle
   A) I only   B) II only   C) Both I and II   D) Neither
   Ans: C

4. Which of the following polygons can tile the plane?
   I: Scalene triangle
   II: Equilateral triangle
   A) I only   B) II only   C) Both I and II   D) Neither
   Ans: C

5. The exterior angle of a regular hexagon has a measure of:
   A) 18°   B) 30°   C) 45°   D) 60°
   Ans: D

6. The exterior angle of a regular pentagon has a measure of:
   A) 18°   B) 30°   C) 60°   D) 72°
   Ans: D

7. The exterior angle of a regular octagon (8-gon) has a measure of:
   A) 18°   B) 30°   C) 45°   D) 60°
   Ans: C

8. The exterior angle of a regular decagon (10-gon) has a measure of:
   A) 18°   B) 36°   C) 45°   D) 54°
   Ans: B

9. Choose the correct word.
   ... pentagons can form a tiling of the plane.
   A) All ...   B) Some ...   C) No ...
   Ans: B

10. Choose the correct word.
    ... hexagons can form a tiling of the plane.
    A) All ...   B) Some ...   C) No ...
    Ans: B

11. Choose the correct word.
    ... non-convex quadrilaterals can form a tiling of the plane.
    A) All ...   B) Some ...   C) No ...
    Ans: A

12. Choose the correct word.
    ... convex quadrilaterals can form a tiling of the plane.
    A) All ...   B) Some ...   C) No ...
    Ans: A

13. Semiregular tilings can tile with:
    I: three different regular polygons.
    II: three different vertex combinations.
    A) I only   B) II only   C) Both I and II   D) Neither
    Ans: A

14. Squares and equilateral triangles can form a tiling that has at every vertex:
    A)   three squares and two triangles.   C)   one square and four triangles.
    B)   two squares and three triangles.   D)   one square and five triangles.
    Ans: B

15. Regular hexagons and equilateral triangles can form a tiling of the plane that has at every vertex:
    A)   three hexagons and one triangle.   C)   two hexagons and three triangles.
    B)   two hexagons and two triangles.   D)   one hexagon and five triangles.
    Ans: B

16. Regular octagons and squares can form a tiling of the plane that has at every vertex:
    A)   two octagons and two squares.   C)   one octagon and two squares.
    B)   two octagons and one square.   D)   one octagon and three squares.
    Ans: B

17. Regular dodecagons (12-gons) and equilateral triangles can form a tiling of the plane that has at every vertex:
    A)   two dodecagons and two triangles.   C)   one dodecagon and two triangles.
    B)   two dodecagons and one triangle.   D)   one dodecagon and three triangles.
    Ans: B

18. A semiregular tiling has one equilateral triangle and two regular p-gons at each vertex. What is p?
    A) 8   B) 9   C) 10   D) 12
    Ans: D

19. A semiregular tiling has one square, one regular hexagon, and one regular p-gon at each vertex. What is p?
    A) 8   B) 9   C) 10   D) 12
    Ans: D

20. A semiregular tiling has two regular octagons and one regular p-gon at each vertex. What is p?
    A) 3   B) 4   C) 5   D) 6
    Ans: B

21. A semiregular tiling has four equilateral triangles and one p-gon at each vertex. What is p?
    A) 3   B) 4   C) 5   D) 6
    Ans: D

22. A semiregular tiling has one square and two regular p-gons at each vertex. What is p?
    A) 5   B) 6   C) 8   D) 10
    Ans: C

23. A scalene triangle ABC tiles the plane. What is a possible configuration of the angles at the vertices?
    I: Three types of vertices: 6 As, or 6 Bs, or 6 Cs
    II: One type of vertex: 2As, 2 Bs, and 2Cs
    A) I only   B) II only   C) Both I and II   D) Neither
    Ans: A

24. A non-convex quadrilateral ABCD tiles the plane. What is a possible configuration of the angles at the vertices?
    I: Two types of vertices: 2 As and 2 Cs; 2 Bs and 2 Ds
    II: One type of vertex: A, B, C, D
    A) I only   B) II only   C) Both I and II   D) Neither
    Ans: A

25. Which of the following form the faces of a regular polyhedron?
    I: Eight squares
    II: Four equilateral triangles
    A) I only   B) II only   C) Both I and II   D) Neither
    Ans: B

26. Which of the following form the faces of a regular polyhedron?
    I: Six equilateral triangles
    II: Eight equilateral triangles
    A) I only   B) II only   C) Both I and II   D) Neither
    Ans: B

27. Which of the following form the faces of a regular polyhedron?
    I: Six squares
    II: Ten pentagons
    A) I only   B) II only   C) Both I and II   D) Neither
    Ans: A

28. A regular polyhedron with 12 faces has what regular polygon as faces?
    A) Triangle   B) Square   C) Pentagon   D) Hexagon
    Ans: C

29. A regular polyhedron with 20 faces has what regular polygon as faces?
    A) Triangle   B) Square   C) Pentagon   D) Hexagon
    Ans: A

30. A regular polyhedron with six faces has what regular polygon as faces?
    A) Triangle   B) Square   C) Pentagon   D) Hexagon
    Ans: B

31. What is a possible way to tile the plane with a right triangle?
    I: Six at every vertex
    II: Four or eight at every vertex
    A) I only   B) II only   C) Both I and II   D) Neither
    Ans: C

32. What is a possible way to tile the plane with a general isosceles triangle?
    I: Six at a vertex
    II: Four or eight at a vertex
    A) I only   B) II only   C) Both I and II   D) Neither
    Ans: A

33. What is a possible way to tile the plane with a parallelogram with 60° and 120° angles?
    I: Four at a vertex
    II: Three or six at a vertex
    A) I only   B) II only   C) Both I and II   D) Neither
    Ans: C

34. What is a possible way to tile the plane with a pentagon with three 90° angles and two equal obtuse angles?
    I: Three at a vertex
    II: Three or four at a vertex
    A) I only   B) II only   C) Both I and II   D) Neither
    Ans: B

35. What is a possible way to tile the plane with a pentagon with two 90° angles and three equal obtuse angles?
    I: Three at a vertex
    II: Three or four at a vertex
    A) I only   B) II only   C) Both I and II   D) Neither
    Ans: B

36. Can the tile below be used to tile the plane?

    A)   No
    B)   Yes, with translations only
    C)   Yes, with translations and half-turns only
    D)   Yes, but reflections must be included
    Ans: B

37. Can the tile below be used to tile the plane?

    A)   No
    B)   Yes, with translations only
    C)   Yes, with translations and half-turns only
    D)   Yes, but reflections must be included
    Ans: A

38. Can the tile below be used to tile the plane?

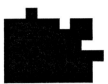

A)   No
B)   Yes, with translations only
C)   Yes, with translations and half-turns only
D)   Yes, but reflections must be included
Ans: C

39. Can the tile below be used to tile the plane?

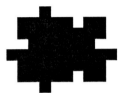

A)   No
B)   Yes, with translations only
C)   Yes, with translations and half-turns only
D)   Yes, but reflections must be included
Ans: C

40. Can the tile below be used to tile the plane?

A)   No
B)   Yes, with translations only
C)   Yes, with translations and half-turns only
D)   Yes, but reflections must be included
Ans: C

41. Penrose Tilings are non-periodic.
    A) True   B) False
    Ans: A

42. Portions of Penrose Tilings can have rotational symmetry.
    A) True   B) False
    Ans: A

43. Most Penrose Tilings require at least 10 differently shaped tiles.
    A) True   B) False
    Ans: B

44. Any finite portion of a Penrose Tiling can be found in another Penrose Tiling.
    A) True   B) False
    Ans: A

45. Escher No. 128 [*Bird*], Figure 20.10 in the textbook, tiles by:
    A)   translations only.
    B)   translations and half-turns only.
    C)   translations and reflections only.
    D)   translations, half-turns, and reflections.
    Ans: A

46. Escher No. 67 [*Horseman*], Figure 20.11a in the textbook, tiles by:
    A)   translations only.
    B)   translations and half-turns only.
    C)   translations and reflections only.
    D)   translations, half-turns, and reflections.
    Ans: C

47. Escher No. 6 [*Camel*], Figure 20.15 in the textbook, tiles by:
    A)   translations only.
    B)   translations and half-turns only.
    C)   translations and reflections only.
    D)   translations, half-turns, and reflections.
    Ans: B

48. Escher No. 88 [*Sea Horse*], Figure 20.16 in the textbook, tiles by:
    A)   translations only.
    B)   translations and half-turns only.
    C)   translations and reflections only.
    D)   translations, half-turns, and reflections.
    Ans: B

49. If you attempt to tile a non-Euclidean surface with eight triangles meeting at each vertex,
    A)   you will find your efforts to be impossible.
    B)   you will be tiling a surface with elliptic geometry.
    C)   you will be tiling a surface with hyperbolic geometry.
    Ans: B

50. If you attempt to tile a non-Euclidean surface with five squares meeting at each vertex,
    A)   you will find your efforts to be impossible.
    B)   you will be tiling a surface with elliptic geometry.
    C)   you will be tiling a surface with hyperbolic geometry.
    Ans: C

51. The interior angle of a regular hexagon has a measure of:
    A) 60°   B) 108°   C) 120°   D) 135°
    Ans: C

52. The interior angle of a regular pentagon has a measure of:
    A) 72°   B) 108°   C) 120°   D) 144°
    Ans: B

53. The interior angle of a regular octagon has a measure of:
    A) 45°   B) 60°   C) 120°   D) 135°
    Ans: D

54. What is a possible way to tile the plane with a hexagon that has four angles measuring 140° and two angles measuring 80°?
    A)   Three at a vertex only
    B)   Four at a vertex only
    C)   Either three or four at a vertex
    D)   This shape will not tile the plane by itself.
    Ans: A

55. Which of the following is a regular tiling of the plane?

A)

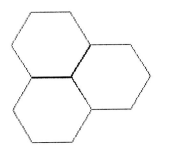

B)

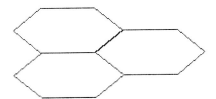

C)

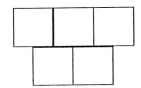

D)

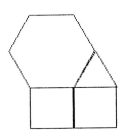

Ans: A

56. Which of the following is a semiregular tiling of the plane?
   A)

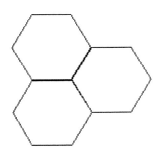

   B)

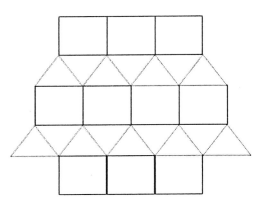

   C)

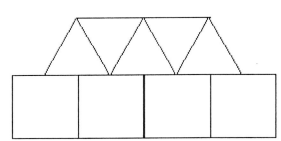

   D)

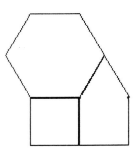

   Ans: B

57. At the vertex of a tiling of the plane there are two regular pentagons and one regular p-gon at each vertex. What is p?
   A) 8   B) 9   C) 10   D) 12
   Ans: C

58. A semiregular tiling has two squares and three regular p-gons at each vertex. What is p?
    A) 3   B) 4   C) 5   D) 6
    Ans: A

59. A semiregular tiling has an equilateral triangle, a regular hexagon and two regular p-gons at each vertex. What is p?
    A) 3   B) 4   C) 5   D) 6
    Ans: B

60. A semiregular tiling has two equilateral triangles and two regular p-gons at each vertex. What is p?
    A) 3   B) 4   C) 5   D) 6
    Ans: D

Chapter 20: Free-Response

1. Tile the plane with a scalene triangle.
   Ans:

   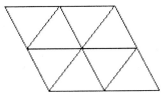

2. Tile the plane with a non-square rhombus.
   Ans:

3. Tile the plane with a (tileable) pentagon.
   Ans:

   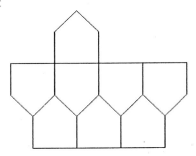

4. Tile the plane with a (tileable) hexagon.
   Ans:

   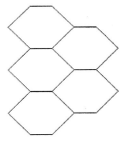

5. Create a non-regular tiling with a right triangle tile.
   Ans:
   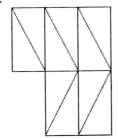

6. Create a non-regular tiling with pentagons.
   Ans: For example:
   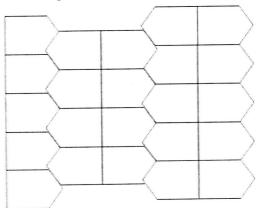

7. Create a non-regular tiling with octagons and squares.
   Ans:
   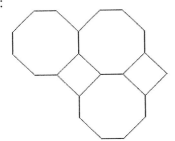

8. Create a tiling with a parallelogram. Is it regular?
   Ans:

   Yes.

9. Create a tiling with a non-convex quadrilateral. Is it regular?
   Ans:

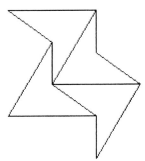

   Yes.

10. Use the figure below to tile the plane, if possible.

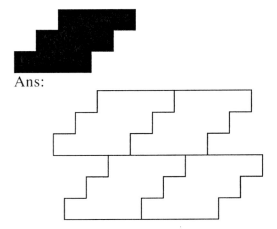

   Ans:

11. Use the figure below to tile the plane, if possible.

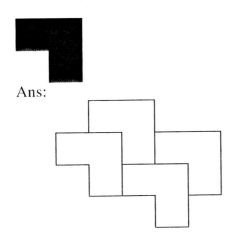

Ans:

12. Use the figure below to tile the plane, if possible.

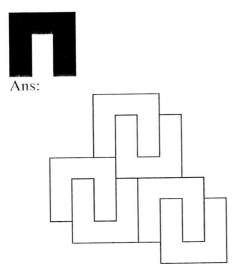

Ans:

13. Choose one of Marjorie Rice's pentagon tiles, and use it to tile the plane.
    Ans: See illustration in Spotlight 20.2, for example.

14. Why are regular pentagons not usable to tile the plane?
    Ans: Angles do not evenly divide 360°.

15. Why are regular octagons not useable to tile the plane?
    Ans: Angles do not evenly divide 360°.

16. Create a tiling of the plane using squares and hexagons, if possible.
    Ans:

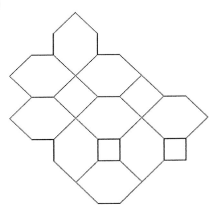

17. Create a tiling of the plane using triangles and octagons, if possible.
    Ans:

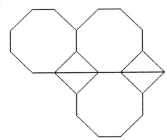

18. Create an Escher-like tiling that uses only translations.
    Ans: See Figure 20.10, for example.

19. Create an Escher-like tiling that uses only translations and half-turns.
    Ans: See Figure 20.15, for example.

20. Create an Escher-like tiling that uses only translations and reflections.
    Ans: See Figure 20.11(a), for example.

21. Why are Penrose tilings of interest to chemists?
    Ans: For example, they describe the structure of quasicrystals.

22. If a tiling has only translations, how could it be classified in wallpaper pattern notation?
    Ans: p1

23. How can you "tile" three dimensions using cubes?
    Ans: For example, stack them as alphabet building blocks.

24. How can you "tile" three dimensions using non-cube solid "tiles"?
    Ans: For example, stack them as cinder blocks.

25. Give a numerical explanation of why a regular decagon (ten sides) cannot tile the plane by itself.

    Ans: A regular decagon has interior angles measuring 144° each. Since 144 does not evenly divide 360°, decagons cannot tile the plane by themselves.

26. At the vertex of a tiling of the plane there is a regular octagon, an equilateral triangle, and one other regular polygon. Which regular polygon is it?

    Ans: A regular 24-gon

27. At the vertex of a tiling of the plane there is a regular pentagon, a square, and one other regular polygon. Which regular polygon is it?

    Ans: A regular 20-gon

28. Explain why the tiling below does not form a semiregular tiling of the plane.

    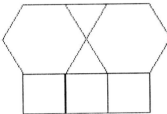

    Ans: Not every vertex figure is the same; for example, at one vertex there are two squares and two hexagons, while a different vertex contains two squares, a triangle, and a hexagon.

29. Explain why the tiling below does not form a semiregular tiling of the plane.

    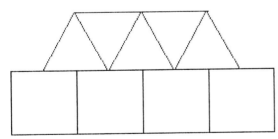

    Ans: The tiles are not edge-to-edge.

30. At the vertex of a tiling of the plane there is a regular octagon, a square, and one other regular polygon. Which regular polygon is it?

    Ans: Another regular octagon

Chapter 21: Multiple-Choice

1. You have $2500 that you invest at 6% simple interest. What is the balance after four years?
A) $310   B) $600   C) $3100   D) $6000
Ans: C

2. You have $3500 that you invest at 7% simple interest. How long will it take for your balance to reach $4235?
A) Two years   B) Three years   C) Four years   D) Five years
Ans: B

3. You have $7000 that you invest at 9% simple interest. What is the balance after 14 years?
A) $12,390   B) $15,820   C) $63,000   D) $882,000
Ans: B

4. You have $4300 that you invest at 5% simple interest. How long will it take for your balance to reach $7525?
A) 14 years   B) 15 years   C) 16 years   D) 17 years
Ans: B

5. Suppose you invest in an account that pays 5% interest, compounded quarterly. You would like your investment to grow to $5000 in 16 years. How much would you have to invest in order for this to happen?
A) $2258   B) $2374   C) $3125   D) $4153
Ans: A

6. Merrie borrowed $1000 from her parents, agreeing to pay them back when she graduated from college in five years. If she paid interest compounded quarterly at 5%, how much would she owe at the end of the five years?
A) $1050   B) $1282   C) $1503   D) $1581
Ans: B

7. Suppose you invest in an account that pays 6% interest, compounded quarterly. You would like your investment to grow to $8000 in 14 years. How much would you have to invest in order for this to happen?
A) $2125   B) $2290   C) $2650   D) $3475
Ans: D

8. Merrie borrowed $500 from her parents, agreeing to pay them back when she graduated from college in four years. If she paid interest compounded daily at 16%, how much would she owe at the end of the four years?
A) $948   B) $1029   C) $1237   D) $1581
Ans: A

9. What is the APY for 5.3% compounded quarterly?
   A) 5.3%   B) 5.4%   C) 5.5%   D) 5.6%
   Ans: B

10. What is the APY for 6% compounded weekly?
    A) 6.00%   B) 6.09%   C) 6.18%   D) 7.25%
    Ans: C

11. What is the APY for 9.6% compounded daily?
    A) 9.6%   B) 10.1%   C) 12.2%   D) 13.0%
    Ans: B

12. What is the APY for 10.2% compounded quarterly?
    A) 9.5%   B) 9.7%   C) 10.2%   D) 10.6%
    Ans: D

13. What is the APY for 7.5% compounded quarterly?
    A) 7.3%   B) 7.5%   C) 7.7%   D) 8.1%
    Ans: C

14. What is the APY for 6.25% compounded daily?
    A) 6.25%   B) 6.45%   C) 6.95%   D) 7.25%
    Ans: B

15. What is the APY for 12.3% compounded weekly?
    A) 11.8%   B) 12.3%   C) 12.7%   D) 13.1%
    Ans: D

16. What is the APY for 9.7% compounded annually?
    A) 9.5%   B) 9.7%   C) 10.2%   D) 10.9%
    Ans: B

17. Tara has $85 deducted from her paycheck at the end of each month and put into a savings account earning 9% interest compounded monthly. She continues these deposits for ten years. How much is the account worth at the end of the 10 years?
    A) $208   B) $2496   C) $16,450   D) $21,150
    Ans: C

18. A man cuts back on his latte habit and instead makes $20 deposits each month into a savings account earning 6% interest compounded monthly. He continues these deposits for eight years. How much will the account be worth after eight years?
    A) $1920   B) $2457   C) $2941   D) $3250
    Ans: B

19. The Martin family has decided to save up for a new swimming pool. They want to save $14,000 in four years. They find a savings account for which interest was compounded daily at 7.6%. How much will they have to deposit each month to meet this goal?
A) $541.84   B) $627.41   C) $689.50   D) $756.86
Ans: A

20. Juanita has $100 deducted from her paycheck at the end of each month and put into a savings account earning 11% interest compounded monthly. She continues these deposits for five years. How much is the account worth at the end of the five years?
A) $7952   B) $9827   C) $10,450   D) $11,150
Ans: A

21. A man makes $10 deposits each month into a savings account earning 8% interest compounded quarterly. He continues these deposits for 12 years. How much will the account be worth after 12 years?
A) $794   B) $827   C) $952   D) $1056
Ans: A

22. The Chavez family has decided to save up for a new spa. They want to save $10,000 in five years. They find a savings account for which interest was compounded monthly at 8.2%. How much will they have to deposit each month to meet this goal?
A) $54   B) $97   C) $135   D) $256
Ans: C

23. Use the geometric series formula to find the sum of $1 + \dfrac{1}{b} + \dfrac{1}{b^2} + \dfrac{1}{b^3}$.

A) $\dfrac{b^3 - 1}{b - 1}$ B) $\dfrac{\frac{1}{b^3} - 1}{\frac{1}{b} - 1}$ C) $\dfrac{b^4 - 1}{b - 1}$ D) $\dfrac{\frac{1}{b^4} - 1}{\frac{1}{b} - 1}$

Ans: D

24. Use the geometric series formula to find the sum of $1 - q + q^2 - q^3 + q^4$.

A) $\dfrac{(-q)^5 - 1}{(-q) - 1}$ B) $\dfrac{q^5 - 1}{q - 1}$ C) $\dfrac{(-q)^4 - 1}{(-q) - 1}$ D) $\dfrac{q^4 - 1}{q - 1}$

Ans: A

25. Use the geometric series formula to find the sum of $1 + \dfrac{1}{4} + \dfrac{1}{4^2} + \dfrac{1}{4^3} + \dfrac{1}{4^4}$.

A) $\dfrac{4^5 - 1}{4 - 1}$ B) $\dfrac{\frac{1}{4^5} - 1}{\frac{1}{4} - 1}$ C) $\dfrac{4^4 - 1}{4 - 1}$ D) $\dfrac{\frac{1}{4^4} - 1}{\frac{1}{4} - 1}$

Ans: B

26. Use the geometric series formula to find the sum of $1 - 2 + 4 - 8 + 16$.

A) $\dfrac{(-2)^4 - 1}{(-2) - 1}$ B) $\dfrac{2^4 - 1}{2 - 1}$ C) $\dfrac{(-2)^5 - 1}{(-2) - 1}$ D) $\dfrac{2^5 - 1}{2 - 1}$

Ans: C

27. A car was purchased in 1980 for $12,000. Its value in current dollars depreciates steadily at a rate of 14% per year. What will the car's value be at the beginning of 2003?
A) $1920.05   B) $745.20   C) $628.52   D) $373.81
Ans: D

28. A computer was purchased in 1999 for $3000. Its value in current dollars depreciates steadily at a rate of 25% per year. What will the computer's value be at the beginning of 2003?
A) $1920.05   B) $949.22   C) $652.28   D) $373.81
Ans: B

29. A car was purchased in 1985 for $15,000. Its value in current dollars depreciates steadily at a rate of 13% per year. What will the car's value be at the beginning of 2003?
A) $1187.25   B) $1223.03   C) $1314.58   D) $1551.05
Ans: B

30. A computer was purchased in 1996 for $2500. Its value in current dollars depreciates steadily at a rate of 30% per year. What will the computer's value be at the beginning of 2003?
A) $205.89   B) $301.20   C) $420.87   D) $580.26
Ans: A

31. Betty bought a house in 1987 for $99,000 and sold it in 2001. If the 1987 CPI is 113.6 and the 2001 CPI is 177.1, how much would the house be worth in 2001 dollars?
A) $165,157   B) $154,339   C) $134,921   D) $102,356
Ans: B

32. Javier bought a house in 1974 for $49,000 and sold it in 1997. If the 1974 CPI is 49.3 and the 1997 CPI is 160.5, how much would the house be worth in 1997 dollars?
A) $159,523   B) $123,086   C) $95,157   D) $65,456
Ans: A

33. In early 2002 the inflation rate was about 1.4%. If you invested in a savings account with an annual interest rate of 4.8%, what was the real growth rate of this investment?
A) 1.66% B) 3.35% C) 4.27% D) 6.12%
Ans: B

34. Buck bought a house in 1967 for $19,000 and sold it in 2001. If the 1967 CPI is 33.4 and the 2001 CPI is 177.1, how much would the house be worth in 2001 dollars?
A) $115,157 B) $100,745 C) $94,921 D) $25,356
Ans: B

35. John bought a house in 1947 for $19,000 and sold it in 1997. If the 1947 CPI is 22.3 and the 1997 CPI is 160.5, how much would the house be worth in 1997 dollars?
A) $115,157 B) $101,086 C) $94,921 D) $25,356
Ans: A

36. In late 2001 the inflation rate was about 2.9%. If you invested in a savings account with an annual interest rate of 9.2%, what was the real growth rate of this investment?
A) 1.66% B) 3.35% C) 4.27% D) 6.12%
Ans: D

37. Candas made an investment with a 10% annual yield. However, the real growth rate of her investment was only 8.2%. What was the inflation rate?
A) 1.66% B) 3.35% C) 4.27% D) 6.12%
Ans: A

38. Sindee wants to make an investment that will have a real growth rate of 9%. If the current inflation rate is 1.97%, what annual interest rate will she need to get on her investment to accomplish her goal?
A) 8.50% B) 7.63% C) 11.15% D) 12.82%
Ans: C

39. Ray wants to make an investment that will have a real growth rate of 5%. If the current inflation rate is 2.5%, what annual interest rate will he need to get on his investment to accomplish his goal?
A) 8.50% B) 7.63% C) 11.15% D) 12.82%
Ans: B

40. Joe wants to make an investment that will have a real growth rate of 7%. If the current inflation rate is 1.4%, what annual interest rate will he need to get on his investment to accomplish his goal?
A) 8.50% B) 7.63% C) 11.15% D) 12.82%
Ans: A

41. Katrina invested in her employer's stock program in 1992. The annual yield for her investment was 9.3%, and the inflation rate was 1.47%. What was the real growth rate of this investment?
A) 6.06%   B) 6.59%   C) 7.48%   D) 7.72%
Ans: D

42. Pat invested in her employer's stock program in 1981. The annual yield for her investment was 6.5%, but the inflation rate was 7.8%. What was the real growth rate of this investment?
A) –1.21%   B) –2.09%   C) –3.30%   D) –4.41%
Ans: A

43. In early 2002 the inflation rate was about 1.4%. If you invested in a savings account with an annual interest rate of 6.5%, what was the real growth rate of this investment?
A) 3.24%   B) 4.19%   C) 4.47%   D) 5.03%
Ans: D

44. In late 2001 the inflation rate was about 2.9%. If you invested in a savings account with an annual interest rate of 7.5%, what was the real growth rate of this investment?
A) 3.24%   B) 4.19%   C) 4.47%   D) 5.03%
Ans: C

45. Karen made an investment with a 12% annual yield. However, the real growth rate of her investment was only 7.5%. What was the inflation rate?
A) 3.24%   B) 4.19%   C) 4.47%   D) 5.03%
Ans: B

46. Brad wants to make an investment that will have a real growth rate of 12%. If the current inflation rate is 2.38%, what annual interest rate will he need to get on his investment to accomplish his goal?
A) 8.65%   B) 9.40%   C) 14.67%   D) 15.82%
Ans: C

47. Monte wants to make an investment that will have a real growth rate of 6%. If the current inflation rate is 2.5%, what annual interest rate will he need to get on his investment to accomplish his goal?
A) 8.65%   B) 9.40%   C) 14.67%   D) 15.82%
Ans: A

48. Charles wants to make an investment that will have a real growth rate of 8%. If the current inflation rate is 1.3%, what annual interest rate will he need to get on his investment to accomplish his goal?
A) 8.65%   B) 9.40%   C) 14.67%   D) 15.82%
Ans: B

49. Stephanie invested in her employer's stock program in 1989. The annual yield for her investment was 8.1%, and the inflation rate was 0.86%. What was the real growth rate of this investment?
A) 6.21%   B) 6.48%   C) 7.18%   D) 7.24%
Ans: C

50. Bonnie invested in her employer's stock program in 1981. The annual yield for her investment was 7.5%, but the inflation rate was 9.8%. What was the real growth rate of this investment?
A) –1.82%   B) –2.09%   C) –2.30%   D) –3.41%
Ans: B

51. John bought a house in 1947 and sold it in 1997 for $80,000. If the 1947 CPI is 22.3 and the 1997 CPI is 160.5, how much would the house be worth in 1947 dollars?
A) $57,578   B) $11,115   C) $28,633   D) $49,844
Ans: B

52. Chris bought a house in 1957 and sold it in 1997 for $115,000. If the 1957 CPI is 28.1 and the 1997 CPI is 160.5, how much would the house be worth in 1997 dollars?
A) $39,096   B) $20,134   C) $25,499   D) $49,667
Ans: B

53. John sold a house in 2003 for twice the amount that he paid for it. When did he purchase the house? (Use table 21.5.)
A) 1980   B) 1981   C) 1983   D) 1986
Ans: B

54. Kim sold a house in 1993 for twice the amount that he paid for it. When did he purchase the house? (Use table 21.5.)
A) 1973   B) 1977   C) 1979   D) 1980
Ans: C

55. When John sold a house in 2003 for $115,000, he received $20,000 more than he paid for it. When did he purchase the house? (Use table 21.5.)
A) 1984   B) 1991   C) 1995   D) 1998
Ans: C

56. In 1999, Rachel had the opportunity to either invest $100,000 for three years in the housing market or in a CD paying 3.5%. If the 1999 CPI is 166.6 and the 2002 CPI is 179.9, which is the better investment?
A)   The housing market   C)   The options are equivalent
B)   The CD   D)   Not enough information given
Ans: B

57. In 1999, Debra had the opportunity to either invest $100,000 for three years in the housing market or in a CD paying 2.5%. If the 1999 CPI is 166.6 and the 2002 CPI is 179.9, which is the better investment?
    A) The housing market
    B) The CD
    C) The options are equivalent
    D) Not enough information given
    Ans: A

58. In 1997, Howard had the opportunity to either invest $100,000 for five years in the housing market or in a CD paying 2.5%. If the 1997 CPI is 160.5 and the 2002 CPI is 179.9, which is the better investment?
    A) The housing market
    B) The CD
    C) The options are equivalent
    D) Not enough information given
    Ans: B

59. In 1997, Alva had the opportunity to either invest $100,000 for five years in the housing market or in a CD paying 2.2%. If the 1997 CPI is 160.5 and the 2002 CPI is 179.9, which is the better investment?
    A) The housing market
    B) The CD
    C) The options are equivalent
    D) Not enough information given
    Ans: A

60. Zeke bought a house in 1981 for $19,000 and sold it in 1997. If the 1981 CPI is 90.9 and the 1997 CPI is 160.5, how much would the house be worth in 1997 dollars?
    A) $26,300   B) $27,860   C) $29,808   D) $33,548
    Ans: D

Chapter 21: Free-Response

1. A man borrowed $29,000 for two years under simple interest. At the end of the two years his balance due was $31,900. What annual simple interest rate did he pay?
   Ans: 5%

2. A man borrowed $9000 for four years under simple interest. At the end of the four years his balance due was $11,160. What annual simple interest rate did he pay?
   Ans: 6%

3. Suppose you invest $6000 and would like your investment to grow to $8000 in five years. What interest rate, compounded monthly, would you have to earn in order for this to happen?
   Ans: 5.77%

4. Suppose you invest $5000 and would like your investment to grow to $10,000 in eight years. What interest rate, compounded weekly, would you have to earn in order for this to happen?
   Ans: 8.67%

5. Michelle invests in a savings account that pays 4% interest compounded monthly. What is the APY for this account?
   Ans: 4.07%

6. Brad invests in a savings account that pays 8% interest compounded quarterly. What is the APY for this account?
   Ans: 8.24%

7. Moira invests in a savings account that pays 6% interest compounded weekly. What is the APY for this account?
   Ans: 6.12%

8. Zoe invests in a savings account that pays 7% interest compounded quarterly. What is the APY for this account?
   Ans: 7.19%

9. Use the geometric series formula to find the sum of $1 - \dfrac{1}{r} + \dfrac{1}{r^2} - \dfrac{1}{r^3} + \dfrac{1}{r^4}$.
   Ans:
   $$\frac{\dfrac{1}{(-r)^5} - 1}{\dfrac{1}{(-r)} - 1}$$

10. Use the geometric series formula to find the sum of $1 - \dfrac{1}{r} + \dfrac{1}{r^2} - \dfrac{1}{r^3} + \dfrac{1}{r^4} + \ldots \pm \dfrac{1}{r^n}$, where the $\pm$ denotes $+$ if n is odd and $-$ if n is even (to fit the pattern of the earlier terms).

Ans:

$$\dfrac{\dfrac{1}{(-r)^n} - 1}{\dfrac{1}{(-r)} - 1}$$

11. Use the geometric series formula to find the sum of $1 - \dfrac{1}{2} + \dfrac{1}{4} - \dfrac{1}{8} + \dfrac{1}{16}$.

Ans: 11/16

12. Use the geometric series formula to find the sum of $1 - \dfrac{1}{2} + \dfrac{1}{4} - \dfrac{1}{8} + \dfrac{1}{16} + \ldots \pm \dfrac{1}{2^n}$, where the $\pm$ denotes $+$ if n is odd and $-$ if n is even (to fit the pattern of the earlier terms).

Ans:

$$\dfrac{\dfrac{1}{(-2)^n} - 1}{\dfrac{1}{(-2)} - 1} \quad \text{or} \quad \dfrac{2 - 2(-2)^n}{3(-2)^n}$$

13. Kamel bought a house in 1982 for $67,000 and sold it in 2001. If the 1982 CPI is 96.5 and the 2001 CPI is 177.1, how much would the house be worth in 2001 dollars?
Ans: $122,961

14. Matthew made an investment with an 8% annual yield. However, the real growth rate of his investment was only 5%. What was the inflation rate?
Ans: 2.86%

15. Margaret made an investment with a 10% annual yield. However, the real growth rate of her investment was only 4.5%. What was the inflation rate?
Ans: 5.26%

16. In 1960 the inflation rate was about 5.1%. If you invested in a savings account with an annual interest rate of 4.9%, what was the real growth rate of this investment?
Ans: –0.19%

17. In 1984 the inflation rate was about –0.24%. If you invested in a savings account with an annual interest rate of 9.4%, what was the real growth rate of this investment?
Ans: 9.66%

18. Michael wants to make an investment that will have a real growth rate of 10%. If the current inflation rate is 11.4%, what annual interest rate will he need to get on his investment to accomplish his goal?
Ans: 22.54%

19. Stephen wants to make an investment that will have a real growth rate of 15%. If the current inflation rate is 5.4%, what annual interest rate will he need to get on his investment to accomplish his goal?
Ans: 21.21%

20. Stephen made an investment with a 9% annual yield. However, the real growth rate of his investment was only 4%. What was the inflation rate?
Ans: 4.81%

21. Marlene made an investment with a 12% annual yield. However, the real growth rate of her investment was only 6.5%. What was the inflation rate?
Ans: 5.16%

22. In 1960 the inflation rate was about 5.1%. If you invested in a savings account with an annual interest rate of 7.3%, what was the real growth rate of this investment?
Ans: 2.09%

23. In 1984 the inflation rate was about –0.24%. If you invested in a savings account with an annual interest rate of 6.8%, what was the real growth rate of this investment?
Ans: 7.06%

24. Alex wants to make an investment that will have a real growth rate of 6.2%. If the current inflation rate is 4.5%, what annual interest rate will he need to get on his investment to accomplish his goal?
Ans: 10.98%

25. Jack wants to make an investment that will have a real growth rate of 8%. If the current inflation rate is 2.1%, what annual interest rate will he need to get on his investment to accomplish his goal?
Ans: 10.27%

26. Mildred bought a house in 1962 for $17,000 and sold it in 2004. If the 1962 CPI is 30.9 and the 2004 CPI is 189.5, how much would the house be worth in 2004 dollars?
Ans: $104,256

27. Nebo bought a house in 1999 for $67,000 and sold it in 2002. If the 1999 CPI is 166.5 and the 2002 CPI is 179.9, how much would the house be worth in 2002 dollars?
Ans: $72,392

28. Owen sold a house in 2003 for $104,000 that he had purchased in 1990. If the 1990 CPI is 130.7 and the 2003 CPI is 184.0, how much would the house be worth in 1990 dollars?
Ans: $73,874

29. In 2000 Patti had the choice to invest $100,000 in the housing market for five years, or invest in a CD paying 4% compounded annually. If the 2000 CPI is 172.2 and the 2005 CPI is 195.0, which is the better choice?
Ans: The CD. The housing market would return $113,240 and the CD would return $121,665.

30. In 2000 Patti had the choice to invest $100,000 in the housing market for five years, or invest in a CD paying 3% compounded annually. If the 2000 CPI is 172.2 and the 2005 CPI is 195.0, which is the better choice?
Ans: The CD. The housing market would return $113,240 and the CD would return $115,927.

Chapter 22: Multiple-Choice

1. Your rich Uncle Ralph is willing to loan you $1000 for two years, and asks that you repay your loan with simple interest at the rate of 12% per year. How much will you repay after two years?
   A) $1024   B) $1240   C) $1254.40   D) $2400
   Ans: B

2. Your rich Uncle Ralph is willing to loan you $5000 for three years, and asks that you repay your loan with simple interest at the rate of 9% per year. How much will you repay after three years?
   A) $5270   B) $5350   C) $5900   D) $6350
   Ans: D

3. Your rich Uncle Ralph is willing to loan you $10,000 for eight months, and asks that you repay your loan with simple interest at the rate of 12% per year. How much will you repay after eight months?
   A) $10,080   B) $10,800   C) $10,120   D) $10,960
   Ans: B

4. Your rich Uncle Ralph is willing to loan you $50,000 for five years, so long as you pay interest each month. He asks for a simple interest rate of 24% per year. How much will you pay each month?
   A) $1000   B) $2000   C) More than $2000   D) Less than $1000
   Ans: A

5. Your rich Uncle Ralph is willing to loan you $1000 for two years, and asks that you repay your loan with annual compounding interest at the rate of 10% per year. How much will you repay after two years?
   A) $1200   B) $1121   C) $1210   D) $1110
   Ans: C

6. Your rich Uncle Ralph is willing to loan you $5000 for 3 1/2 years, and asks that you repay your loan with quarterly compounding interest at the rate of 8% per year. How much will you repay after 3 1/2 years?
   A) $6545.66   B) $5358.84   C) $6442.56   D) $6597.39
   Ans: D

7. Your rich Uncle Ralph is willing to loan you $50,000 for five months, and asks that you repay your loan with monthly compounding interest at the rate of 24% per year. How much interest will you pay?
   A) $5204   B) $5760   C) $5200   D) $5496
   Ans: A

8. If college tuition increases by 3% per year, how does your fourth-year tuition compare to your first-year tuition?
   A) It is 12% more.
   C) It is about 9.3% more.
   B) It is 9% more.
   D) It is about 12.5% more.
   Ans: C

9. If college tuition increases by 4% per year, how does your fourth-year tuition compare to your first-year tuition?
   A) About 12.5% more
   C) About 17% more
   B) About 16% more
   D) About 12% more
   Ans: A

10. Which of these savings rates is most favorable?
    A) 5% compounded annually
    C) 5% compounded quarterly
    B) 5% compounded semi-annually
    D) 5% compounded monthly
    Ans: D

11. Which of these savings rates is most favorable?
    A) 4% compounded quarterly
    C) 4% compounded monthly
    B) 4% compounded semi-annually
    D) 4% compounded annually
    Ans: C

12. Which of these savings rates is most favorable?
    A) 4% compounded annually
    C) 3.9% compounded quarterly
    B) 3.9% compounded monthly
    D) 3.8% continuously compounded
    Ans: A

13. Which of these savings rates is most favorable?
    A) 5% compounded annually
    C) 4.8% compounded quarterly
    B) 4.9% compounded monthly
    D) 4.8% continuously compounded
    Ans: B

14. Which of these savings rates is most favorable?
    A) 6% compounded annually
    C) 5.9% compounded quarterly
    B) 5.8% compounded monthly
    D) 5.8% continuously compounded
    Ans: C

15. Which of these loan rates is most favorable?
    A) 12% compounded annually
    C) 12% compounded quarterly
    B) 12% compounded monthly
    D) 12% continuously compounded
    Ans: A

16. Which of these loan rates is most favorable?
    A)   12% compounded annually   C)   11.5% compounded quarterly
    B)   11.5% compounded monthly   D)   11% continuously compounded
    Ans: D

17. Karana takes out a conventional loan to purchase a car. The interest rate is 6.4% compounded monthly and Karana has 10 years to repay the $27,000 she borrowed. What are Karana's monthly payments?
    A) $385.07   B) $305.21   C) $186.49   D) $171.48
    Ans: B

18. Moe takes out a conventional loan to purchase a car. The interest rate is 8.3% compounded monthly and Moe has eight years to repay the $12,000 he borrowed. What are Moe's monthly payments?
    A) $385.07   B) $305.21   C) $186.49   D) $171.48
    Ans: D

19. Ellie takes out a conventional loan to purchase a car. The interest rate is 7.5% compounded monthly and Ellie has four years to repay the $12,000 she borrowed. What are Ellie's monthly payments?
    A) $95.46   B) $139.33   C) $169.53   D) $290.15
    Ans: D

20. May takes out a conventional loan to purchase a car. The interest rate is 6.8% compounded monthly and May has six years to repay the $10,000 she borrowed. What are May's monthly payments?
    A) $95.46   B) $139.33   C) $169.53   D) $290.15
    Ans: C

21. Suppose a student loan has an interest rate of 7% compounded monthly with monthly payments and the borrower has 10 years to repay. If $12,000 is borrowed, what are the monthly payments?
    A) $95.46   B) $139.33   C) $169.53   D) $290.15
    Ans: B

22. Suppose a student loan has an interest rate of 5% compounded monthly with monthly payments and the borrower has 10 years to repay. If $9000 is borrowed, what are the monthly payments?
    A) $95.46   B) $139.33   C) $169.53   D) $290.15
    Ans: A

23. Suppose a student loan has an interest rate of 5.8% compounded monthly with monthly payments and the borrower has 10 years to repay. If $35,000 is borrowed, what are the monthly payments?
    A) $385.07   B) $305.21   C) $186.49   D) $171.48
    Ans: A

24. Suppose a student loan has an interest rate of 6.2% compounded monthly with monthly payments and the borrower has 10 years to repay. If $5000 is borrowed, what are the monthly payments?
    A) $45.28   B) $56.01   C) $68.92   D) $73.10
    Ans: B

25. A credit card bill shows a balance due of $980 with a monthly interest rate of 1.91%. What is the APR?
    A) 18.36%   B) 19.99%   C) 22.92%   D) 25.49%
    Ans: C

26. A credit card bill shows a balance due of $980 with a monthly interest rate of 1.91%. What is the EAR?
    A) 18.36%   B) 19.99%   C) 22.92%   D) 25.49%
    Ans: D

27. A credit card bill shows a balance due of $2500 with a monthly interest rate of 1.53%. What is the APR?
    A) 18.36%   B) 19.99%   C) 22.92%   D) 25.49%
    Ans: A

28. A credit card bill shows a balance due of $2500 with a monthly interest rate of 1.53%. What is the EAR?
    A) 18.36%   B) 19.99%   C) 22.92%   D) 25.49%
    Ans: B

29. A credit card bill shows a balance due of $750 with a minimum payment of $15 and a monthly interest rate of 1.62%. What is the APR?
    A) 17.28%   B) 18.72%   C) 19.44%   D) 21.26%
    Ans: C

30. A credit card bill shows a balance due of $750 with a minimum payment of $15 and a monthly interest rate of 1.62%. What is the EAR?
    A) 17.28%   B) 18.72%   C) 19.44%   D) 21.26%
    Ans: D

31. A credit card bill shows a balance due of $1200 with a minimum payment of $24 and a monthly interest rate of 1.44%. What is the APR?
    A) 17.28%   B) 18.72%   C) 19.44%   D) 21.26%
    Ans: A

32. A credit card bill shows a balance due of $1200 with a minimum payment of $24 and a monthly interest rate of 1.44%. What is the EAR?
    A) 17.28%   B) 18.72%   C) 19.44%   D) 21.26%
    Ans: B

33. Find the future value of an annuity with monthly deposits of $350, made over a period of five years, with 4% interest compounded monthly.
    A) $13,721   B) $23,205   C) $23,292   D) $30,707
    Ans: B

34. Find the future value of an annuity with monthly deposits of $250, made over a period of eight years, with 6% interest compounded monthly.
    A) $13,721   B) $23,205   C) $23,292   D) $30,707
    Ans: D

35. Find the future value of an annuity with monthly deposits of $150, made over a period of 10 years, with 5% interest compounded monthly.
    A) $13,721   B) $23,205   C) $23,292   D) $30,707
    Ans: C

36. Find the future value of an annuity with monthly deposits of $75, made over a period of 10 years, with 8% interest compounded monthly.
    A) $13,721   B) $23,205   C) $23,292   D) $30,707
    Ans: A

37. How much would you have to invest each month in an annuity earning 5% monthly to earn $30,000 at the end of 30 years?
    A) $14.32   B) $36.05   C) $39.82   D) $40.26
    Ans: B

38. How much would you have to invest each month in an annuity earning 5% monthly to earn $5000 at the end of 18 years?
    A) $14.32   B) $36.05   C) $39.82   D) $40.26
    Ans: A

39. How much would you have to invest each month in an annuity earning 6% monthly to earn $40,000 at the end of 30 years?
    A) $14.32   B) $36.05   C) $39.82   D) $40.26
    Ans: C

40. You invest $150 each month into an annuity earning 5.4% each month. How much do you have at the end of 18 years?
    A) $48,826   B) $54,582   C) $64,651   D) $68,461
    Ans: B

41. You invest $100 each quarter into an annuity earning 8% each quarter. How much do you have at the end of 30 years?
    A) $48,826   B) $54,582   C) $64,651   D) $68,461
    Ans: A

42. Find the future value of an annuity with monthly deposits of $150, made over a period of four years, with 5.2% interest compounded monthly.
    A) $5777.18   B) $7984.39   C) $7706.18   D) $8254.28
    Ans: B

43. Find the future value of an annuity with monthly deposits of $60, made over a period of 10 years, with 8.1% interest compounded monthly.
    A) $11,038.21   B) $17,234.56   C) $29,668.96   D) $58,843.96
    Ans: B

44. Find the future value of an annuity with monthly deposits of $250, made over a period of 30 years, with 6.1% interest compounded monthly.
    A) $153,264.36   B) $198,328.32   C) $231,235.54   D) $255,986.36
    Ans: D

45. Find the future value of an annuity with monthly deposits of $75, made over a period of five years, with 9.8% interest compounded monthly.
    A) $5777.18   B) $7984.39   C) $7706.18   D) $8254.28
    Ans: A

46. How much would you have to invest each month in an annuity earning 6.5% monthly to earn $30,000 at the end of 15 years?
    A) $84.77   B) $98.83   C) $146.93   D) $152.15
    Ans: B

47. How much would you have to invest each quarter in an annuity earning 5% quarterly to earn $20,000 at the end of 20 years?
    A) $84.77   B) $98.83   C) $146.93   D) $152.15
    Ans: C

48. How much would you have to invest each month in an annuity earning 7.4% monthly to earn $15,000 at the end of 10 years?
    A) $84.77   B) $98.83   C) $146.93   D) $152.15
    Ans: A

49. You invest $75 each month into an annuity earning 6.2% each month. How much do you have at the end of 18 years?
    A) $11,038.21   B) $17,234.56   C) $29,668.96   D) $58,843.96
    Ans: C

50. You invest $300 each quarter into an annuity earning 8.1% each quarter. How much do you have at the end of 20 years?
    A) $11,038.21   B) $17,234.56   C) $29,668.96   D) $58,843.96
    Ans: D

51. You invest $200 each quarter into an annuity earning 8.1% each quarter. How much do you have at the end of 20 years?
    A) $39,229   B) $19,779.31   C) $11,489.70   D) $7,358.81
    Ans: A

52. You have established an annuity plan that will accumulate to $50,000 in 10 years by investing $100 a month. If you instead invest $200 a month, what would your annuity accumulate?
    A) More than $160,000   B) $150,000   C) $100,000   D) Less than $90,000
    Ans: C

53. You have established an annuity plan that will accumulate to $30,000 in 10 years by investing $100 a month. If you instead invest $200 a month, what would your annuity accumulate?
    A) $50,000   B) $60,000   C) More than $70,000   D) Less than $45,000
    Ans: B

54. Which of these savings rates is most favorable?
    A)   5% compounded annually   C)   5% compounded quarterly
    B)   5% compounded semi-annually   D)   5% compounded monthly
    Ans: D

55. Which of these savings rates is most favorable?
    A)   4% compounded quarterly   C)   4% compounded monthly
    B)   4% compounded semi-annually   D)   4% compounded annually
    Ans: C

56. Which of these savings rates is most favorable?
    A)   4% compounded annually   C)   3.9% compounded quarterly
    B)   3.9% compounded monthly   D)   3.8% continuously compounded
    Ans: A

57. Which of these savings rates is most favorable?
    A)   5% compounded annually   C)   4.8% compounded quarterly
    B)   4.9% compounded monthly   D)   4.8% continuously compounded
    Ans: B

58. Which of these savings rates is most favorable?
    A)   6% compounded annually   C)   5.9% compounded quarterly
    B)   5.8% compounded monthly   D)   5.8% continuously compounded
    Ans: C

59. Which of these loan rates is most favorable?
    A)   12% compounded annually   C)   12% compounded quarterly
    B)   12% compounded monthly   D)   12% continuously compounded
    Ans: A

60. Which of these loan rates is most favorable?
    A)   12% compounded annually   C)   11.5% compounded quarterly
    B)   11.5% compounded monthly   D)   11% continuously compounded
    Ans: D

Chapter 22: Free-Response

1. Your Great Aunt Sally loans you $1000 for two years and asks that you repay it with simple interest at the rate of 5% per year. How much do you repay her after two years?
   Ans: $1100

2. Your Great Aunt Sally loans you $5000 for three years and asks that you repay it with simple interest at the rate of 8% per year. How much do you repay her after three years?
   Ans: $6200

3. Your Great Aunt Sally loans you $1000 for seven months and asks that you repay it with simple interest at the rate of 1% per month. How much do you repay her after seven months?
   Ans: $1070

4. Your Great Aunt Sally loans you $1000 for two years and asks that you repay it with annually compounding interest at the rate of 5% per year. How much do you repay her after two years?
   Ans: $1102.50

5. Your Great Aunt Sally loans you $5000 for three years and asks that you repay it with annually compounding interest at the rate of 8% per year. How much do you repay her after three years?
   Ans: $6298.56

6. Your Great Aunt Sally loans you $1000 for seven months and asks that you repay it with monthly compounding interest at the rate of 1% per month. How much do you repay her after seven months?
   Ans: $1072.14

7. If you borrow $10,000 for three years at a quarterly compounding interest rate of 4% per year, how much interest will you pay?
   Ans: $1268.25

8. If you borrow $50,000 for three months at a monthly compounding rate of 18% per year, how much interest will you pay?
   Ans: $ 2283.92

9. If you borrow $10,000 for two years under the condition that no interest is charged for the first six months, and a quarterly compounded interest rate of 12% applies for the remainder of the period, how much interest will you pay?
   Ans: $1940.52

10. Which is more costly: paying 12% simple interest for two years, or 11% annual compounding interest for two years?
Ans: 12% simple

11. Which is more costly: paying 11.5% simple interest for four years, or 10% annual compounding interest for four years?
Ans: 10% annual compounding

12. Which is more costly: paying 2.5% simple interest for a six-month loan, or 2.4% monthly compounding interest for six months?
Ans: 2.5% simple

13. Bill takes out a conventional loan to purchase a car. The interest rate is 5.2% compounded monthly and Bill has 10 years to repay the $15,000 he borrowed. What are Bill's monthly payments?
Ans: $160.57

14. David takes out a conventional loan to purchase a car. The interest rate is 4.8% compounded quarterly and David has four years to repay the $8000 he borrowed. What are David's quarterly payments?
Ans: $552.52

15. David takes out a conventional loan to purchase a car. The interest rate is 4.8% compounded quarterly and David has four years to repay the $12,000 he borrowed. What are David's quarterly payments?
Ans: $828.78

16. Yvette takes out a conventional loan to purchase a car. The interest rate is 6.2% compounded monthly and Yvette has five years to repay the $9600 she borrowed. What are Yvette's monthly payments?
Ans: $186.49

17. How much would you have to invest each month in an annuity earning 6% monthly to earn $50,000 at the end of 30 years?
Ans: $49.78

18. How much would you have to invest each quarter in an annuity earning 5% quarterly to earn $5000 at the end of five years?
Ans: $221.60

19. Find the future value of an annuity with weekly deposits of $12, made over a period of five years, with 3.8% interest compounded weekly.
Ans: $3434.72

20. You invest $325 each quarter into an annuity earning 9% each quarter. How much do you have at the end of ten years?
    Ans: $20,730.51

21. How much would you have to invest each month in an annuity earning 4.9% monthly to earn $35,000 at the end of 20 years?
    Ans: $86.14

22. How much would you have to invest each quarter in an annuity earning 5.4% quarterly to earn $8000 at the end of 10 years?
    Ans: $152.15

23. Find the future value of an annuity with weekly deposits of $50, made over a period of four years, with 6.8% interest compounded weekly.
    Ans: $11,942.94

24. You invest $100 each quarter into an annuity earning 8% each quarter. How much do you have at the end of 30 years?
    Ans: $48,825.82

25. You invest $20 each month into an annuity earning 9.2% each month. How much do you have at the end of 15 years?
    Ans: $7706.18

26. Which is a more favorable savings rate: 4.5% compounded monthly or 4.6% compounded annually?
    Ans: 4.6% compounded annually. 4.5% compounded monthly is equivalent to 4.594% compounded annually.

27. Which is a more favorable savings rate: 3.5% compounded monthly or 3.6% compounded annually?
    Ans: 3.6% compounded annually. 3.5% compounded monthly is equivalent to 3.5567% compounded annually.

28. Which is a more favorable savings rate: 3.5% compounded monthly or 3.55% compounded quarterly?
    Ans: 3.55% compounded quarterly

29. Which is a more favorable savings rate: 4.5% compounded monthly or 4.52% compounded quarterly?
    Ans: 4.52% compounded quarterly

30. Which is a more favorable savings rate: 6% compounded monthly or 6.05% compounded quarterly?
    Ans: 6.05% compounded quarterly

Chapter 23: Multiple-Choice

1. The population of a small town was 1500 at the beginning of 2007. Assuming an average growth rate of 2.3% per year, what will the population be at the beginning of 2015?
   A) 1621   B) 1799   C) 2137   D) 3197
   Ans: B

2. The population of a small town was 3000 at the beginning of 2007. Assuming an average growth rate of 0.8% per year, what will the population be at the beginning of 2015?
   A) 1621   B) 1799   C) 2137   D) 3197
   Ans: D

3. The population of a small town was 1200 at the beginning of 2009. Assuming an average growth rate of 4.2% per year, what will the population be at the beginning of 2019?
   A) 1426   B) 1811   C) 2037   D) 2139
   Ans: B

4. The population of a small town was 4500 at the beginning of 2009. Assuming an average growth rate of 0.8% per year, what will the population be at the beginning of 2019?
   A) 4751   B) 4923   C) 5071   D) 5120
   Ans: D

5. The population of the state of Georgia in 2001 was about 8,384,000. The average growth rate from 2000 to 2001 was 2.4%. What was the approximate population in 2000?
   A) 6,238,100   B) 7,284,700   C) 8,028,200   D) 8,187,500
   Ans: D

6. In 2001 the population of the state of Alabama was about 4,467,000 and the growth rate was approximately 0.4%. What is the projected population of Alabama in 2020?
   A) 4,565,454   B) 4,797,419   C) 5,224,386   D) 6,187,500
   Ans: B

7. In 2001 the population of the state of Washington was about 5,594,000 and the growth rate was approximately 1.6%. What is the projected population of Washington in 2005?
   A) 2,465,421   B) 5,617,428   C) 6,280,366   D) 7,187,500
   Ans: C

8. The population of the state of New York in 2000 was about 18,976,000. In 2001, the population was about 19,011,000. What was the average growth rate over that period of time?
   A) 0.18%   B) 1.16%   C) 1.90%   D) 2.30%
   Ans: A

9. The population of the state of California in 1980 was about 23,237,000. In 2001, the population was about 34,501,000. What was the average growth rate over that period of time?
   A) 0.3%   B) 1.2%   C) 1.9%   D) 2.3%
   Ans: C

10. The population of the United States in 2000 was about 281,422,000. In 2001, the population was about 284,797,000. What was the average growth rate over that period of time?
    A) 1.2%   B) 1.4%   C) 1.9%   D) 2.4%
    Ans: A

11. The population of the state of Texas in 1993 was about 17,778,000. In 2001, the population was about 21,325,000. What was the average growth rate over that period of time?
    A) 0.3%   B) 1.2%   C) 1.9%   D) 2.3%
    Ans: D

12. The population of the state of Alaska in 1700 was about 302,583. In 2000, the population was about 634,900. What was the average growth rate over that period of time?
    A) 1.2%   B) 1.4%   C) 1.9%   D) 2.4%
    Ans: D

13. The population of the world in 1800 was about 900,000,000. The average growth rate from 1800 to 1900 was 0.51%. What was the approximate population in 1990?
    A) 925,000,000   B) 946,000,000   C) 951,000,000   D) 1,500,000,000
    Ans: D

14. In 1999 the population of the Ukraine was about 49,800,000 and the growth rate was approximately –0.62%. What is the projected population of the Ukraine in 2010?
    A) 46,506,993   B) 47,165,236   C) 49,203,421   D) 50,120,215
    Ans: A

15. In 1999 the population of the Marshall Islands was about 65,500 and the growth rate was approximately 3.86%. What is the projected population of the Marshall Islands in 2010?
    A) 70,165   B) 99,351   C) 101,203   D) 120,032
    Ans: B

16. The population of Mexico in 1900 was about 18,000,000. In 2000, the population was about 100,000,000. What was the average growth rate over that period of time?
    A) 0.85%   B) 1.36%   C) 1.73%   D) 2.74%
    Ans: C

17. The population of British Columbia in 1997 was about 3,959,700. In 2001, the population was about 4,095,900. What was the average growth rate over that period of time?
   A) 0.85%   B) 1.36%   C) 1.73%   D) 2.74%
   Ans: A

18. The population of Laos in 1996 was about 5,200,000. In 2001, the population was about 5,952,520. What was the average growth rate over that period of time?
   A) 0.85%   B) 1.36%   C) 1.73%   D) 2.74%
   Ans: D

19. The population of Ontario in 1997 was about 11,249,500. In 2001, the population was about 11,874,400. What was the average growth rate over that period of time?
   A) 0.85%   B) 1.36%   C) 1.73%   D) 2.74%
   Ans: B

20. The population of the United States in 1700 was about 600,000,000. In 2000, the population was about 6,000,000,000. What was the average growth rate over that period of time?
   A) 0.23%   B) 0.77%   C) 5.4%   D) 10%
   Ans: B

21. Suppose the world demand for iron is about 420,000,000 tons per year. The known global reserves are 100,000,000,000 tons. What is the static reserve for iron?
   A) 93.3   B) 128.4   C) 238.1   D) 420.0
   Ans: C

22. Suppose the world demand for iron is about 420,000,000 tons per year. The known global reserves are 100,000,000,000 tons. The demand for iron is increasing at a rate of 1.8%. What is the exponential reserve for iron?
   A) 93.3   B) 128.4   C) 238.1   D) 420.0
   Ans: A

23. Suppose the world demand for silver is about 343,750,000 troy ounces per year. The known global reserves are 5,500,000,000 troy ounces. What is the static reserve for silver?
   A) 3.44   B) 14.2   C) 16.0   D) 51.5
   Ans: C

24. Suppose the world demand for silver is about 343,750,000 troy ounces per year. The known global reserves are 5,500,000,000 troy ounces. The demand for silver is increasing at a rate of 2.7%. What is the exponential reserve for silver?
   A) 3.44   B) 14.2   C) 16.0   D) 51.5
   Ans: B

25. Suppose the world demand for copper is about 8,600,000 tons per year. The known global reserves are 308,000,000 tons. What is the static reserve for copper?
A) 21.62   B) 35.81   C) 65.47   D) 96.55
Ans: B

26. Suppose the world demand for copper is about 8,600,000 tons per year. The known global reserves are 308,000,000 tons. The demand for copper is increasing at a rate of 4.6%. What is the exponential reserve for copper?
A) 21.62   B) 35.81   C) 65.47   D) 96.55
Ans: A

27. Suppose the world demand for chromium is about 1,845,000 tons per year. The known global reserves are 775,000,000 tons. What is the static reserve for chromium?
A) 98.15   B) 110.02   C) 420.05   D) 604.51
Ans: C

28. Suppose the world demand for chromium is about 1,845,000 tons per year. The known global reserves are 775,000,000 tons. The demand for chromium is increasing at a rate of 2.6%. What is the exponential reserve for chromium?
A) 21.62   B) 35.81   C) 65.47   D) 96.55
Ans: D

29. Suppose the world demand for cobalt is about 16,360,000 pounds per year. The known global reserves are 1,800,000,000 pounds. What is the static reserve for cobalt?
A) 98.15   B) 110.02   C) 420.05   D) 604.51
Ans: B

30. Suppose the world demand for cobalt is about 16,360,000 pounds per year. The known global reserves are 1,800,000,000 pounds. The demand for cobalt is increasing at a rate of 1.5%. What is the exponential reserve for cobalt?
A) 21.62   B) 35.81   C) 65.47   D) 96.55
Ans: C

Use the following to answer questions 31-33:

Use the following reproduction curve for a population to answer the question(s). Units are in thousands.

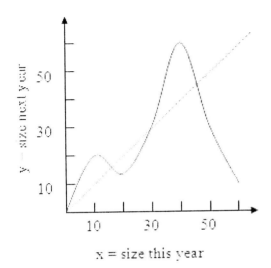

x = size this year

31. The maximum sustainable yield is approximately:
    A) 10,000   B) 20,000   C) 30,000   D) 40,000
    Ans: D

32. A population equilibrium corresponds to:
    A) 10,000   B) 20,000   C) 30,000   D) 40,000
    Ans: B

33. The sustainable yield corresponding to a population of size 10,000 remaining after the harvest is approximately:
    A) 10,000   B) 20,000   C) 30,000   D) 40,000
    Ans: D

Use the following to answer questions 34-36:

Use the following reproduction curve for a population to answer the question(s). Units are in thousands.

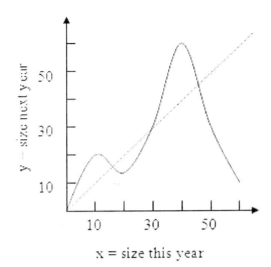

x = size this year

34. The maximum sustainable yield is approximately:
    A) 10,000   B) 20,000   C) 30,000   D) 40,000
    Ans: B

35. A population equilibrium corresponds to:
    A) 10,000   B) 20,000   C) 30,000   D) 40,000
    Ans: C

36. The sustainable yield corresponding to a population of size 10,000 remaining after the harvest is approximately:
    A) 10,000   B) 20,000   C) 30,000   D) 40,000
    Ans: A

Use the following to answer questions 37-39:

Use the following reproduction curve for a population to answer the question(s). Units are in thousands.

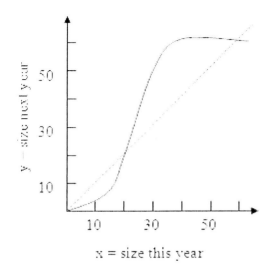

x = size this year

37. The maximum sustainable yield is approximately:
    A) 20,000   B) 30,000   C) 40,000   D) 50,000
    Ans: A

38. A population equilibrium corresponds to:
    A) 20,000   B) 30,000   C) 40,000   D) 50,000
    Ans: A

39. The sustainable yield corresponding to a population of size 40,000 remaining after the harvest is approximately:
    A) 20,000   B) 30,000   C) 40,000   D) 50,000
    Ans: A

40. A small change in initial conditions of a system can make an enormous difference later on. This is called:
    A) Fisher's effect.   B) a steady state.   C) the butterfly effect.   D) equilibrium.
    Ans: C

41. A population grows according to a logistic growth model, with population parameter $\lambda = 2.4$ and $x = 0.35$ for the first year. The value of x after the second year is:
    A) 0.273   B) 0.546   C) 0.608   D) 0.994
    Ans: B

42. A population grows according to a logistic growth model, with population parameter $\lambda = 4.0$ and $x = 0.7$ for the first year. The value of x after the fourth year is:
    A) 0.273   B) 0.546   C) 0.608   D) 0.994
    Ans: D

43. A population grows according to a logistic growth model, with population parameter $\lambda = 1.3$ and $x = 0.7$ for the first year. The value of x after the second year is:
    A) 0.273   B) 0.546   C) 0.608   D) 0.994
    Ans: A

44. A population grows according to a logistic growth model, with population parameter $\lambda = 3.8$ and $x = 0.8$ for the first year. The value of x after the second year is:
    A) 0.273   B) 0.546   C) 0.608   D) 0.994
    Ans: C

45. A population grows according to a logistic growth model, with population parameter $\lambda = 3.7$ and $x = 0.8$ for the first year. The value of x after the second year is:
    A) 0.433   B) 0.592   C) 0.827   D) 0.967
    Ans: B

46. A population grows according to a logistic growth model, with population parameter $\lambda = 2.5$ and $x = 0.28$ for the first year. The value of x after the fourth year is:
    A) 0.210   B) 0.501   C) 0.586   D) 0.702
    Ans: C

47. A population grows according to a logistic growth model, with population parameter $\lambda = 1.8$ and $x = 0.34$ for the first year. The value of x after the third year is:
    A) 0.433   B) 0.592   C) 0.827   D) 0.967
    Ans: A

48. A population grows according to a logistic growth model, with population parameter $\lambda = 4.0$ and $x = 0.67$ for the first year. The value of x after the fourth year is:
    A) 0.433   B) 0.592   C) 0.827   D) 0.967
    Ans: D

49. A population grows according to a logistic growth model, with population parameter $\lambda = 2.2$ and $x = 0.61$ for the first year. The value of x after the third year is:
    A) 0.228   B) 0.549   C) 0.627   D) 0.724
    Ans: B

50. A population grows according to a logistic growth model, with population parameter $\lambda = 4.1$ and $x = 0.72$ for the first year. The value of x after the second year is:
    A) 0.433   B) 0.592   C) 0.827   D) 0.967
    Ans: C

51. What is the world demand for iron, if the known global reserves are 100,000,000,000 tons and the static reserve is 238?
    A)   About 300,000,000 tons   C)   About 500,000,000 tons
    B)   About 400,000,000 tons   D)   About 600,000,000 tons
    Ans: B

52. Suppose the world demand for iron is about 420,000,000 tons per year and the static reserve is 238. However, the demand for iron is increasing at a rate of 1.8%. What is the exponential reserve for iron?
    A) 420   B) 238   C) 145   D) 93.3
    Ans: D

53. Suppose the world demand for silver is about 343,750,000 troy ounces per year and the static reserve is 16. What are the known global reserves for silver?
    A)   About 5 billion troy ounces   C)   About 5 trillion troy ounces
    B)   About 5.5 billion troy ounces   D)   About 5.5 trillion troy ounces
    Ans: B

54. Suppose the world demand for silver is about 343,750,000 troy ounces per year and the static reserve is 16. However, the demand for silver is increasing at a rate of 2.7%. What is the exponential reserve for silver?
    A) 3.44   B) 14.2   C) 16.0   D) 51.5
    Ans: B

55. Suppose the world demand for copper is about 8,600,000 tons per year and the static reserve is about 36. What are the known global reserves for copper?
    A)   About 310 million tons   C)   About 239 million tons
    B)   About 360 million tons   D)   Less than 220 million tons
    Ans: A

56. Suppose the world demand for copper is about 8,600,000 tons per year and the static reserve is about 36. However, the demand for copper is increasing at a rate of 4.6%. What is the exponential reserve for copper?
    A) About 22   B) About 36   C) About 65   D) About 97
    Ans: A

57. Suppose the world demand for chromium is about 1,845,000 tons per year and the static reserve is 420. What are the known global reserves for chromium?
    A)   412 million tons   C)   439 million tons
    B)   420 million tons   D)   775 million tons
    Ans: D

58. Suppose the world demand for chromium is about 1,845,000 tons per year and the static reserve is 420. If the demand for chromium is increasing at a rate of 2.6%, what is the exponential reserve for chromium?
A) 21.62   B) 35.81   C) 65.47   D) 96.55
Ans: D

59. Suppose the world demand for cobalt is about 16,360,000 pounds per year and the static reserve is 110. What are the known global reserves for cobalt?
A) 1600 million tons   C) 1600 billion tons
B) 1800 million tons   D) 1800 billion tons
Ans: B

60. Suppose the world demand for cobalt is about 16,360,000 pounds per year and the static reserve is 110. The demand for cobalt is increasing at a rate of 1.5%. What is the exponential reserve for cobalt?
A) 21.62   B) 35.81   C) 65.47   D) 96.55
Ans: C

Chapter 23: Free-Response

1. A colony of penguins had 352 members at the beginning of 1998. The colony is expanding at an average rate of 1.2% per year. How many penguins will there be at the beginning of 2005?
Ans: 383

2. A colony of penguins had 541 members at the beginning of 1994. At the beginning of 2001 the colony had grown to 670 members. What was the average growth rate over that period of time?
Ans: 3.1%

3. A colony of penguins had 1024 members at the beginning of 2001. The colony is expanding at an average rate of 3.4% per year. How many penguins will there be at the beginning of 2003?
Ans: 1095

4. A colony of penguins had 534 members at the beginning of 1998. At the beginning of 2001 the colony had grown to 721 members. What was the average growth rate over that period of time?
Ans: 10.53%

5. The population of the state of Virginia was 7,187,700 at the beginning of 2002. Assuming an average growth rate of 1.5% per year, what will the population be at the beginning of 2020?
Ans: 5,497,955

6. The population of a small town was 4200 at the beginning of 2002. Assuming an average growth rate of 0.2% per year, what will the population be at the beginning of 2020?
Ans: 4354

7. Suppose the world demand for gold is about 32,000,000 troy ounces per year. The known global reserves are 100,000,000,000 troy ounces. What is the static reserve for gold?
Ans: 11.03

8. Suppose the world demand for gold is about 32,000,000 troy ounces per year. The known global reserves are 100,000,000,000 troy ounces. The demand for gold is increasing at a rate of 4.1%. What is the exponential reserve for gold?
Ans: 9.29

9. Suppose the world demand for zinc is about 5,000,000 tons per year. The known global reserves are 123,000,000 tons. What is the static reserve for zinc?
Ans: 24.6

10. Suppose the world demand for zinc is about 5,000,000 tons per year. The known global reserves are 123,000,000 tons. The demand for zinc is increasing at a rate of 2.9%. What is the exponential reserve for zinc?
    Ans: 18.84

11. Suppose the world demand for aluminum is about 16,800,000 tons per year. The known global reserves are 1,700,000,000 tons. The demand for aluminum is increasing at a rate of 6.4%. What is the exponential reserve for aluminum?
    Ans: 32.43

12. Suppose the world demand for coal is about 2,174,000,000 tons per year. The known global reserves are 5,000,000,000,000 tons. What is the static reserve for coal?
    Ans: 2299.91

13. Suppose the world demand for coal is about 2,174,000,000 tons per year. The known global reserves are 5,000,000,000,000 tons. The demand for coal is increasing at a rate of 4.1%. What is the exponential reserve for coal?
    Ans: 113.41

Use the following to answer questions 14-16:

Use the following reproductive curve for a population to answer the question(s) below. Units are in thousands.

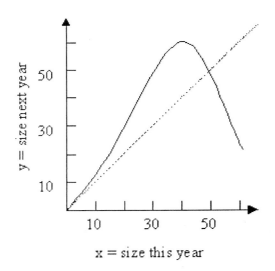

14. Estimate the maximum sustainable yield.
    Ans: 20,000

15. Estimate the equilibrium population size.
    Ans: 50,000

16. Estimate the sustainable yield corresponding to a population of size 20,000 remaining after the harvest.
    Ans: 10,000

Use the following to answer questions 17-19:

Use the following reproductive curve for a population to answer the question(s) below. Units are in thousands.

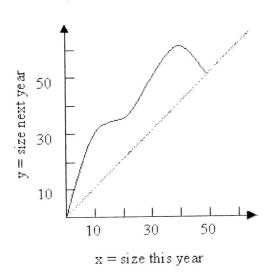

17. Estimate the maximum sustainable yield.
    Ans: 20,000

18. Estimate the equilibrium population size.
    Ans: 50,000

19. Estimate the sustainable yield corresponding to a population of size 40,000 remaining after the harvest.
    Ans: 20,000

20. A population grows according to a logistic growth model, with population parameter $\lambda = 4.1$ and $x = 0.9$ for the first year. Find the value of x after the second year.
    Ans: 0.369

21. A population grows according to a logistic growth model, with population parameter $\lambda = 1.4$ and $x = 0.05$ for the first year. Find the value of x after the second year.
    Ans: 0.067

22. Suppose the world demand for aluminum is about 16,800,000 tons per year. The known global reserves are 1,700,000,000 tons. What is the static reserve for aluminum?
Ans: 101.19

23. A population grows according to a logistic growth model, with population parameter $\lambda = 3.9$ and $x = 0.84$ for the first year. Find the value of x after the second year.
Ans: 0.524

24. A population grows according to a logistic growth model, with population parameter $\lambda = 1.4$ and $x = 0.05$ for the first year. Find the value of x after the third year.
Ans: 0.087

25. A population grows according to a logistic growth model, with population parameter $\lambda = 2.4$ and $x = 0.01$ for the first year. Find the value of x after the third year.
Ans: 0.056

26. A population grows according to a logistic growth model, with population parameter $\lambda = 3.1$ and $x = 0.9$ for the first year. Find the value of x after the second year.
Ans: 0.624

27. A population grows according to a logistic growth model, with population parameter $\lambda = 1.9$ and $x = 0.05$ for the first year. Find the value of x after the second year.
Ans: 0.156

28. Suppose the world demand for aluminum is about 16,800,000 tons per year and the static reserve is 100. What are the known global reserves for aluminum?
Ans: 1,680,000,000 tons

29. Suppose the world demand for coal is about 2,174,000,000 tons per year and the static reserve is 2300. What are the known global reserves for coal?
Ans: 5,000,200,000,000 tons

30. A population grows according to a logistic growth model, with population parameter $\lambda = 1.4$ and $x = 0.15$ for the first year. Find the value of x after the third year.
Ans: 0.2284